WITHDRAWN

W9-BYQ-278

ILLINOIS CENTRAL COLLEGE
PN6120.H7M56
STACKS
Modern plays for special days;
A12900 302599

MODERN PLAYS
for
SPECIAL DAYS

Other books by
HELEN LOUISE MILLER

PRIZE PLAYS FOR TEEN-AGERS
EASY PLAYS FOR BOYS AND GIRLS
GOLD MEDAL PLAYS FOR HOLIDAYS
ON STAGE FOR TEEN-AGERS
FIRST PLAYS FOR CHILDREN
HOLIDAY PLAYS FOR TEEN-AGERS
PLAYS FOR LIVING AND LEARNING
POINTERS ON PRODUCING THE SCHOOL PLAY

Modern Plays for Special Days

A collection of royalty-free, one-act holiday plays for teen-agers

By **HELEN LOUISE MILLER**

Publishers *PLAYS, INC.* Boston

CAUTION

All material in this volume is fully protected by copyright law. All rights, including motion picture, recitation, television, public reading, radio broadcasting, and rights of translation into foreign languages, are strictly reserved.

NOTICE FOR AMATEUR PRODUCTION

These plays may be produced by schools, clubs, and similar amateur groups without payment of a royalty fee.

NOTICE FOR PROFESSIONAL PRODUCTION

For any form of non-amateur presentation (professional stage, radio or television), permission must be obtained in writing from the publisher. Inquiries should be addressed to PLAYS, INC., 8 Arlington Street, Boston 16, Massachusetts.

Library of Congress Catalog Card Number: 64-23738

MANUFACTURED IN THE UNITED STATES OF AMERICA

CONTENTS

MODERN PLAYS
for
SPECIAL DAYS

The Curse of Hag Hollow

Characters

SABILLA, AURILLA, VANILLA — *the witches of Hag Hollow*
TERRY BAXTER, *the curse of Hag Hollow*
CASPER CRAMER
DRUSILLA DEANE

SETTING: *The cave of the three witches.*

AT RISE: SABILLA *is seated at a table, eating a dish of cereal. The label of the giant cereal box facing the audience reads* GHOST TOASTIES. AURILLA *is hobbling about, half-heartedly sweeping with the traditional witch's broom. From time to time she pauses to take a drink of red liquid from an enormous goblet.*

SABILLA (*Pushing back her bowl*): I can't swallow another mouthful. In the past week I've eaten my way through a dozen boxes of Ghost Toasties. You and Vanilla will have to finish them.

AURILLA (*Pausing to take a drink*): Don't count on me. I'm still on my diet. Three glasses of Skinnycal a day!

SABILLA: Humph! I can't see that it's doing much for you. You're sneaking too many salted rat tails on the side.

AURILLA: You're just jealous. That's all that ails you.

SABILLA: I'm comfortable just as I am, thank you. Besides, at our age, a little extra weight is becoming.

AURILLA: Nonsense! Who ever heard of a fat witch? And one of these days you're not going to get off the ground. Haven't you noticed how your broomstick creaks and groans at every take-off? There's a limit to what a witch's broom can carry.

SABILLA: Well, there's definitely a limit to the amount of Ghost Toasties I can eat, and I've reached it.

AURILLA: But think of all the Green Slaving Stamps! Twenty-four with every package.

SABILLA: Green Slaving Stamps or no Green Slaving Stamps, I've had it!

AURILLA: But, Sabilla, as soon as we fill our last book we can get another Green Slave.

SABILLA: So what? The last one we had was more bother than she was worth. We had to get rid of her.

AURILLA: I'll admit she was a mistake. But this one will be different. I'm going to pick her out myself.

SABILLA: None of these flesh-and-blood girls make good slaves. They're all afraid of work.

AURILLA: Afraid of work, and afraid of everything else. That was the trouble with our last one. She had a fear complex. Scared to death of mice, bats, toads, spiders, frogs, worms, and snakes! She was in a panic the whole time she was here.

SABILLA: And a terrible cook! Horrors! What a mess she made of a simple dish of Toad Stew and Kippered Spiders!

AURILLA: The next one will be better. I'm going to pick

her out myself, and we'll have no more screaming-meemies about the place.

VANILLA (*Offstage*): Yoo-hoo! Look what I have here!

SABILLA: Great-grandfather's ghost! Here comes Vanilla! What is she screeching about now? (VANILLA *enters, driving the new* GREEN SLAVE *ahead of her with a broomstick. The* SLAVE *is dressed as a scrub woman, with head tied up in a dustcloth; wears a long, green coverall apron and carries a mop and pail.*)

VANILLA (*Chuckling*): Faster, my girl, faster! We'll have no sluggards in Hag Hollow. Pick up your feet!

SABILLA: What is the meaning of this? Who is this earthworm?

VANILLA: It's our new Green Slave. What do you think of her?

AURILLA: I thought it was my turn to make the selection.

VANILLA: Don't be cross, Aurilla. I had the stamp books with me, and when I saw this creature, I was afraid someone else might snap her up. Just look at those muscles.

SABILLA: All brawn and no brain, if you ask me!

VANILLA: At least this one isn't afraid of her own shadow.

AURILLA: We'll soon see about that. Go fetch me the market basket. (VANILLA *exits.*)

SABILLA: What's your name, creature? Don't you have a tongue?

TERRY: Sure, I have a tongue, but this is the first chance I've had to use it.

AURILLA: Ummph! A saucy one! Well, we'll soon teach you some manners. Now, what is your name?

TERRY: My name is Terry—Terry Baxter.

AURILLA: Terry, eh? Well, now, Terry, we'll soon see if you'll make a suitable slave for a witches' den. (VANILLA *enters with basket from which* AURILLA *draws forth a big, black spider which she dangles in front of* TERRY'S *face.*)

AURILLA (*Cackling*): Do you know what this is, my pretty?

TERRY: Of course, I know what it is. It's an *Arachnida.* And don't call me "pretty."

SABILLA: Hold your tongue, slave. That's a spider. Aren't you afraid of it?

TERRY: I said it was a spider, didn't I? I told you it was an *Arachnida.* And why should I be afraid of it? After all, it's nothing more than an arthropod that happens to be able to spin a web.

VANILLA: But aren't you afraid it will bite you?

TERRY: Don't be silly. This is merely a garden spider, and certainly not poisonous. Now if it were a *Latrodectus mactans,* or, as you would say, a *black widow,* that would be a different story.

SABILLA: This is mighty strange talk coming from a slave, Vanilla. What sort of creature have you brought home?

VANILLA: At least there's no screeching and screaming at the mere sight of a spider. That's better than the last one we had.

AURILLA: If you're not afraid of spiders, how do you like this fellow? (*Dangles a frog in front of* TERRY'S *eyes*)

TERRY: I must say you ladies go in for unusual pets. Frogs are ugly but harmless little creatures, just tailless vertebrates known as *Amphibia* or *Anura.*

SABILLA: Maybe we have something here, girls—a green slave who has no fear of creepy, crawly things.

VANILLA: What about cooking? Do you think you could make Toad Stew and Kippered Spiders?

TERRY: Probably. I've cut up plenty of frogs in biology class, but I've never actually cooked any.

AURILLA (*Returning basket to* VANILLA): Put these back in the kitchen, Vanilla, and I'll get her started on the cleaning. Come along, slave, and I'll show you where to start. (VANILLA *exits.*)

TERRY: Just a minute. So far, you've done all the talking. Now it's my turn.

AURILLA: Slaves don't have turns. Do as you're told, speak when you are spoken to, and we'll get along all right.

TERRY: But I don't get it. Who are you and what is this bit about my being a slave?

SABILLA: I don't see why we should bother with introductions, but I guess it won't do any harm to tell you our names. We are the three witches of Hag Hollow. I am Sabilla. This is Aurilla, and the one who brought you here is Vanilla, our youngest sister.

AURILLA: We just filled our last book of Green Slaving Stamps, and she had them redeemed for you.

VANILLA (*Re-entering*): Since we're all getting older, we need a strong, husky girl for the heavy work and the cooking. Now bring your brush and pail and get on with the job.

TERRY: Not so fast! Not so fast! I have news for you . . . big news. In the first place, I am not a slave, green or otherwise! And in the second place, I am not a strong, husky girl! I am a boy!

ALL: A what?

TERRY: You heard me. I'm a boy!

SABILLA: But you're wearing a dress!

AURILLA: And an apron!

VANILLA: And you said your name is Terry.

TERRY: But I'm a boy, just the same. (*Removes head covering and unrolls trouser legs which have been rolled up above the knees*) This crazy outfit is my costume for the school Halloween party to which I was going when your Slave Snatcher shanghaied me. And Terry happens to be a nickname for Terence. Now are you convinced? (*Witches run around stage, screaming in terror.* AURILLA *and* SABILLA *jump on stools as if escaping a mouse.* VANILLA *crouches behind a table.*)

ALL WITCHES: A boy! A boy! Help! Help! Mercy on us! A boy! A boy!

TERRY: What's the matter? Have you all gone mad?

AURILLA (*Trembling with fright*): You're a boy!

SABILLA (*Shuddering with horror*): A real, live boy!

VANILLA (*Quaking with terror*): And you're right here in our cave!

TERRY: So what? You brought me here, didn't you? Why all the fuss?

WITCHES (*Each pointing a finger at* TERRY): You are the Curse of Hag Hollow.

TERRY: Who? Me? The what?

ALL WITCHES (*Solemnly*): The Curse of Hag Hollow!

TERRY (*Laughing*): Now I've heard everything! I've been called a lot of names in my time, but this takes the cake! "The Curse of Hag Hollow!" Wow!

AURILLA: Stop that laughing.

SABILLA: This is no laughing matter!

VANILLA (*Sobbing*): And to think it was I who brought this curse upon my innocent sisters! (*She weeps wildly.*)

TERRY: Will you stop that caterwauling and tell me what this is all about? First I'm a Green Slave and now I'm the Curse of Hag Hollow! No wonder I'm mixed up.

WITCHES (*Pointing at* TERRY *and chanting in sepulchral tones*):

When a boy, in girl's disguise,
Fools your ears and blinds your eyes,

Then will come a quick disaster!
Then the slave will be the master!
Then will black misfortune follow!
This the Curse upon Hag Hollow!

TERRY: It all sounds like mumbo-jumbo to me. Doesn't make a grain of sense.

SABILLA: That's what Papa said until the day he was taken in by a masquerader and saw Great-grandmamma dissolved in a pail of water, right before his very eyes.

AURILLA: Hold your tongue, sister. You'll be giving him ideas.

VANILLA: What difference does it make now? Our only hope is to throw ourselves on his mercy. (*All drop to their knees in elaborate salaams.*)

ALL WITCHES: All hail to the Master of Hag Hollow!

AURILLA: We are yours to command—body and broomstick!

SABILLA: You are our leader!

VANILLA: Your wish is our law!

TERRY: I must be on the *Twilight Zone* program! When does the commercial come on? (AURILLA *indicates tallest stool for* TERRY *to sit on.*)

AURILLA: Sit here, master, and issue your royal decrees.

SABILLA (*Putting mop in his hand*): This shall be your scepter, sire, the symbol of your power over us.

VANILLA: You have only to speak and we will do your bidding.

TERRY: But I don't know what to say. I've never been in a situation like this before.

AURILLA: Maybe you would like to go home.

SABILLA: We can return you in a jiffy.

VANILLA: And we will never trouble you again.

TERRY (*Settling himself*): No, no. I think I'll stay—at least for a while. I'm beginning to like it here. In fact, I think this whole deal may have possibilities.

AURILLA: Surely there is something we can do for you.

TERRY: Like what?

SABILLA: Have you no enemies?

TERRY (*Pondering*): Well, not exactly, but there *are* one or two people who have been getting in my hair lately. Just what did you have in mind?

AURILLA: You have only to name them, and their cows will never give another drop of milk.

SABILLA: Their chickens will never lay another egg!

VANILLA: Their crops will dry up and wither away!

TERRY: That's no good. The people I have in mind don't have any cows or chickens and they don't raise any crops. Can't you think of anything else?

AURILLA: We can put a spell on anybody you name. A thousand pins and needles will be pricking their arms and legs. Mysterious pains will shoot through their bodies!

TERRY: Oh, no! I wouldn't want anything like that.

VANILLA: How about a nice transformation?

TERRY: What do you mean?

VANILLA: Sabilla is very good at changing people into animals and insects.

AURILLA: Remember that fat little spider I showed you? That's really old Mrs. Flanders. Used to live next door to a friend of ours. Quite a nice woman in her way, until she developed the nasty habit of stealing our friend's knitting patterns and passing them off as her own. Well, Sabilla fixed her, but good!

VANILLA: And that frog? Did you notice how nice and fat he was?

TERRY: Don't tell me he used to be a person!

VANILLA: Of course. Quite a horrible little man, really. Used to drive his neighbors crazy playing the tuba. Now, thanks to Sabilla, he can croak to his heart's content without disturbing a soul!

TERRY: This may be the very thing! Yes, the more I think of it, the better I like it.

SABILLA (*Rubbing her hands with glee*): Goody! Goody! I can hardly wait to get started. Who is this enemy you wish me to destroy?

TERRY: His name is. . . . Now, wait a minute! I wouldn't want him destroyed permanently. I just want him out of the way for the time being. Can you change him back again later on?

SABILLA: Oh, sure. Any time you say the word. (*Snapping her fingers*) Just like that!

TERRY: O.K. I'll give it a try. His name is Casper Cramer and he lives at 922 East Maple Street, Harristown, Pennsylvania.

SABILLA: Casper Cramer? Can you tell me a little more about him? I take pride in matching my transformations with my victims' personalities.

TERRY: I guess you might say that Casper is quite a guy, at least in his own opinion. He's . . . well . . . I hate to admit this, but he's good-looking . . . at least all the girls seem to think so. He's tall, dark, plays basketball, and he's quite a singer. In fact, he was to be the soloist at our Halloween party tonight—the same party I was going to when this character (*Indicates* VANILLA) so rudely interrupted me.

SABILLA: Um-m-m! Tall, dark and handsome! Likes to play with a ball! Fast on his feet! Likes to sing . . . um-m!

I've got it! I've got it! I've got it! Casper the Cat! How does that appeal to you?

TERRY: Fine! In fact, that's great! Boy, oh boy, I can just see old Casper ducking the boots and shoes people will throw at him when he starts yowling! And wait till he catches his first mouse. Hurry up! Let's get this show on the road!

SABILLA: I'm practically there, master.

AURILLA: Do you have your magic spray gun?

SABILLA: Right here in my pocket.

VANILLA: I'll meet you in front of the cave and give your broomstick an extra push. (SABILLA *and* VANILLA *exit.*)

TERRY: How long do you think it will take?

AURILLA: Sabilla will be back with her report before you can say "Scat!" This Casper must be a deadly enemy. What evil has he done you, master?

TERRY: He's done plenty, the rat! . . . er . . . I mean . . . the cat! He's stolen my girl, that's what he's done.

AURILLA: No wonder you wanted him catapulted into oblivion.

TERRY: You see, I made a date for this Halloween party two weeks ago, and then, at the last minute, Drusilla fell for this big operator, Casper Cramer.

AURILLA: Drusilla?

TERRY: Drusilla Deane. (*With rapture*) Man, oh man! You should see her!

AURILLA: Is she beautiful?

TERRY: She's a knockout. Red hair . . .

AURILLA (*With excitement*): Red hair?

TERRY: Gorgeous red hair, big green eyes . . .

AURILLA (*Even more excited*): Green eyes?

TERRY: Well, maybe not exactly green, but a greenish blue . . .

AURILLA: Tell me, does she have a wart on her chin—something like mine?

TERRY: Ye gods, no! Drusilla doesn't have any warts at all. But she does have a dimple . . . and it *is* in her chin.

AURILLA: I thought as much.

TERRY: You sound as if you know Drusilla. Why are you asking all these questions?

AURILLA: I just like to hear you talk about her. You make her sound so bewitching. By the way, does she like to go swimming?

TERRY (*Surprised*): Now that's a funny thing for you to ask. As it happens, Drusilla hates the water. She won't even walk in the rain if she can help it.

AURILLA: This is very interesting, very interesting, indeed.

VANILLA (*Re-entering*): Well, she's off! I gave her a good, big shove and sent her up in the air like a rocket.

AURILLA: Our master has another problem, Vanilla. You and I have work to do.

VANILLA: More enemies?

AURILLA: Quite the opposite. Our young master is suffering from unrequited love.

VANILLA: Excellent! Excellent! It will give us a chance to try out our new formula.

TERRY: Now, look here, I don't want anything to happen to Drusilla.

VANILLA: *Drusilla!* Did you say *Drusilla?*

AURILLA: Yes, our lord and master has fallen victim to the charms of a young lady by the name of Drusilla . . . Drusilla Deane.

VANILLA: But wasn't that the name of . . .

TERRY: What goes on here? You both sound as if you know Drusilla.

AURILLA: Pray don't jump to conclusions, master.

TERRY: I want it distinctly understood she's not to be changed into any beast, bird, or fish. I like her the way she is.

VANILLA: Nothing will happen to Drusilla. I promise you.

TERRY: Then what's all this about a formula?

AURILLA: It's just a simple little love potion Vanilla and I have dreamed up.

TERRY: I won't have you experimenting on my girl.

VANILLA: Who said anything about your girl! We'll give *you* the potion. Once you drink it, you will become positively irresistible.

TERRY: How do I know this isn't some trick to get rid of me?

AURILLA: Go get the bottle, Vanilla. Which do you prefer, master, strawberry or chocolate?

TERRY: Chocolate. But wait a minute! (*As* VANILLA *exits*) Wait a minute! I haven't said I'll drink any of the stuff.

AURILLA (*In a soothing voice*): Now, now, master. Vanilla and I know our business. We've been making love potions of one kind or another for hundreds of years and this is the best batch we've ever brewed, if I do say so myself. You want this girl to fall for you, don't you?

TERRY: Sure, but . . .

AURILLA (*Taking bottle and spoon from* VANILLA *as she enters, and pouring out a spoonful of liquid*): Then take this, master, and Drusilla won't have eyes for another boy in the whole world.

TERRY (*Doubtfully, as* AURILLA *stands poised with the spoon*): Are you sure?

AURILLA: Positive.

VANILLA: It never fails.

TERRY: Then here goes! (*Takes dose of liquid*) Mm-m-m!

Not bad! In fact, it's delicious. How about another spoonful?

AURILLA (*Corking bottle and handing it to* VANILLA): It's high-powered stuff, master. We don't want to overdo it.

TERRY: Well, do I look any different? Am I getting irresistible?

VANILLA: You'll have to wait a while for it to begin to work.

AURILLA: Of course we find you irresistible already. But the real test will be when you meet Drusilla.

TERRY: I can hardly wait!

VANILLA: Then we will have her here immediately, my lord.

TERRY: You mean you'll bring her here?

AURILLA: Of course.

TERRY: But she's at the Halloween party. She won't want to come. How will you manage?

VANILLA: We have our methods.

TERRY: But I don't want her harmed.

VANILLA: You made the journey without any discomfort, didn't you?

TERRY: Yes, but . . .

AURILLA: We promise you no harm will come to the girl while she is in our care. May we proceed?

TERRY: No! Yes . . . O.K., go ahead. But I'm warning you . . .

AURILLA: Prepare for flight, Vanilla. In the meantime I'll see to our young master's costume.

TERRY: What's wrong with my costume?

VANILLA: Well, you must admit that outfit you're wearing isn't the most romantic get-up in the world. Even with our potion at work, I can't see a beautiful young girl falling for someone who looks like you!

TERRY: Maybe you're right. I decided to wear this only after Drusilla turned me down.

AURILLA: If you'll step into the next room, master, you will find any disguise you wish. We have skeletons in armor, robes of ermine, uniforms of state . . . you have only to help yourself.

VANILLA: And by the time you are dressed, Drusilla will be here to greet you.

TERRY: If this stuff works as you say it will, we should have a ball. (*He exits.*)

AURILLA (*Clutching* VANILLA's *arm*): Go bring her at once, Vanilla. Don't let her escape your clutches.

VANILLA: Do you really think she's the same one?

AURILLA: She has to be. Red hair . . . green eyes . . . goes by the name of Drusilla.

VANILLA: Then we've found her . . . after all these years.

AURILLA: The Fourth Witch of Hag Hollow!

VANILLA: This time we'll never let her escape. Where's my broomstick? (SABILLA *enters, somewhat breathless.*)

SABILLA: The deed is done. Casper the Cat is out catching his first mouse (*Cackling*) and I hope he enjoys it! Where are you going, Vanilla?

VANILLA: No time to explain, sister. Aurilla will tell you what it's all about. I'll be back as soon as I can. (*She exits.*)

AURILLA: Better sit down, Sabilla. I have some shocking news.

SABILLA: It's that wretched boy! The curse is already at work.

AURILLA: Not exactly. But he has found Drusilla.

SABILLA: No! I can't believe it. Not after all these years. There must be some mistake.

AURILLA: There's no mistake, Sabilla. I knew her at once

from his description. Ever since she left us to take on mortal form, I knew some day we would find her.

SABILLA: The boy? Does he know?

AURILLA: Of course not. She has managed to bewitch him into accepting her as a real girl. The poor stupid oaf is quite enamored.

SABRILLA: How can you be sure?

AURILLA: Everything fits . . . the same red hair, the same green eyes, the same power to enthrall and bewitch every young man she meets. Oh, it's Drusilla all right.

SABILLA: I just can't believe it.

AURILLA: With any luck at all, Vanilla should have her here in a few minutes. Then you can judge for yourself.

TERRY (*Entering resplendent in a Romeo costume*): Well, how do I look? Do you think Drusilla will like it?

AURILLA: A very wise choice, master. And with our potion bubbling away inside of you, you'll not only look like Romeo, you'll *be* Romeo.

SABILLA: And a very dashing one, too. (*Offstage siren.*)

TERRY: What in the world is that?

AURILLA: It's the all-clear for Vanilla. She's making a perfect one-point landing.

TERRY: I wonder if she has Drusilla. (DRUSILLA *enters in Juliet costume, cuddling a small kitten in her arms.*)

DRUSILLA: Terry! How in the world did you get here? And where did you get that simply stunning costume? Why, you look positively handsome.

TERRY: Thanks, Drusilla. I might say the same thing to you and even ask you the same question. The last I saw of you, you were headed for the Halloween dance with Casper.

DRUSILLA: Casper! Don't mention that horrible boy's name to me *ever!* Such a thing never happened to me in my whole life. He told me he was going to bring me a glass of punch, and that was the last I ever saw of him. Imagine, he left me cold!

TERRY: And where, may I ask, did you get that disgusting animal you're carrying?

DRUSILLA: Disgusting animal indeed! (*Holding kitten against her face and cooing over it*) This is a dear, little, precious kitten. I found him wandering in the street as I left the gym, and I just scooped him up and brought him along, didn't I, sweetums? I certainly couldn't let any nasty old automobile run over this precious baby. Besides, I adore cats. They're my favorite pets.

TERRY: Drusilla, will you put that creature down and come here? I want you to meet my friends.

DRUSILLA: Why, Terry, what a way to talk about a poor innocent, defenseless, adorable pussycat!

TERRY: It's a horrible cat! Probably has fleas! Put it down, I say.

DRUSILLA (*Puts cat on floor.* VANILLA *picks up cat and carries it offstage*) : Why, Terry, I never knew you could be so masterful! But then everything that's happening tonight seems strange. I don't even know where I am or how I got here. I just stepped out for a breath of air, and woosh! The next thing I knew, here I was. Who are these friends of yours, and what is this place?

AURILLA: You know perfectly well who we are, Drusilla.

DRUSILLA: Maybe I'd know you if you took off that horrible mask!

AURILLA: Take off my mask, indeed! This is my face.

SABILLA: Stop bluffing, Drusilla. You know who we are.

DRUSILLA: Good heavens! There are two of you!

VANILLA (*Entering*): Three, to be exact, sister mine.

TERRY *and* DRUSILLA: Sister!

DRUSILLA: How dare you call me sister?

VANILLA: Because you *are* our sister.

AURILLA: Our long-lost sister who decided she was too good to be a witch and changed herself into a human being.

SABILLA: Drusilla . . . the fourth Witch of Hag Hollow.

DRUSILLA (*Running to* TERRY): Terry, who are these creatures? What are they talking about?

TERRY: This must be some sort of joke. (*Turning to witches*) I would advise you to stop clowning. You're frightening Drusilla.

WITCHES (*Mocking*): "Frightening Drusilla!" That's the laugh of the century!

TERRY: As Master of Hag Hollow, I command you to put an end to this funny business and behave yourselves. This joke has gone far enough.

AURILLA: It's no joke, master. This girl is really our long-lost sister, Drusilla.

SABILLA: It's common knowledge that witches sometimes assume human shape and form.

VANILLA: But this one carried things too far. She has been gone for three hundred years. It's high time she came back and took up her responsibilities as a witch.

TERRY: This is the most ridiculous thing I ever heard of. Drusilla is not and never was a witch. She's a real girl.

AURILLA: How do you know? How do you know what she does or what shape she assumes after everyone else is asleep?

SABILLA: Look at her. Look at that hair—those eyes.

VANILLA: You said yourself she never goes near the water if she can help it.

AURILLA: She just told you that cats are her favorite pets. She's never without one.

SABILLA: And look at that wart on her chin—just like ours!

DRUSILLA (*Furious*): Wart! I'll have you know that's not a wart. It's a dimple!

TERRY: And a most enchanting dimple.

SABILLA: So you call it a dimple. We call it an inverted wart!

TERRY: Stop it, you fiends! You're insulting Drusilla and proving nothing. There are probably hundreds of red-haired girls who dislike swimming and love cats.

AURILLA: And how many of them are named Drusilla? Answer me that.

TERRY: Well, I've never made a survey, but I should say plenty.

VANILLA: Name two.

TERRY: I—I can't . . . not on the spur of the moment, but this is just plain stupid. Come on, Drusilla, let's get out of here.

VANILLA: How?

TERRY: You forget I am the Master here. I order you to return us both at once.

AURILLA: Leave Drusilla with us and we will return you to your home immediately.

DRUSILLA: Terry, Terry, don't leave me here with these dreadful hags!

TERRY: I wouldn't dream of such a thing. Take us home at once! Do you hear me?

SABILLA: We are asking only for what is ours.

VANILLA: Whether she admits it or not, Drusilla is one of us.

AURILLA: She belongs here with her own skin and bones.

DRUSILLA: Terry, don't let them have me.

TERRY: Don't be afraid, Drusilla. I'll get us both out of here—and fast! (*Seizes scrub bucket.*) With one good dousing, I can destroy them all, and when I get home, I'll report this cave to our speleological society and have the place sealed shut forever.

SABILLA: And what about Casper?

DRUSILLA: Casper? What does he have to do with it?

VANILLA: Do you want to be blamed for his disappearance?

TERRY: Ye gods! I forgot all about Casper. Bring him back here right away.

AURILLA: On one condition.

TERRY: You're not in any position to bargain. Do as I say.

VANILLA: Destroy us and Casper will be catching mice forever.

TERRY: How did I ever get into such a mess!

SABILLA: We are prepared to be reasonable. If you are so sure Drusilla is not a witch, why not try the water treatment on her?

TERRY: What do you mean?

AURILLA: You know exactly what she means.

VANILLA: If you think you can destroy a witch with water, try it on Drusilla and see what happens.

TERRY: I wouldn't dare.

SABILLA: Then you really believe she is our long-lost sister.

TERRY: I believe nothing of the sort.

AURILLA: Then why aren't you throwing the water on her?

DRUSILLA: Terry Baxter, don't you dare.

TERRY: Let me see Casper in human form, and I'll do it!

SABILLA: You swear?

TERRY: I swear.

SABILLA: Very well. We'll see. (*Squints and intones*)

Casper, Jasper,
Meow, meow,
Back to nature
Come right now!

(CASPER *enters with paper cup in his hand. He goes directly to* DRUSILLA.)

CASPER: So there you are! I've been looking everywhere for you.

DRUSILLA (*Turning away from him*): You can drink your own punch. I'm going home with Terry.

CASPER: Going home with Terry! But you have a date with me!

DRUSILLA: I can't help it, Casper. Somehow I find Terry positively irresistible.

TERRY: Oh, Drusilla, do you really mean it?

DRUSILLA: Of course I mean it, Terry. You are the most delightful boy I've ever met.

WITCHES: It's now or never, Terry!

TERRY: Oh, gosh, please forgive me, Drusilla, but I have to do this. (*Throws water on her*)

DRUSILLA (*Squealing and brushing her dress*): No! No! Terry, what are you doing? You're ruining my hair. . . . Oh, look . . . my dress is all spotted.

TERRY (*Shaking finger at witches*): See, see . . . nothing happened. She's not a witch. She's still the same. Now, you horrible, wicked creatures, you get us all out of here on the double!

AURILLA: I guess we'll have to keep our word.

SABILLA: I'm still not convinced.

VANILLA: But we have no proof. Come along, master, you may ride on *my* broomstick.

AURILLA: I'll take Casper.

SABILLA: And Drusilla will ride with me.

DRUSILLA: Wait a minute. I must get my kitten.

CASPER: Meow, meow! Here I am.

DRUSILLA: I don't understand.

TERRY: Don't stop to ask questions now, Drusilla. I'll explain later. (*A siren sounds offstage and there is a black-out. The witches shriek, "We're off!" When lights go on, the curtains are closed and* TERRY *and* DRUSILLA *are strolling in front of curtain, arm in arm.*)

TERRY: It's been a wonderful evening, Drusilla, although a bit weird in spots.

DRUSILLA: Just look at that moon. Isn't it gorgeous?

TERRY (*Gazing upward*): A real October moon.

DRUSILLA: Does the moon ever make you feel funny, Terry?

TERRY: How do you mean, "funny"?

DRUSILLA: Oh, I don't know. But when there's a full moon, I always feel . . . well . . . sort of strange. As if I could fly higher and higher and higher. . . .

TERRY (*Shuddering*): Please, Drusilla, don't mention flying.

DRUSILLA: Do you think the moon could cast a spell on anyone, Terry?

TERRY: A spell? What ever made you think of such a thing?

DRUSILLA: Oh, I don't know. There's something so bewitching about a moon!

TERRY: Why must you keep using those awful words? You never talked this way before.

DRUSILLA: I've never been out with you on a moonlit night before. (*Sound of meowing*) Listen . . . do you hear a cat?

TERRY: No, I don't. Yes, I do.

DRUSILLA: Wait a minute. I must find it. You know how much I love cats.

TERRY: Forget it. For heaven's sake, Drusilla, what's got into you?

DRUSILLA: Nothing's got into me. I was always like this.

TERRY (*Looking at her closely*): Drusilla, you look so strange! Your eyes are positively glowing.

DRUSILLA: That's because I'm with you, Terry. Take a good look at me, Terry. Is that really a dimple in my chin?

TERRY (*Cupping her chin in his hands*): Of course it's a dimple . . . a most bewitching dimple. Bewitching . . . now, why did I use that word? Drusilla, tell me the truth. Are you . . . could you possibly be. . . .

DRUSILLA: Be what, Terry?

TERRY: Oh, hang it all, what difference does it make? (*Putting his arm around her*) All I really wanted to know is this: Could you possibly go to the rest of the school dances with me this winter?

DRUSILLA: But of course, Terry. I was just wondering how long it would take you to ask me.

TERRY (*Laughing and giving her a quick hug*): Drusilla, you really *are* a little witch. But go right ahead and keep me under your spell. I love it! (*They exit.*)

THE END

Production Notes

The Curse of Hag Hollow

Characters: 2 male; 4 female.

Playing Time: 30 minutes.

Costumes: The witches wear traditional black witch costumes. Terry first enters dressed as a scrub woman, with his head tied up in a dustcloth. He wears a long coverall apron and carries a mop and pail. (His trousers are rolled up beneath the apron.) Later Terry wears a Romeo costume. Drusilla wears a Juliet costume. Casper may wear a dark suit.

Properties: Giant cereal box with large label, "Ghost Toasties," enormous goblet (the type used as an ornamental planter) filled with red liquid; bowl and spoon; brooms; basket containing a large black spider and a frog; bottle and spoon; kitten for Drusilla; paper cup for Casper.

Setting: A cave. The furnishings include a table and several stools of different heights. The backdrop may be painted to represent rocks, and large spiders' webs may be hung about the cave.

Lighting: Just before the end of the play, there is a complete blackout.

Sound: Offstage siren.

Haunts for Hire

Characters

FRANK FRANKENSTEIN
VELMA VAMPIRE
CARL
BONY
WARDROBE MISTRESS
HEADLESS HARRY
CHILLY WILLY
REPRESENTATIVE OF A.F. OF G.
MRS. VANDERMEER
OFFICER
MRS. MARBLE
MARY } *her daughters*
MOLLY }
MESSENGER

TIME: *Halloween afternoon.*
SETTING: *The office of Haunts for Hire, a flourishing Halloween enterprise.*
AT RISE: FRANK FRANKENSTEIN *is frantically taking calls on four phones at a large table, above which hangs a big*

sign, YOU DARE 'EM, WE SCARE 'EM! *His secretary,* VELMA VAMPIRE, *is folding and stacking sheets at a long table cluttered with wigs, costumes, masks, props, etc. The* WARDROBE MISTRESS *is draping* BONY *in a long, red velvet cloak.* BONY'S *back is toward the audience.* CARL, *a third assistant, is untangling a mass of chains and packing them in boxes.*

FRANK (*At phone*): Haunts for Hire. Frankenstein speaking. (*Picking up second phone as it rings*) Sorry, we're completely out of regulation black cats and witches. (*Answering third phone*) Haunts for Hire. Frankenstein speaking. (*Pause*) Yes, yes, we can give you three ghosts at three dollars each, but clanking chains will be extra. (*Back to first phone*) Sorry, ma'am, we were interrupted. (*Pause*) Yes, we'll put you down for a Midnight Murder Special. (*Pause*) Of course not! We never use anything as obvious as *ketchup!* (*Laugh*) Oh, we have our little trade secrets, you know! (*Pause*) Thank you and goodbye. (*Fourth phone rings.*) Haunts for Hire. Frankenstein speaking. (*Pause*) What? What's that? (*Pause*) A.F. of G.? Never heard of it. What does it stand for? (*Pause*) Amalgamated Federation of Ghosts? No, no, I'm afraid we wouldn't be interested. We are strictly nonunion. (*Picks up first phone as it rings.*) Haunts for Hire. Frankenstein speaking. (*Pause*) Just a minute. I'll see. (*With hand over mouthpiece*) Velma, how many clean sheets do we have left?

VELMA: We'll have to call the laundry. Only six left and I have three more orders to fill.

FRANK (*Returning to phone*): Sorry, I'm afraid we're fresh out of ghosts. But we do have a nice, mildewed corpse we could let you have. (*Pause*) But naturally, he's terrific. Remember our slogan: "They're wild! They satisfy." (*Pause*) Yes, indeed, we stand behind every haunt! O.K. What's that address? (*To* VELMA) Velma, get this, will you please? (VELMA *comes to desk with memo pad.*) Two twenty-two Ocean Terrace.

VELMA: Ocean Terrace! That's way on the other side of town, Frank. Charge them ten percent extra for transportation.

FRANK (*At phone*): Sorry, but Ocean Terrace is pretty far out. We'll have to make an extra charge for transportation. (*Pause*) Very well. I know you'll be pleased. O.K. madam, twelve o'clock sharp! (*Hangs up and mops forehead*) Phew! This is driving me crazy. Can you take the phones for a while, Velma?

VELMA: Sorry, Frank. I have to work in the stockroom. The rest of the girls went home early. Those phantom costumes aren't ready and the spider webs are in a mess. Let Carl do it.

CARL (*Busy with chains*): Not me. I'm strictly sound effects, remember?

FRANK: Only too well. If you can't get a better recording of hysterical laughter, you're fired.

CARL: Take it easy, boss. By the way, what was that bit about the Amalgamated Federation of Ghosts?

FRANK: Some crazy coot thinks we should join a union—a ghost union. Can you beat that?

VELMA: Oh, I forgot to tell you. I had a call from that same outfit this morning, and a man came to see me about it this afternoon.

FRANK: What did you tell him?

VELMA: The usual. I told him you did the hiring and firing and that he'd have to come back later.

FRANK: He'll only be wasting his time with me. Has Chilly Willy come in yet?

VELMA (*As she goes to right exit*): He's due any minute now. If you need me, I'll be in the workroom. (*She exits.*)

WARDROBE MISTRESS: Do you have time to take a look at this, Frank? It's still a bit lopsided, but it's the best I could do. (*Stands back from* BONY)

FRANK (*Inspecting* BONY): Not bad, considering you made it out of an old pair of drapes. What's he supposed to be?

WARDROBE MISTRESS: I'm not quite sure. We have orders for the Masque of the Red Death and the Phantom of the Opera.

FRANK: He looks a long time dead. (*Picking up plumed hat from table and putting it on* BONY) Put this hat on him, and he can be both—at different times, of course. (BONY *faces audience, revealing skeleton mask.*)

BONY: If I do both, I get double pay.

FRANK: Natch. Let me see the order blanks. (WARDROBE MISTRESS *hands him the blanks.*) Good! You're in, Bony. Red Death at eleven, Phantom of the Opera at one. (*Looking at watch*) Take a break and be back in twenty minutes.

BONY: Hey, Frank, for five bucks extra, I'll play my flute on the Phantom of the Opera job.

FRANK: Nothing doing. All musical haunts are handled by Evelyn and her Tragic Violin.

WARDROBE MISTRESS: Now take it easy getting out of that costume, Bony. Let me help you. (*Helps* BONY *out of costume as phone rings*)

FRANK (*At phone*): Haunts for Hire. Frankenstein speaking. (*Pause*) Who? Oh, it's you, Harry. (*Pause*) What do you mean you lost your head? (*Pause*) Well, stop at the nearest supermarket and get another one. (*Pause*) O.K., O.K.! We'll charge it up to expenses, but don't be so careless. Now, get back on the job. We're snowed under with calls. (*Hangs up*) That Harry would lose his head even if it *were* fastened on to him. That's the third pumpkin he's bought this week for The Man with His Head Tucked Underneath His Arm. Remind me to send someone else next time we have a call for detachable heads. (CHILLY WILLY *enters. He wears a dripping raincoat, and carries a soaking wet sponge in each hand. He is sneezing violently. Each time he sneezes, he tries to cover his mouth with his hand, and water drips on the floor from the sponges.*)

WARDROBE MISTRESS (*As she folds up costume*): Watch where you're going, Willy. I don't want you dripping all over this red velvet.

CHILLY WILLY: Don't worry. I'm down to my last drip. In other words, I've had it. (*Sneeze*) I quit.

FRANK: But you can't quit now, Willy. You're booked solid.

CHILLY WILLY: I'm no longer a solid. I'm a liquid. I've disintegrated. I tell you I'm finished, once and for all. Somebody help me out of these wet things before *rigor mortis* sets in.

BONY: Here, I'll give you a hand, but don't drip on me. I don't want to catch cold. (*Helps* CHILLY WILLY *remove coat*)

VELMA (*Entering*): Oh, you poor dear. Let me help you. (*Takes sponges*) You really are soaked. Maybe you should go home and change your clothes.

CHILLY WILLY: I'm going home all right, and I'm going to stay there.

FRANK: You can't be serious. Your Drowned Demon of the Deep is a sensation. We just had a call on your last job. Three gals fainted when you dribbled that wet seaweed down their backs.

CHILLY WILLY: Flattery will get you nowhere. (*Sneezes*) I'm going home.

WARDROBE MISTRESS: Come on, Willy. I'll hang these wet things on the radiator in the workroom and make you a nice hot cup of tea. Then you'll feel better.

VELMA: You'll have plenty of time to dry out.

CHILLY WILLY: You're so right! I'll have the rest of my life. I tell you I'm finished—washed up!

FRANK: But you can't leave us now. I've just signed you up for a job on Ocean Terrace as the Mildewed Corpse! We'll lose a customer.

CHILLY WILLY: Don't cry on my shoulder, Frank. I'm damp enough already. All I want is my pay check.

CARL: I sure hate to see you go, chum. I just worked out a neat recording of sea gull cries and dashing waves for your entrance.

BONY: What's a little discomfort, old man? We all knew we'd have to suffer for our art when we signed up for this Haunts for Hire hassle.

VELMA: And think of what we're doing for the Dramatic Club Scholarship Fund!

WARDROBE MISTRESS: To say nothing of the percentage we keep for ourselves—and all the fun we're having. This is the most successful Halloween project the club has ever had.

CHILLY WILLY: Congratulations! But count me out.

FRANK (*Moving to desk and writing out check*): O.K., Willy. Here's your check. I can see your mind's made up.

CHILLY WILLY: Thanks, thanks a lot. No hard feelings I hope.

FRANK: Of course not. We'll manage somehow.

CHILLY WILLY: Thanks, pal. And good luck! (*He exits.*)

CARL: What are you going to do about Ocean Terrace?

FRANK (*To* BONY): Maybe we could double again with you, Bone Head.

BONY: Not me. I'm afraid of water.

WARDROBE MISTRESS: I could rig up an outfit for Harry if he gets back in time. (*Blackout. Lights go back on almost immediately.*)

VELMA: What was that?

CARL: Did we forget to pay the light bill?

REPRESENTATIVE (*Standing in doorway. He wears a business suit with lapels, pockets, tie, and cuffs of phosphorescent material. He coughs apologetically*): Excuse me. (*As everybody jumps*) Did I startle you? (*Handing card to* FRANK) I represent the A.F. of G.— Amalgamated Federation of Ghosts.

FRANK: Oh! Er—yes. I believe we had a phone call from your organization a while ago. (*Puts card in pocket*)

REPRESENTATIVE (*Indicating* VELMA): This young lady suggested I call on you, sir. It's about joining the Federation.

FRANK: Sorry you made the trip, sir. But we're not interested.

REPRESENTATIVE: But our organization has many advantages.

FRANK: Perhaps so. But we're just a small outfit, strictly non-professional.

REPRESENTATIVE: Non-professional? But I understand you charge regular fees for your services.

VELMA: Yes, yes, we do, but we keep only a small percentage for ourselves. The rest goes to our Dramatic Club.

REPRESENTATIVE: Nevertheless, the fee does take you out of the amateur class.

FRANK: I'm afraid you are wasting your time. We are not interested.

REPRESENTATIVE: If you'll pardon my saying so, sir, I might point out several *disadvantages* of operating outside the Federation.

FRANK: What are you trying to do? Threaten us?

REPRESENTATIVE: Not at all, sir. I was merely pointing out the risks you are taking.

FRANK: Risks? What risks?

REPRESENTATIVE: Haunting is a risky business, even for professionals.

FRANK: This is nonsense. Now, as I told you before, we're just not interested.

REPRESENTATIVE: Is that your last word, sir?

FRANK: That's my last word, mister.

REPRESENTATIVE: Very well, sir. But just in case anything happens, please remember we gave you a chance.

FRANK: What chance?

REPRESENTATIVE (*Blandly*): Why, the chance to join the Amalgamated Federation of Ghosts. (*Blackout. When lights go on,* REPRESENTATIVE *has disappeared.*)

VELMA: Well, what do you make of that?

CARL: That was a funny one.

BONY: What a creep!

WARDROBE MISTRESS: He gave me the jitters, that one!

FRANK: Don't get yourselves in an uproar. We have work to do. Now, let's get on with it. Velma, get on the phone and see if you can reach Harry at his last call. Bony, you'd better get moving. (MRS. VANDERMEER *enters. She is a nervous, fussy woman, highly excited.*)

MRS. VANDERMEER: Is this the office of Haunts for Hire?

FRANK (*Heartily*): Yes, yes, it is. What can we do for you?

MRS. VANDERMEER: Do for me? Well, my goodness, you've already done it. And I must say you have done a fabulous job—absolutely fabulous. Young man, you simply *made* my party.

FRANK: I—er—I am afraid I don't quite understand, Mrs. —er—what did you say your name was?

MRS. VANDERMEER: Vandermeer. Mrs. J. W. Vandermeer of Vandermeer Drive. You know, the big brownstone house at the top of the hill where you sent the mummy.

ALL: Mummy?

MRS. VANDERMEER: Yes, mummy. Oh, I do wish you could have seen my guests when that horrible creature stepped out of the mummy case in the front hall and gibbered at them.

FRANK: I'm afraid I still don't understand, ma'am. Velma, do we have a Vandermeer on our list?

VELMA (*At desk, consulting book*): Vandermeer? No—no order for that name or address.

MRS. VANDERMEER: Oh, dear! How careless of Howard. Howard's my husband. I asked him to place an order here, and he didn't seem a bit keen on it at the time. But when that mummy case arrived, I knew he had been here. I wonder how your driver ever found us without an address.

FRANK: Driver? We don't even have a driver.

MRS. VANDERMEER: But you must have a driver. You absolutely must have a driver and a truck, too. Otherwise, how will you ever get that mummy case out of our front hall and off the premises?

FRANK: But my dear lady, we didn't put it there in the first place.

MRS. VANDERMEER: Now, young man, let's not play games. Of course you put it there. (*Producing card from bag*) Here's your card, "Haunts for Hire." It was on the mummy case when it was delivered. I see your rates are three dollars an hour. Very reasonable. (*Puts three dollars on desk*) Now there's your fee and I'll expect that mummy case to be taken out of there within the hour.

VELMA: Look, Mrs. Vandermeer, we don't even own a mummy case.

WARDROBE MISTRESS: Or a mummy.

MRS. VANDERMEER: Well, you own one now—the case, I mean. You see, when my guests asked the mummy to remove his wrappings, well—he just wasn't there any more. (*Giggles*) It was fabulous! Simply fabulous. I don't see how you young folks think up these things. I guess it's all this science they're teaching in the schools these days.

FRANK: Mrs. Vandermeer, please listen to me.

MRS. VANDERMEER: I simply must run, young man. But let me tell you one thing, I'm telling everybody about Haunts for Hire. You are simply fabulous. Fabulous! (*Exits*)

CARL: Gee, boss, it will cost at least twenty bucks to get a moving van to haul that mummy case from Vandermeer Drive.

VELMA: Twenty bucks! And she gave us three!

BONY: That's making money fast.

WARDROBE MISTRESS: I don't understand it!

FRANK (*Sinking into chair at desk*): Neither do I. (*Phone rings.*) Haunts for Hire. Frankenstein speaking. (*Pause*) What? (*Sputtering*) What's that? What's that you say?

(*Pause*) A monster in your swimming pool? What kind of monster? (*Pause*) But that's impossible. We don't have any monsters that big. No, no. It couldn't have come from Haunts for Hire. (*Pause*) What? What's that? You're sending us a bill? No, no! (*Jiggling phone*) Listen. Wait a minute. Operator! Operator!

VELMA: What is it, Frank? What's wrong?

FRANK (*In a daze*): Some joker out on Parmalee Drive claims he was having a Halloween party and a twenty-foot monster rose up out of his swimming pool.

CARL: Boy, oh boy! What kind of cider were they serving at that party?

FRANK: The man wasn't kidding, Carl. The monster had a tag around its neck—"Haunts for Hire"—with our address!

ALL: Oh, no!

FRANK: Oh, yes! And he's sending us a bill for one cracked swimming pool! (*As they stare at each other in amazement,* HARRY *enters.*)

HARRY (*Frantically*): Frank! Frank! This thing has gone too far. Frank, wait till you hear what happened!

VELMA: Don't tell us you lost your head again.

HARRY: Yes, yes, this time I really lost it! And how! (*Sits down, wipes brow with handkerchief*) Boy, I wouldn't have believed it.

CARL: Well, get on with it. What happened?

HARRY: Right after I got my new head at the supermarket, I went out to that place on Pleasant Hill Road. It was a kid's party, so I did my usual bit with the head—you know—twisting it all around and finally throwing it through an open window. Well, that's when it happened.

CARL: I can guess. You forgot to open the window.

HARRY: If that were all! No, the window was open all right, but when I threw the head—now, I know you won't believe this, but so help me—

FRANK: We'll believe almost anything today, Harry. What happened?

HARRY: Well, the thing took off like—like a regular rocket.

BONY: What do you mean?

HARRY: I mean it zoomed around and around and then went off into space. Boy! You should have seen that living room. It knocked down two lamps, hit the chandelier, bounced down on the floor, zoomed up again, sideswiped two pictures and the last I saw of it, it was heading upstairs.

VELMA: What do you mean—the last you saw of it?

HARRY: You don't think I stuck around to see the finish, do you? Not Headless Harry. I high-tailed it out of there before the lady could call the cops.

VELMA: Frank, what are we going to do? (*Phone rings.*)

WARDROBE MISTRESS: Don't answer it.

CARL: Let's get out of here.

BONY: This is no place for us. (*Phones ring insistently*)

FRANK (*Answering one after the other*): Haunts for Hire. Sorry, we're closed until further notice. Sorry, closed till further notice.

HARRY: It's no good, Frank. Just don't answer any more. Carl's right. We have to get out of here.

FRANK: But why should we run? We've done nothing wrong.

HARRY: Try telling that to the people on Pleasant Hill Road.

BONY: And the man with the cracked swimming pool.

VELMA: I'll get my things. (*Everyone scrambles to collect belongings.*)

FRANK (*Rising*): O.K., we'll go. (OFFICER *enters with* CHILLY WILLY.)

OFFICER: Nobody's going any place until you answer a few questions.

CHILLY WILLY: Frank, tell this officer I am not a juvenile delinquent!

ALL (*Ad lib*): Willy! What's the matter? (Etc.)

OFFICER: So you know this character, do you? He told me you would vouch for him, but unless you can do some pretty fast talking, I'll take the whole crowd of you downtown.

FRANK: What's the charge, Officer?

OFFICER: Vandalism! Pure, outrageous vandalism. If you have anything to say for this young hoodlum, speak up.

VELMA: What happened, Willy?

FRANK: Willy doesn't even work here any more, Officer. He quit.

CHILLY WILLY: Oh, if I only had quit, Frank. But after I left you, I began thinking of how I had let you down. So—well—I guess I had a change of heart. Anyhow, I went out to that place on Ocean Terrace. The lady was a little surprised to see me so early, but I explained that I always liked to get my act set up before the party started, so she told me to come in. I started to show her my trick with the sponges.

OFFICER: Some trick, I'd say!

FRANK: But, officer, it was all in fun and perfectly harmless.

OFFICER: If that's your idea of fun, buster, I'm not laughing.

CHILLY WILLY: Neither am I, Frank. It was awful. I started to show her how I dropped the seaweed around and squeezed a little water out of these sponges, when, holy catfish—it was just as if Boulder Dam broke loose. Before I knew what was happening, we were up to our ankles in water. Water everywhere. It came down from the ceiling and out of the walls just like a sprinkler system.

OFFICER: Fortunately, I was right in front of the house and when the lady screamed and this young vandal came tearing out of the house, I grabbed him.

CHILLY WILLY: Tell him, tell him, Frank.

FRANK: Tell him what?

CHILLY WILLY: Tell him I didn't do it. Tell him I couldn't have done it. Tell him it's only a little trick—a sort of joke.

FRANK: It's no joke, Willy. We're in trouble. (MRS. MARBLE, MARY, *and* MOLLY *enter, wearing scarves on their heads. The girls are crying.*)

MRS. MARBLE (*In a loud, angry voice*): So this is Haunts for Hire. Thank goodness, there's an officer in the place.

VELMA: Excuse me, madam, but who are you?

MRS. MARBLE: My name doesn't matter in a case like this, but I'll be glad to tell this officer who I am. I am Mrs. Mabelline Marble, and these are my daughters.

OFFICER: What's the trouble, ma'am?

MRS. MARBLE: I want these young people arrested, Officer. They are a menace to the community.

OFFICER: Have they flooded your property?

MRS. MARBLE: I don't know anything about a flood, but when I tell you my story, I know you will put them in jail where they can't do any more damage.

OFFICER: Let's have your story, ma'am. Suppose we start with your address.

MRS. MARBLE: We live in Oak Heights—328 Oak Lane. My daughters were giving a Halloween party and about an hour ago, a young entertainer showed up from this agency.

VELMA: But we didn't send anyone to that address, Mrs. Marble.

MRS. MARBLE (*Producing card from handbag*): Here is your card. The young man gave it to me.

OFFICER: What did this young man look like, ma'am?

MRS. MARBLE: I can't tell you exactly, Officer. He wore a mask.

WARDROBE MISTRESS: Was he wearing any sort of costume? I'd know if it was one of ours.

MRS. MARBLE: He wore a long, white coat like a barber's coat. In fact, he called himself The Demon Barber of Death Valley.

MARY (*Crying*): He said he would give Halloween Hairdos to our guests.

MOLLY (*Crying*): We thought it would be something different.

MRS. MARBLE: It was different all right. The girls were tickled with the idea, so he said he'd start with us.

GIRLS: And now, just look at us! See what he did! (*They strip off the scarves from their heads. Both girls, who should have short haircuts, have brushed their hair straight up and sprayed it with hair spray so it stands on end. The mother wears a skin-colored bathing cap which makes her look bald. Gasps and cries of astonishment from all.*)

OFFICER: I'll take the lot of them down to the station, ma'am. You can come along and prefer charges.

FRANK: But, Officer, please! We're doing this for our Dramatic Club. We've never been in any trouble before, honest! (*Reaches in pocket for card*) Please, at least call my father. He's a lawyer. Here—here is his card. (*Hands it to* OFFICER)

OFFICER (*Looking at card*): What's this? More of your jokes? "A.F. of G.!" Amalgamated Federation of Ghosts! Now you come along with me, young man.

FRANK (*Seizing card*): That's it! That's it!

OFFICER: That's what? What are you talking about?

FRANK: That's it, kids. We've been framed! It's the A.F. of G. at work!

CARL: You're right, Frank. The Federation has pulled these tricks on us.

VELMA: That man said we'd be sorry if we didn't join.

BONY: I knew he was a shady character.

WARDROBE MISTRESS: Gave me goosebumps, he did!

FRANK: Man, oh, man! If only we knew how to get in touch with that guy.

VELMA: Let me see that card. (*Takes it from* FRANK *and reads it*) No address! No phone number! Wait—wait a minute. See here—on the other side.

FRANK (*Leaning over*): What does it say?

VELMA (*Reading*): It says, "If you change your mind, *whistle*!"

BONY: What a joker!

CARL: Do you suppose he means that?

FRANK: Only one way to find out. Officer, please, blow that whistle like blue blazes! Come on, gang, all together! One! Two! Three! (*All join in loud whistle; the lights go out and when they come on again, the* REPRESENTATIVE *is standing center stage, smiling and rubbing his hands in an obsequious fashion.*)

REPRESENTATIVE (*Bowing to* FRANK): You sent for me, sir?

FRANK (*Pointing*): There, Officer, there is your man! This is the guy you're looking for.

CARL: He's responsible for that cracked swimming pool and Chilly Willy's flood.

MRS. MARBLE: He's not the man who gave us those awful haircuts.

REPRESENTATIVE: Of course not, Mrs. Marble. I never go out on jobs in person, but I assure you, it was one of our staff.

OFFICER: So you admit it?

REPRESENTATIVE: I claim full credit, in the name of the Federation, of course.

HARRY: What about my head? Are you responsible for that, too?

REPRESENTATIVE: When a man has two heads, my friend, it is a good thing to share the responsibility with someone else. Yes, I can also claim credit for that remarkable manifestation on Pleasant Hill Road.

BONY: And the mummy out at Mrs. Vandermeer's place?

REPRESENTATIVE: Just one more modest service of the A.F. of G.

WARDROBE MISTRESS: There, you see, Officer, you have a complete confession.

OFFICER: I don't get it. What's going on here?

REPRESENTATIVE: Just a little conflict, sir, between the natural and the supernatural. These young people, with their ridiculous Haunts for Hire and their bag of parlor tricks, have muscled in on a legitimate business reserved for spooks only. In other words, they are operating outside of their own territory and the Federation won't stand for it.

FRANK: You mean we are taking work away from regular ghosts?

REPRESENTATIVE: Exactly! Every ghost and goblin, every witch and banshee, every haunt and horror in this area is up in arms against you.

CHILLY WILLY: I say a real spook is welcome to my job any time he wants it.

REPRESENTATIVE: That's a very sensible viewpoint, Willy, and I only wish your associates were as reasonable. As it is, they are operating without a license, so the Federation is closing them down.

OFFICER: What's all this talk about Federations and licenses? I came here to investigate a charge of property damage and that's what I'm going to do. (*To* REPRESENTATIVE) If you say you're responsible for these goings-on, then you'll have to come along with me.

REPRESENTATIVE: One minute, Officer. I think I can save you a lot of time and trouble. (*To* FRANK) If I interpreted your distress signal correctly, Haunts for Hire is ready to join the A.F. of G.

FRANK: What else can we do? If you don't close us down, the police will. What must we do? How much are the dues?

REPRESENTATIVE: That's all you human beings think about. Money! Money! Money! It's our professional reputation that is at stake. We can't have our Happy Haunting Grounds invaded by a bunch of impostors!

FRANK: You mean you want us to go out of business entirely?

REPRESENTATIVE: Of course not. (*Pointing to phones*) You have plenty of good connections. We could use them. We also like your nice, warm office. It's snug and dry, no dampness, no mould, no mildew, no worms! Quite different from our own headquarters. And we also like your staff. This lady (*Indicating* WARDROBE MISTRESS) is very handy with the needle. We have any number of shrouds she could fix up for us. And this fellow (*Indicating* CARL) is a genius with his recording machine. We have some sound effects of our own that I am sure he could handle very nicely for us. Yes, all in all, I think we could do business together.

FRANK: Do business together?

REPRESENTATIVE: But naturally. When you join the Federation, we'll be partners, subject to the same rules and regulations. You let us use some of your equipment, and we'll teach you some of our better tricks. You do the booking and the billing, and we'll take care of the haunting.

CARL: Sounds good to me, boss. Let's sign up.

VELMA: I'm afraid, Frank. He makes me nervous.

REPRESENTATIVE: Nonsense, my dear young lady. You'll like taking dictation from me, and I'll teach you how to do it in invisible ink.

BONY: What do you say, Frank?

FRANK: How do we know they won't get us into more trouble with the police?

REPRESENTATIVE: The A.F. of G. is a reputable organization, young man. When you play by our rules, we play by yours. (*Phone rings.*) If you don't believe me, pick up your telephone.

FRANK: Haunts for Hire. Frankenstein speaking. (*Pause*) Who? (*Pause*) Oh, yes, yes, he's here. (*Away from phone*) Officer, it's for you.

OFFICER (*At phone*): Sergeant Brown speaking. (*Pause*) Who? (*Pause*) Oh, yes, yes, ma'am. Well, now, I'm mighty glad to hear that. *(Aside, to others)* It's the lady from Ocean Terrace. Says the water's completely disappeared from her house. *(At phone)* How about the damage? *(Pause)* Well, now, that's hard to believe. Everything dry as a bone, you say, and not a mark or stain to be seen? *(Pause)* No, no, I haven't done anything with the boy. Very well, ma'am. I'll dismiss the charge, if you say so. Thank you for calling. Goodbye. *(Hangs up. To* CHILLY WILLY*)* Well, there's a break for you, son. The lady withdraws all charges. Says there's no damage at all.

CHILLY WILLY: Thanks, Officer, thanks a lot.

REPRESENTATIVE: Better thank me, Willy. Thank me and the A.F. of G. I just wanted to prove to you that we spooks can operate within the law.

MRS. MARBLE: What about me? What about me and my daughters? Can you undo the mischief you have done us?

REPRESENTATIVE: Why, beautiful lady, no harm was ever intended to you or your charming daughters. *(Drapes scarves over their heads)* Just step out into the hallway and look at yourselves in the mirror. You'll see a real transformation has taken place.

GIRLS: Hurry, Mother. Hurry.

MRS. MARBLE *(As they rush out)*: Dear me! I do feel something very unusual stirring in the atmosphere. *(As* MRS. MARBLE *and her daughters exit, a* MESSENGER *enters carrying a box.)*

MESSENGER: Special messenger service for Haunts for Hire.

VELMA: I'll take it.

MESSENGER: I can hardly make out the address, ma'am, but I think it says, Headless Harry.

HARRY: That's for me. Let me have it. *(Opens package)*

Why, it's my head! They've sent back my head. (*Displays pumpkin in box*) And look, here's a note. (*Reads*) "To whom it may concern: Enclosed find regular fee for the most unusual and clever entertainment at my son's Halloween party. The animated head was simply astounding, and all of us were delighted, especially after we realized our furnishings were undamaged in the performance. Please feel free to call on us for testimonials on your outstanding service. We will certainly recommend you to our friends. Very truly yours. . . ." Well, that fixes that. I suppose your Federation did this, Mr. A.F. of G.

REPRESENTATIVE (*Modestly*): Just the sort of service we give our members.

MESSENGER: Oh, I almost forgot. I ran into a lady downstairs who was on her way up here. She says to thank you for your prompt service in removing the mummy case from her front hall. It didn't make much sense to me, but she seemed to know what she was talking about.

FRANK (*Tipping* MESSENGER): It makes good sense to us all right, and thanks.

MESSENGER: You're welcome, and thank you, sir. (*Exits*)

BONY: There's just one thing that worries me, boss.

FRANK: What's that, Bony?

BONY: That cracked swimming pool.

REPRESENTATIVE: Forget it, my boy. Forget it! Once you have signed on the dotted line (*Produces contract from briefcase*) your worries are over.

FRANK: Where do we sign?

REPRESENTATIVE (*Putting contract on desk and handing pen to* FRANK): Right here, sir. (*Each person signs in turn.*) There you are! And welcome to the Amalgamated Federation of Ghosts! (*He and* FRANK *shake hands.*) Now that you are all members in good standing, I should say we are open for business under new management. And this time you'll be operating under the Good House-Haunting Seal of Approval!

OFFICER (*Scratching his head*): Say, I still don't get this. Are you kids serious?

REPRESENTATIVE: Haunting houses is a serious business, Officer. What can we do for you?

OFFICER: Well, the boys down at the station are getting up a party tomorrow night. I was thinking it might be a good idea to throw a scare into them—nothing serious, you know, but—well—just for kicks.

FRANK: We could let you have Chilly Willy or Headless Harry here.

BONY: What about me? I'd love to haunt a station house.

REPRESENTATIVE: Child's play! Child's play! Nothing but the best for our men in blue. You forget there's no limit to what you can do now that you belong to the A.F. of G. Come over here, sir, and take a look at our catalogue. (*Moves to table. He and* OFFICER *look at catalogue.*) Now here's something very special—The Hangman's Holiday. Or, we could rig up a nice floating corpse bathed in blue light. He'll float right through the air and disappear in a puff of smoke.

OFFICER: I think the boys would go for that. (*Phones start ringing.*)

REPRESENTATIVE: Answer that, please, Frank, will you? Velma, your order book, please.

FRANK (*At one phone after the other*): Haunts for Hire, Frankenstein speaking. (*Curtain.*)

THE END

Production Notes

HAUNTS FOR HIRE

Characters: 8 male; 6 female.

Playing Time: 30 minutes.

Costumes: Frank and the Representative are dressed in business suits. Velma Vampire and the Wardrobe Mistress wear dresses. Carl wears work clothes. Bony wears tights, a red velvet cloak, and a skeleton mask. Harry wears black suit, gloves, and a cape over his head. Chilly Willy wears a raincoat over sports clothes. Mrs. Vandermeer is in a suit and furs and carries a purse and gloves. Mrs. Marble, Mary Marble, and Molly Marble are in party clothes and wear scarves on their heads. Under their scarves, the girls have their hair sprayed stiff to stand on end, and Mrs. Marble wears a skin-colored bathing cap. Policeman and Messenger are in appropriate uniforms.

Properties: Order blanks, wet sponges, pen, briefcase containing contract, calling cards, three dollar bills, whistle, memo pad, and box containing pumpkin and note, checkbook, handbag for Mrs. Marble, handkerchief, change for Messenger's tip.

Setting: The office of Haunts for Hire. Desk with four telephones is at left. Above it is sign saying YOU DARE 'EM, WE SCARE 'EM! At right is large table cluttered with sheets, wigs, costumes, masks, props, and catalogue. Chains and boxes are on floor at side of table.

Lighting: Blackouts as indicated.

Damsels in Distress

Characters

ELLEN
LADY-IN-WAITING
ELLEN'S FATHER
SIR STEPHEN TRENT
ROBIN HOOD
ALLAN-A-DALE
GWENNY
LORNA DOONE
JOHN RIDD
ANNE OF AUSTRIA
CONSTANCE BONACIEUX
PAGE
CHARLES DARNAY
SYDNEY CARTON
SPY
NARRATOR

BEFORE RISE: NARRATOR *enters in front of curtain.*

NARRATOR:

In days of old when knights were bold,
And ladies passing fair,
Strange tales were told of secret gold,
And deeds of "do and dare."

Whenever knight would chance to sight
A damsel in distress,

He'd straightway fight to ease her plight,
And save her from duress.

The heroes brave all fought to save
Their ladies from their fate.
Yes, knight and knave, their lives they gave
And did not hesitate.

And now we show from long ago
Some ladies in dismay.
We hope you know each dame and beau
Who came to save the day.

We say adieu as we review
These damsels in distress.
What did they do and who is who?
It's up to you to guess.

Yes, stories of romance and adventure are always bound to include the rescue of a lovely lady in distress. Our library shelves contain countless stories of rescues by brave and handsome heroes. Sometimes a knight does battle with his mortal enemy to win the fair lady's hand. But whether the lady is rescued from a watery grave, snatched from a burning building, or saved from the clutches of the wicked villain, the rescue always takes place just in the nick of time.

Today, as part of our celebration of Children's Book Week, we are going to present some famous damsels in distress with their equally famous rescuers. But we are not going to disclose their names until the end of the program. It's up to you to guess who they are.

Our first lady is in a pitiful plight indeed. It is the morning of her wedding day, the day which *should* be the happiest of her life. But alas! The beautiful bride is in tears. Her Lady-in-Waiting tries to comfort her, but the words fall on deaf ears. (NARRATOR *walks to stage left, as curtains open.*)

* * * * *

SCENE 1

SETTING: ELLEN'S *dressing room. A vanity table with mirror, and a chair may stand at stage right.*

AT RISE: ELLEN *sits on chair in front of vanity table, looking into mirror. Her* LADY-IN-WAITING *stands behind her and adjusts* ELLEN'S *veil.*

LADY-IN-WAITING: Please, mistress, please dry thine eyes and permit me to adjust the veil. Thy father will be angry if we keep him waiting.

ELLEN: He is already angry. He ne'er looks at me without a frown. His only thought is to marry me off to that bandy-legged Sir Stephen Trent.

LADY-IN-WAITING: It is a fine marriage, milady. Sir Stephen is the richest knight in the valley.

ELLEN: Aye, and the oldest! And the ugliest! Fie! I would not have him for my lord were he the last man on earth.

LADY-IN-WAITING: Alas, my lady, thy father's heart is set on this match, and we must make haste. It is time to leave for the church. (ELLEN'S FATHER *enters and walks over to her.*)

FATHER (*Standing beside* ELLEN): Come, child. The horses are saddled and at the door. It will not do to keep the bridegroom waiting.

ELLEN: Pray, Father, pray have mercy, I entreat thee. Do not force me to become Sir Stephen's bride.

FATHER (*Impatiently*): What saucy talk is this? All has

been settled between us. Sir Stephen has honored our house by requesting thy hand in marriage.

ELLEN: But, Father, my heart is pledged to another.

FATHER: Speak not of thy pledges. I will hear no more talk of that languishing minstrel lad who tried to steal thy heart. Sir Stephen is a good knight and true. He will make thee a good husband.

ELLEN: Please, Father, it will break my heart to wed Sir Stephen Trent.

FATHER: Tush! Tush! We'll hear no more of broken hearts. I am thy father and thou wilt do my bidding. Now there's an end to it. (*Walks to exit left.*) I bid thee follow me at once. (FATHER *exits.*)

LADY-IN-WAITING: Alack, my lady, thy cause is lost.

ELLEN: Truly, and my heart is lost with it. I will obey my father, but always I will wear this broken sixpence on its silver chain . . . (*Indicates locket*) just as my beloved wears the other half of this same coin. It is our pledge to be true to each other as long as we both shall live. (LADY-IN-WAITING *and* ELLEN *exit.*)

NARRATOR (*To audience, from his position left stage*): Will nothing save this fair lady from a loveless marriage? Will no one rescue her from this tragic fate? (*There is a trumpet blast offstage.* ROBIN HOOD *enters, his arm about the shoulders of* ALLAN-A-DALE. *He is laughing heartily.*)

ROBIN (*To audience*): Oh, oh, my good friends! It was as good as a play to see the rescue of this fair maiden. That horn ye just heard was the signal to my merry men to meet me at the church. Ah, ye should have seen it! There was the bridegroom, the wizened old Sir Stephen! And there was the good Edward with his reluctant daughter! And the great Lord Bishop of Hereford ready to say the holy words. When all of a sudden . . . (*Offstage trumpet*) down the aisle of the church came eighteen of my stout yeomen all clad in Lincoln green, with this brave lad here (*Clapping* ALLAN *on the shoulder*) at their head, bearing my trusty bow of yew. The bride's father was in a towering rage. (*Enter* FATHER, SIR STEPHEN *and* ELLEN.)

FATHER (*To* ALLAN-A-DALE): Is it thou, young varlet, who hast bred this trouble in the church?

ROBIN: Nay, 'tis not the lad, but myself ye have to reckon with. But (*Indicating* ALLAN) here is thy daughter's betrothed husband. I vow she shall marry him or death shall be bred to some of you this day.

FATHER: Now I say nay! I am her father, and she shall wed with no man but Sir Stephen Trent.

SIR STEPHEN: Nay, fellow. Thou mayst take thy daughter back again. I would not marry her after this day's doings, could I gain all merry England thereby. Maiden, if thou dost rather choose a beggarly minstrel than a high-born knight, thou art welcome to thy choice. (SIR STEPHEN *exits.*)

ELLEN (*Running to* ALLAN): A choice, in truth, I never shall regret.

ALLAN (*Seizing her hand*): At last we both may keep our pledge.

ROBIN (*To* FATHER): Now give thy blessing to thy daughter's marriage to this yeoman, and all will be well. Allan, give me the purse of gold. (ALLAN *tosses him a purse.* ROBIN *shakes gold coins into his hand from purse and shows them to* ELLEN'S FATHER.) Here are two hundred bright golden angels. Give thy blessing, and I will count them out to thee as thy daughter's dower. Give not thy blessing, and she shall be married all the same, but not so much as a cracked farthing shall cross thy palm. Choose.

FATHER (*After a moment's hesitation*): Let be what will be. I will give her my blessing when she is duly wed.

ROBIN: Then straightway to the altar. (*In a loud voice*) Friar Tuck! Friar Tuck! To the chapel at once! There's work to be done . . . and a happier day's work this sun shall never see! (*All exit as curtains close and* NARRATOR *steps in front of curtain.*)

NARRATOR: So ends the happy story with jolly Friar Tuck reading the marriage vows while the brave rescuer stands by to wish the couple long life and happiness.

We hope, by this time, you have guessed the name of the damsel in distress, her bridegroom, and her rescuer. But if you have not identified them, just wait for our official roll call at the end of the show.

In the meantime, we journey to Exmoor in the south of England, the year of the great winter. Our heroine and her little serving maid are snowbound within a robber stronghold deep in the hills. Although the outlaws may force their way into the cottage at any moment, our leading lady prefers death by starvation to the possibility of marriage with the robber chieftain.

* * * * *

SCENE 2

SETTING: *A sparsely furnished room with two chairs and a table.*

AT RISE: LORNA DOONE *walks back and forth wringing her hands in despair.* GWENNY, *her maid, tries to comfort her.*

GWENNY: Do not despair, mistress. I know someone who has not forgotten us.

LORNA: So do I, Gwenny. But even such a stout-hearted lad could not make his way into our valley through all this snow. Is there no more wood for the fire?

GWENNY: 'Tis almost burned to ashes. Not enough embers left to bake us a pastry, even if we had one.

LORNA: Pray stop talking of food, Gwenny. 'Tis more than I can bear.

GWENNY: Mayhap I could find a bit of firewood were I to venture out and prowl around a bit.

LORNA: We dare not risk opening the door, even if it is to save our lives. (*Knock*) What's that? What's that?

GWENNY: Hide in the other room, ma'am. I'll see who it is. (*Exit* LORNA.) Who's there? Who's there?

JOHN (*From offstage*): Only me. (*Rattles latch*) There's no need to be afraid. Quick! Let me in. Open the door! (GWENNY *goes to door and opens it;* JOHN RIDD *enters.*)

GWENNY (*Stepping back and speaking to* LORNA): Oh, mistress, come quickly and see who's here. (LORNA *re-enters.*)

LORNA (*Rushing to* JOHN): How did you ever get here? Gwenny said you'd come, but I feared you'd never make it in the snow.

JOHN (*Indicating snowshoes*): I never would have managed without these. You should have heard Mother and Lizzie laugh as they watched me floundering my way through the drifts. I had to see how you fared and make sure you were safe.

LORNA: I never expected to see you again. I had made up my mind to die without your knowing it. Oh, you look so well, so strong . . . almost . . .

GWENNY: Almost good enough to eat! Those red cheeks

of his remind me of good rich sirloin! I declare, I might even eat you up.

JOHN (*Unpacking basket*): No need for that, Gwenny. Mother and Lizzie have packed a basket of food. (*Holding up pie*) Smell! Did you ever sniff anything so delicious in all your life? And wait till ye taste it. It's mince meat and golden apples, and the best spices . . .

LORNA: Stop it. Stop it or I shall faint.

JOHN: What is the meaning of this?

LORNA: The meaning is sad enough, and I see no way out of it. We are both to be starved until I choose to marry Carver.

JOHN: That would be a slow death for you.

LORNA: Not a slow death . . . a quick one. I hate him with such bitterness that less than a week would kill me.

JOHN: If I guarantee to take you safely out of this, will you come with me?

LORNA: I have small choice—to go with you or starve.

JOHN: Gwenny, do you have the courage for it—to go with your mistress?

GWENNY: Think you I would stay behind with those ruffians out there watching the house?

LORNA: Look! Even now they are lighting their bonfires. There they will be roistering, drinking, singing their wild songs well into the night.

JOHN: 'Tis all for our good. In three hours or more the fire will sink and cast friendly shadows. As the cold increases, the outlaws will cling together more closely. They will not venture far away on inspection. Now heed my words. In two hours' time I will be with you again. Keep the bar on the door, and have Gwenny ready to answer only when I knock. You are safe while they are eating and drinking with each other, and before they have done with that I shall be with you again. Have everything you care to take in one small bundle. I shall knock loudly and then wait a little, and then knock twice, very softly. (*Knocks on table to demonstrate*)

LORNA: We will do just as you say.

GWENNY: I will open the door to no one but you.

JOHN: Remember . . . just two hours . . . and I will be back to take you away from here forever. (JOHN *exits, as curtains close.*)

NARRATOR (*Before curtain*): The young man was as good as his word. By morning, Gwenny and her young mistress were safe with our hero's mother and sister in their snug farmhouse. If you can identify these two young lovers who made their way through an ice-blocked valley, just keep your secret until the end of our program. Right now, we take you to Paris, France, only a few years after the Pilgrims had landed at Plymouth Rock. These were the days when a gentleman proved his courage by his sword, and a lady's smile could be just cause for a duel to the death. Our scene is the Hotel de Ville where a certain royal lady is in a desperate predicament. (*Offstage minuet music*) Although there is a court ball in progress, our leading lady has withdrawn to an alcove off the main ballroom, where she paces the floor in apparent distress.

* * * * *

SCENE 3

SETTING: *An alcove blocked off from rest of stage by folding screens on three sides. A small gilt table and chair stand at center of alcove.*

AT RISE: ANNE OF AUSTRIA *paces back and forth nervously, twisting a handkerchief in her hands.*

QUEEN: I am lost! I am lost. The King will know everything! Perhaps he knows even now, or he would not have ordered me to wear the twelve diamond studs! Someone has betrayed me. Someone saw me give the jewel casket to the Duke of Buckingham! Someone who knows it would be impossible for me to get them back from London in time. (*Sits at table. Buries her face in her hands*) Oh, what a foolish, foolish gift! How could I have done such a thing?

PAGE (*Halting at entrance of screens and speaking from outside*): Your Majesty, I have a message from His Gracious Majesty, the King.

QUEEN: I do not wish to be disturbed.

PAGE: It is urgent, Your Majesty. The King demands to know why you do not wear your diamond studs this evening as he requested.

QUEEN: You may tell His Majesty that in a crowd like this, I feared something might happen to them.

PAGE: His Majesty bade me tell you that since he gave you the jewels himself, the responsibility is his. He bids you adorn yourself at once, and join him in the main ballroom.

QUEEN: Inform His Majesty that I shall send to the Louvre at once for the diamonds. His wishes will be obeyed.

PAGE: Very good, Your Majesty. The Ballet begins in less than half an hour. (PAGE *exits.*)

QUEEN: This is the end. I will be banished—sent into exile. Oh, where is that wretched messenger? Surely he has had time to get to England and back again. (*Enter* CONSTANCE BONACIEUX. *She wears a long black cape with a hood and carries a mask which she holds to her face by means of a small handle. Under her arm is a small box.*)

CONSTANCE (*Pausing at edge of screens, and speaking in a half whisper*): Your Majesty!

QUEEN: Madame! Is it you?

CONSTANCE: It is I, Your Majesty. Permit me to enter.

QUEEN (*Drawing* CONSTANCE *into playing area*): Quick! Quick! Do you have them?

CONSTANCE: I have them, Your Majesty. But at what a price. (*Hands box to* QUEEN.)

QUEEN (*Opening box*): I am saved. I am saved. Are they all here? All twelve of them?

CONSTANCE: Every single one, Your Majesty. Even the two which were stolen from the Duke of Buckingham have been replaced. No one could tell the difference.

QUEEN (*Taking from box ribbon on which are pinned twelve diamond clips or pins*): Help me adjust them. Quickly. The King has sent for me.

CONSTANCE (*Pinning ribbon on shoulder*): There! You are ready to face the King, the Cardinal, and the entire court.

QUEEN (*As she turns to go*): How can I ever thank you, Madame?

CONSTANCE: You owe me no thanks, Your Majesty. It is your faithful messenger who has done the impossible.

QUEEN (*Removing ring from her finger*): You will see this messenger again?

CONSTANCE: I hope so, Your Majesty.

QUEEN (*Handing her the ring*): Then give him this, Madame, as a pledge of my undying gratitude. (CONSTANCE *curtsies, as* QUEEN *exits and curtains close.*)

NARRATOR: Now *your* job (*Indicating audience*) is to identify the unseen messenger who risked his life and the lives of his three friends in a daring and successful attempt to rescue a lovely lady from disgrace and the King's displeasure.

Our next Damsel in Distress is also living in Paris, but at the moment we meet her, she is trying her best to leave that hateful place. Her own escape seems certain but the fate of her husband is sealed. He is a prisoner of the French Revolution and will die on the guillotine unless a miracle happens. If such a miracle takes place, it will be a double rescue, the rescue of a man from death, the rescue of a woman from heartbreak. The scene is a prison cell. The prisoner awaits the hour of his execution. Imagine his amazement when the door opens and he beholds the last man on earth he ever expected to see—a man he didn't even know was anywhere near the city of Paris.

* * * * *

Scene 4

SETTING: *A prison cell. There is a cot at one side, and a small table, chair and a bench stand at center.*

AT RISE: CHARLES DARNAY *is seated at table. He rises as* SYDNEY CARTON *enters.*

DARNAY: You! I can scarcely believe it! Surely you are not a prisoner.

CARTON: No. I was able to gain a power over one of your jailers by something I knew of his past. By that means I stand before you. I come from your wife. I bring you a request from her.

DARNAY: What is it?

CARTON: I have no time to explain the why's and wherefores. You must obey without question. Take off those boots you wear and draw on these of mine. (*He pushes* DARNAY *into chair and they exchange boots.*)

DARNAY: There is no escaping from this place. It never can be done. You will only die with me. It is madness.

CARTON: I do not ask you to walk out that door. I ask you only to do as I tell you. First, change your scarf for mine. (*They exchange scarves and put them on.*) Now that coat for this one. (*They exchange coats.*)

DARNAY: It is madness, madness, I say. It has been attempted before, and it has always failed. I beg you, do not add your death to the bitterness of mine.

CARTON (*Opening drawer of table for pen and paper*): Here are pen and paper. Is your hand steady enough to write?

DARNAY: It was when you came in.

CARTON: Then write as I dictate. Quickly. (*He stands behind* DARNAY *who sits at table. As he writes,* CARTON *suddenly draws a handkerchief from his pocket, and he holds it close to* DARNAY's *face.*)

DARNAY: To whom do I address it?

CARTON: To no one. Now write. "If you remember the words that passed between us years ago, you will readily understand this when you see it. You do remember them, I know. It is not in your nature to forget."

DARNAY (*Half turning toward* CARTON): Is that a weapon in your hand?

CARTON: No, I am not armed.

DARNAY: What is in your hand?

CARTON: You shall know directly. Please write on. "I am thankful the time has come when I can keep my promise. That I do so is no reason for grief." (*His hand passes close to* DARNAY.)

DARNAY (*Rubbing his face*): What vapor is that?

CARTON: I am conscious of nothing. Take up the pen and finish. Hurry. Hurry.

DARNAY: The pen feels like lead. I can scarcely see. (*Starts to rise*) What is the matter? (*Sinks back in chair.* CARTON *quickly presses cloth over his face and holds him until he goes limp. Then he takes a cloak and wraps him in it, also removes his hat and puts it on* DARNAY. *He puts the note in* DARNAY's *pocket. Runs to door and makes a signal.* SPY *enters.*)

SPY: Make haste, sir. This is dangerous business.

CARTON: It will be over in a minute. All you have to do is get me out of here and take me to the coach at Tellson's Bank.

SPY: *You,* sir?

CARTON (*Pointing to* DARNAY *slumped over the table*): This one here with whom I have exchanged places. You go out by the same gate by which you brought me in?

SPY: Of course.

CARTON: The guards noticed that I was weak and faint when we came in. I am now fainter when you take me out. This parting interview with my friend has brought on a heart attack. Such a thing has happened before. Once clear of the guards, call for assistance.

SPY: You swear not to betray me?

CARTON: I swear. Take him yourself to the carriage. Tell Mr. Lorry to give him no medicine but air. Bid him to drive away without the slightest hesitation or delay. (SPY *pulls* DARNAY *to his feet, and puts his arm around* DARNAY's *shoulders to support him.*)

SPY: He's a heavy load, sir, but I'll do my best.

CARTON: Your life depends on it, lad.

SPY (*At door*): And yours, sir? Why are you doing this?

CARTON: I once promised a certain young lady that I would give my life to keep a life she loved beside her. The time has come for me to fulfill my pledge.

SPY: It is a brave thing you're doing, sir. You must know there is no escape for you.

CARTON: It is a far, far better thing that I do, than I have ever done; it is a far, far better rest that I go to, than I have ever known. (*Curtain closes.*)

NARRATOR (*In front of curtain*): We draw the curtains on this last act of an unselfish hero and invite our players to pass before you. This time, they will identify themselves. (*Enter* ROBIN HOOD *and* ALLAN-A-DALE *with* ELLEN *walking between them. Each wears a placard with his name written on it.*)

ROBIN HOOD: I'm Robin Hood in my suit of bright green,
And this is fair Ellen, a brave hero's dream.

ELLEN: My good thanks to Robin who came without fail,
And married me safely to Allan-a-Dale.

ALLAN: I hope you all liked us, and if we were good,
You'll read more adventures of bold Robin Hood.
(ROBIN, ELLEN *and* ALLAN *bow and exit opposite side of stage.*)

NARRATOR: Our next hero and heroine take center stage. (JOHN RIDD *and* LORNA DOONE *enter hand in hand.*)

JOHN: My name is John Ridd and with love I will swoon
For a lovely young lady they call Lorna Doone.

LORNA: My John is the hero who risked death for himself.
Our story is found in the library shelf. (LORNA *and* JOHN *bow and exit.*)

NARRATOR: For stories of mystery and intrigue, you can't beat Alexandre Dumas. (*The* QUEEN *enters with* CONSTANCE BONACIEUX.)

QUEEN: "The Austrian Queen" they called me in France.

Without our fine hero I hadn't a chance.
And Constance here was the fair go-between.
Who found a brave man to help rescue the Queen.

CONSTANCE: Our hero is D'Artagnan, well worthy of cheers,
His deeds fill the novel—*The Three Musketeers.*
(QUEEN *and* CONSTANCE *exit.*)

NARRATOR: Although our last Damsel in Distress did not actually appear on stage, we are sure you must have guessed she was Lucie Manette from *A Tale of Two Cities* by Charles Dickens. Her rescuer and the rescuer of her husband, Charles Darnay, is here to speak for himself. (SYDNEY CARTON *enters.*)

CARTON: *A Tale of Two Cities* will never grow old,
As pages of plotting and vengeance unfold.
My name's Sydney Carton, the hero am I.
For Lucy Manette I was willing to die.
Those reading my story again and again
Remember me always, the bravest of men. (CARTON *exits.*)

NARRATOR: We trust indeed that you will read
These stories in our play.
So get with speed the books you need.
Begin without delay.
The hour has run; our play is done,
And so we rest our cause.
Now, everyone who's had some fun,
Please give us your applause.
(NARRATOR *bows and exits on applause.*)

THE END

Production Notes

DAMSELS IN DISTRESS

Characters: 9 male; 6 female; Narrator may be male or female.

Playing Time: 30 minutes.

Costumes: Medieval clothing, for Ellen, Lady-in-Waiting, Ellen's Father, and Sir Stephen Trent. Green tights and tunic, for Robin Hood and Allan-a-Dale; green hat with feather in it, for Robin Hood. Long skirts, blouses, and shawls, for Gwenny and Lorna Doone. Heavy coat, cap, gloves, boots and snowshoes, for John Ridd. Court costumes for Anne of Austria, Constance Bonacieux, and Page. Trousers, coats, boots, neck-cloths, cloaks for Charles Darnay and Sydney Carton.

Properties: Veil and locket, for Ellen. Purse of gold, for Allan-a-Dale. Basket of food, for John Ridd. Handkerchief, for Anne of Austria. Box and ribbon with diamond pins, for Constance. Pen, paper, and handkerchief, for Sydney Carton. Placards with names, for Robin Hood, Allan-a-Dale, Ellen, John Ridd, Lorna Doone, Anne of Austria, Constance Bonacieux, and Sydney Carton.

Setting: Scene 1: Bare stage, or vanity table with mirror and chair for first part. Scene 2: Sparsely furnished room, with table and two chairs. Scene 3: The area is blocked off on three sides by folding screens. A small gilt table and chair are the only furnishings. Scene 4: Prison cell, with a table, cot, chair, and bench.

Lighting: No special effects.

Sound: Offstage trumpet; minuet music.

Horn of Plenty

Characters

TONY HILL
MRS. HILL, *his mother*
SALLY, *his sister*
SAM, *his friend*
KIM, *his girl friend*
AUNT ABIGAIL
OFFICER DUGAN
OFFICER RILEY
MR. RAMSEY, *owner of the Swap Shop*
MR. PLUNK, *owner of music store*

SETTING: *The Hill living room.*

AT RISE: TONY HILL *and his friend* SAM *are piling assorted items into cartons.*

SAM (*Holding up a worn baseball glove*): You'll never get a nickel for this old glove. It has a hole in it.

TONY: Toss it in that box of junk along with the water wings, the fire engine and the inner tube. And don't let old man Ramsay give you a cent less than three bucks for this tennis racket.

SAM: He'll spot that busted string the minute he looks at it.

TONY: Where's your sales technique, Sam? It's all in your approach. You've got to soften him up a bit at the very beginning.

SAM: How?

TONY: Wish him a Happy Thanksgiving. Get him in a holiday mood. Appeal to his generous nature—then shove this racket in with some of the better stuff and hope it gets by.

SAM: Old man Ramsay never heard of Thanksgiving. He's strictly cold turkey all the way.

TONY (*Ignoring him and holding up small radio*): Try to get ten bucks for this radio, but I'll take five.

SAM: But it doesn't play.

TONY: It will, if you give it a good whack right before you turn it on. And be sure not to move the dial. I have it set for the one station it gets.

SAM: What about this alarm clock? He had at least fifty of them, when I was in yesterday.

TONY: Then he should have fifty-one today. Get him in the Thanksgiving spirit and this should bring two and a half.

SAM: You can buy them new for a dollar, any day in the year. Now look, Tony, this guy Ramsay is a smart operator. He knows his merchandise.

TONY: Then he should know a good typewriter when he sees one. Hold out for fifty smackers on this baby.

SAM: But you can't sell your typewriter!

TONY: Why not? It's mine. I bought it with my own money.

SAM: But what will your mother say? And how can you type your papers if you sell it?

TONY: Mom hardly goes up to my room except to change the bed. That was part of the deal when I took over the third floor. As for the typing, I can always count on Kim. That's the beauty of having a girl in the Business Ed Department.

SAM: The more I think about this, Tony, the less I like it! And the less I like your boy Ramsay. He . . . he sort of gives me the creeps.

TONY: What do you mean?

SAM: The way he looked at me yesterday, when I took your camera down there, sort of fishy-eyed—it made me feel guilty somehow.

TONY: Guilty? What's to feel guilty about? I have a right to sell this stuff.

SAM: Then take it down yourself. Why send me?

TONY: I've told you a hundred times. He knows Mom, and he knows me. I don't want anybody finding out about this. You know how women are—especially mothers. They ask a thousand questions.

SAM: How come I always get the dirty end of the deal?

TONY: Look who's talking! It was all your fault the horn was stolen in the first place. You didn't lock the station wagon.

SAM: How could I lock it, when you had the keys? If you hadn't hung around talking to Kim for half an hour—

TONY: And if you had stayed in the car, instead of going for a Coke!

SAM: If! If! If!

TONY: Look, Sam, do you want to help me, or don't you? Can't you see I'm desperate? I've got to put a hundred dollars on that sousaphone by noon, or the jig's up!

SAM: I said from the beginning you should have reported it to the police!

TONY: And have everybody in town find out I lost a school instrument through sheer carelessness.

SAM: But the school carries insurance! They could collect!

TONY: And in the meantime, what happens to me? Mr. Carl would throw me out of the band so fast I'd bounce!

SAM: But you'll have to tell him sooner or later.

TONY: Naturally I'm going to tell him—not sooner, but later—much later—after the Thanksgiving Day Parade. Do you think I want to miss that trip to New York City with the Brewster Pilgrim Band?

SAM: But he needs you for the parade. He couldn't possibly fire you now. What's a marching band without a tuba player?

TONY: He's got Fuzzy Jenkins—willing, able, and ready to blow!

SAM: Fuzzy Jenkins! I can just see him flat-footing it up Broadway. He wouldn't last two blocks!

TONY: And I won't even make it to the bus station unless I can replace that lost horn. Explanations can come later.

SAM: You couldn't have stalled this long, if I hadn't dreamed up that story about getting the valves fixed.

TONY: Good thing I had Big Bertha on tap for practice. (*Indicates old-style tuba on table*)

SAM: Hey, Tony, you don't suppose—

TONY (*As he struggles to open toy bank*): Suppose what?

SAM: How about using Big Bertha in the parade? She's old and beat up, but she still has a good tone.

TONY: Are you out of your mind? The Brewster Pilgrims would be the laughingstock of the whole parade!

SAM: Yeah, I guess you're right. I can hardly see Big Bertha on coast-to-coast TV. (*Seeing bank*) Where did you get that?

TONY: Had it ever since I was a kid. It has a combination like a real safe, only it doesn't work any more. (*Banging it*) There! That does it! (*Counting*) Golly! Only a dollar sixty, but every little bit helps.

SAM: Mr. Ramsay has a lot of metal banks in his shop.

TONY: He does? Then take this one along. Maybe he'll buy it. (*Doorbell rings.*) And hurry. Get this stuff out of here! Scram! Out the back way! Somebody's at the front door! Hurry up! (SAM *tries to pick up everything at once. The bank falls to the floor unnoticed.*)

SAM: I'm hurrying as fast as I can. (*As he drops something else*) What do you think I am—an octopus?

TONY (*Picking up a box*): Here, clumsy, I'll give you a hand. Now hurry and get back here as soon as you can. (*Doorbell rings again*)

SAM: But suppose your mother's here.

TONY: If you hurry, she won't be. She and Aunt Abby have gone shopping. And if she is, remember the password for Operation Sousaphone!

SAM (*Singing loudly*): "If you knew Susie like I know Susie. . . ." (TONY *helps* SAM *off at left, then crosses right to admit* SALLY *and* KIM)

SALLY: For goodness' sake! Where were you? You certainly took long enough to answer the door.

TONY: What's the idea? Don't you have a key? Hiya, Kim.

KIM: Hiya, Tony. How come you had yourself locked in?

TONY: Oh, Mom has to keep the place locked up tight as a drum, with Aunt Abby here.

SALLY: Aunt Abby's scared of her shadow, sees a burglar back of every bush.

KIM: I didn't know your aunt was here.

TONY: She always comes for Thanksgiving, and since we're

having Turkey Day today instead of Thursday, because of the parade, she arrived early.

SALLY: Poor Mom! I don't see how she stands all this locking and unlocking! If you hadn't answered the door soon, Kim and I would have used the painters' ladder and had a go at my bedroom window.

TONY: That's how I got in. I never can remember to carry a key. How come you're home?

SALLY: Not enough money. Mom gave me a Thanksgiving shopping list a mile long. Cranberries, celery, olives, sweet potatoes—the works—but not enough cash. You don't happen to have any money, do you?

TONY: Are you kidding?

SALLY (*Opening desk drawer and removing small change purse*): Not even a dollar here. I wonder what she left in the kitchen change purse. I'll go look. (*Goes to exit left*) Tell Tony about your dress for tonight, Kim. (*Exits*)

KIM: Oh, Tony, you'll adore it. It's your favorite color, blue, so if you make my corsage those tiny French irises . . .

TONY (*Blankly*): Corsage? French irises?

KIM: Oh, well, if you've already ordered something else, it's all right. Any flowers look pretty with blue.

TONY (*Clapping hand to forehead*): Oh, my gosh!

KIM: What's the matter?

TONY: The dance! You're talking about the dance!

KIM: What else? Oh, Tony, I'm so thrilled! I've had other party dresses, lots of them, but never a long one! It makes me feel so absolutely elegant!

TONY: Listen, Kim, I've got something to tell you. Maybe you'd better sit down.

KIM: Sit down? What ever for?

TONY: This . . . this will be a shock, Kim, but, please, please, try to understand.

KIM: What is this? Understand what? Tony, what's got into you?

TONY: Nothing—nothing's got into me, Kim, but, well, I—er—we—that is—well, we just can't go to the dance!

KIM: Can't go? For heaven's sake, why not?

TONY: Because I don't have the money. I'm broke—absolutely and totally flat broke!

KIM: But we had a date! You asked me weeks ago!

TONY: I know. I know I did, but—

KIM: Tony Hill, you can't do this to me. This is the biggest dance of the year—the Thanksgiving Ball!

TONY (*Miserably*): I'm sorry, Kim, honest!

KIM: And besides, it's the big send-off for the band! Everybody will be there!

TONY: Please, Kim, try to understand. Let me explain.

KIM: You could talk for a year and you could never explain a thing like this!

TONY: If you'd just listen, Kim.

KIM: There's nothing you can say to me that I want to hear—not now or ever! Tony Hill, I'll never speak to you again as long as I live. Never! Never! Never! (*Runs off stage right*)

TONY (*Shouting*): Kim, please, come back. Kim, please, I have to talk to you.

SALLY (*Entering with purse*): Thank goodness, Mom left ten dollars in the kitchen change purse. Where's Kim?

TONY: Gone! And I've got to catch her. I've got to explain. (*Races off stage right*)

SALLY (*Shrugging*): Crazy people! Well, it looks as if I'll have to finish my shopping alone. (*Tosses empty purse on table and puts the money into her own purse*) Better take my keys, in case I get home ahead of Mom. (*Takes keys from drawer in phone table as phone rings*) Hello. Yes, this is the Hill residence. (*Pause*) Can you speak more plainly? Who? Tony? No, he's not here. This is his sister. (*Pause*) Tell him what? That he's to pick up Susie? Susie who? (*Pause*) I'm sorry, you must have the wrong number. (*Pause*) Yes, he lives here, but he's not home just now. Well, I can't tell you exactly. All right, you call later. 'Bye. (*As she hangs up*) So that's it! Another girl! Susie! Just wait till Kim hears about this! Men! They're all alike! Even my own brother! (*Exits right. After a brief pause* AUNT ABIGAIL *enters left, carrying a dress box.*)

AUNT ABIGAIL: I can't understand it, Kathy. I'm sure that kitchen door was locked when we left. I tried it myself.

MRS. HILL (*From kitchen*): Just wait a minute, Abby, till I put the cream in the refrigerator. (*Entering*) What did you say?

AUNT ABIGAIL: That kitchen door. I tell you it was locked when we went out.

MRS. HILL: You must have been mistaken, dear. You have to slam it extra hard.

AUNT ABIGAIL: But I did slam it, and I tried the lock. Kathy, there's something wrong.

MRS. HILL: Wrong with what? Don't tell me you're not satisfied with that dress you bought. You tried on at least a dozen.

AUNT ABIGAIL: It's not the dress, Kathy. It's this house. Someone's been in here.

MRS. HILL: Honestly, Abby, you're getting downright simple-minded on the subject of locks and doors.

AUNT ABIGAIL: Simple-minded or not, somebody's been in this house. I can tell.

MRS. HILL: All right. All right. How can you tell?

AUNT ABIGAIL (*Standing stock-still and looking around*): I don't know exactly, but I have a sixth sense about things like this. There's something in this room that isn't the way we left it.

MRS. HILL: For heaven's sake, Abby, come on upstairs and lie down. You'll want to get that dress out of the box before it wrinkles, and I have a million things to do. If I don't get that turkey in the oven, we'll never eat by five o'clock, and the children are going to the dance. Now come along.

AUNT ABIGAIL (*Grabbing* MRS. HILL'S *arm*): Don't go upstairs, Kathy. Please!

MRS. HILL: Abby, you're trembling. If you keep on like this, I'm going to have you see a doctor.

AUNT ABIGAIL: Don't you understand? Whoever came in the house might still be up there.

MRS. HILL: Now look, Abby, enough is enough! You're my own sister, and I love you dearly, but if you go on like this, people will think you're as crazy as a crumpet!

AUNT ABIGAIL: Crazy am I? Kathy, look! (*Pointing to purse on table*) Isn't that your kitchen purse?

MRS. HILL (*Picking it up*): Well how in the world did that get in here?

AUNT ABIGAIL: Now do you believe me?

MRS. HILL (*Examining purse*): It—it's empty. Abby, I had ten dollars in there.

AUNT ABIGAIL: You have to call the police.

MRS. HILL: The police!

AUNT ABIGAIL: You've been robbed! Heaven only knows

what else has been taken! Call the police! Call the police!

MRS. HILL: Take it easy, Abby. We don't want to sound a false alarm. Nothing else seems to be disturbed. (*Opens desk drawer and takes out coin purse which she holds up and shakes*) Good grief! The money for the paper boy is gone, too!

AUNT ABIGAIL: What did I tell you? The whole house has probably been ransacked.

MRS. HILL: Maybe we'd better take a look around. You take the dining room.

AUNT ABIGAIL: The silver! I'll bet there's not a piece left! (*Exits left*)

MRS. HILL: I don't care what Abby says. I'm going upstairs. (*Stumbles on toy bank*) What in the world? (*Picks it up in amazement*) Why, it's Tony's dime bank! And it's been forced open.

AUNT ABIGAIL (*Excitedly as she enters*): Kathy! Kathy! I've found out how they got in! A ladder! There's a ladder propped up against the dining room windows.

MRS. HILL: Good heavens! The painters' ladder.

AUNT ABIGAIL: But it was on the ground when we left. I saw it. Now it's propped against the side of the house. Someone got in through a bedroom window!

MRS. HILL: I still can't believe it!

AUNT ABIGAIL: Kathy Hill, I'm not staying in this house another minute unless you call the police.

MRS. HILL: All right, Abby. All right. (*As she reaches for phone, it rings*) Hello? Yes, yes, this is Mrs. Hill. (*Pause*) Why, certainly, Mr. Ramsay, I remember you. (*Pause*) Yes, yes, my son does have a typewriter. It's an old Royal portable. But I'm sure it's in his room. (*Pause*) A camera? What kind? (*Pause*) Well, yes, he has one like that . . . but . . . Look, Mr. Ramsay, I just came in, and there are signs of breaking and entering here, but I haven't checked yet to see just what has been taken. If you have a suspicious character there, hang on to him, and I'll call you back. Yes, yes, I will. And thanks so much for calling. (*Hangs up*) Well, Abby, you don't need to worry about our thief hiding upstairs. That was Mr. Ramsay calling from the Swap Shop. He thinks some young thug is trying to unload stolen goods and he recognized Tony's initials on the back of his typewriter case. I'm going to take a look upstairs. (*Exits*)

AUNT ABIGAIL: This is a case for the police. (*Picks up receiver and dials. Pause*) Police Headquarters? This is Miss Abigail Simms, 422 Locust Lane. I wish to report a robbery. (*Pause*) Yes, officer, my sister and I came home a few minutes ago and discovered someone had broken into the house by way of a second story window. (*Pause*) Well, officer, I can't tell you exactly what all has been taken, but there is very definitely some money missing. (*Pause*) Right away? Thank you, officer. I certainly will appreciate it.

MRS. HILL (*Entering left, greatly excited*): Abby! Abby! Someone has stripped Tony's room practically bare. Everything is cleaned out—his camera, typewriter, radio! His tennis racket and baseball stuff are gone out of his closet. The toy chest has been rifled—even his alarm clock is gone!

AUNT ABIGAIL: I've already called the police. They're sending the cruise car.

MRS. HILL: Good! I'll call Mr. Ramsay. (*Dialing*) Hello, Mr. Ramsay? This is Mrs. Hill. Mr. Ramsay, you're right! Every one of those items you described belongs to my son! (*Pause*) You still have him? Says he's a friend of Tony's? Humph! A likely story! Well, please hold him. My sister called the police, and I'll send the officer over there when he comes. (*Pause*) Oh, you'll bring him here for identification? Well, maybe that will be better, if it's not too much trouble. (*Pause*) Good. Then we'll expect you. Goodbye. (*Hangs up*)

AUNT ABIGAIL (*Dramatically*): It's a mercy we weren't all murdered in our beds!

MRS. HILL: Don't make things worse than they are, Abby. After all, it's broad daylight, and nothing's been touched except the money and Tony's things.

AUNT ABIGAIL: Thank goodness they didn't take Uncle Joshua's old tuba.

MRS. HILL: Even a thief wouldn't want that old thing, Abby.

AUNT ABIGAIL: Is that so? I'll have you know that's a very valuable instrument—a real antique! I'm surprised you don't make Tony take better care of it.

MRS. HILL: He hardly ever uses it any more except when the school instrument is out for repairs. Poor Tony! I do wish we could afford to get him a sousaphone of his own. He should have one next year when he goes away to college.

AUNT ABIGAIL: Sousaphone! Humph! This tuba is worth more than any such new-fangled contraption.

MRS. HILL: That may be, Abby, but this thing belongs in a museum instead of a modern band. (*Offstage siren*)

AUNT ABIGAIL: The police! They're here. (*Jumping up*) I'll let them in. (*Exits right and returns with* OFFICER RILEY) Do come in, officer.

OFFICER RILEY (*As he walks center*): Good morning, ladies. I am Officer Riley. My partner is checking the ladder at the side of the house. Have you listed the missing articles?

MRS. HILL: Only the money is missing, officer. The other articles taken from my son's room have already turned up at Ramsay's Swap Shop. He's holding the boy who brought them in.

AUNT ABIGAIL: And bringing him here for identification.

OFFICER RILEY: Probably one of our regulars! (OFFICER DUGAN *enters.*) Well, Dugan, what did you find?

OFFICER DUGAN: No question about that ladder. It leads straight to an unlocked window. (TONY *and* SALLY *enter.*)

TONY (*Breathlessly*): Mom! What's going on? Why are the police here?

SALLY (*Excitedly*): Are you all right? What's happened?

MRS. HILL: Now don't panic, dear. No one is hurt. We've just had a robbery.

TONY *and* SALLY (*Together*): A robbery!

AUNT ABIGAIL: Maybe after this you won't think it's so funny to keep the doors and windows locked.

MRS. HILL: Someone broke into the house through your bedroom window, Sally, and stole practically everything of value out of Tony's room.

SALLY: But, Mother. . . .

TONY (*Collapsing into the nearest chair*): Oh, my gosh!

MRS. HILL: It's nothing to be upset about, Tony. Everything but the money has been recovered.

SALLY: The money!

MRS. HILL: Yes. (*Picks up kitchen change purse*) Ten dollars is missing from the kitchen change purse, and the money for the paper boy is gone, too. (*Pointing to bank*) Even your dime bank was broken open.

SALLY: But, Mother. . . .

AUNT ABIGAIL (*To* OFFICER RILEY): Aren't you going to take fingerprints?

MRS. HILL: Why should they, Abby? The thief has already been caught red-handed—with the goods!

TONY (*Leaping to his feet*): Caught with the goods! But they can't do this! (MR. RAMSAY *enters, pushing* SAM *ahead of him.*)

MR. RAMSAY: Here he is, Mrs. Hill! The minute I set eyes on him I knew he was up to no good!

ALL (*Except policemen*): Sam!

SAM: You get me out of this, Tony Hill!

OFFICER RILEY: You know this boy?

TONY: Know him? He's my best friend.

MRS. HILL: Sam, how could you do such a thing? What will your poor mother say?

OFFICER DUGAN: What is your name, young man?

SAM: I'm not answering any questions. It's up to Tony to do the talking. Go ahead, Tony, tell them what happened.

TONY: Look, Mom, there's been a terrible mistake. Sam didn't steal anything. I sent him down to the Swap Shop to sell that stuff. He was only doing me a favor.

AUNT ABIGAIL: But the ladder! The window!

TONY: Thanks to your locking and bolting every door in sight, that was the only way I could get into the house.

SALLY: And as for the money—I took it! You didn't give me enough for the Thanksgiving shopping list, so I came back to the house and took all the small change I could find anywhere around.

SAM (*Shaking his head, mournfully*): Gee, Mrs. Hill, you should have known I wouldn't steal anything.

MRS. HILL: Of course you wouldn't, Sam. I apologize. In fact, I apologize all around. I guess you gentlemen think my sister and I are a pair of old women.

OFFICER RILEY: You did exactly the right thing in calling the police, and there's no need to apologize. It's our duty to investigate unusual happenings.

AUNT ABIGAIL: Then there was no crime after all!

OFFICER DUGAN: Don't sound so disappointed, ma'am. That's the best news a police officer could possibly hear. But I'm afraid this young man has some explaining to do to his mother.

MRS. HILL: What made you do such a thing, Tony? Why would you want to sell your typewriter, your camera, and your radio?

MR. RAMSAY: And why didn't you bring them in yourself instead of throwing suspicion on your friend here?

SAM: I told you he was giving me a fishy look from the very start.

MR. RAMSAY: In my business, I have to be suspicious.

TONY: It's all so mixed up, but I had to have money and had to have it fast.

MRS. HILL: But why? Are you in some kind of trouble?

TONY: And how! (MRS. HILL *looks alarmed.*) But it's not half as serious as you think, Mom. I had to have the money for a new horn.

MRS. HILL (*Unhappily*): But I promised we'd try to get you one for next year.

TONY: I had to have it now—today! (*Enter* MR. PLUNK *with sousaphone*)

MR. PLUNK: Excuse me. I rang, but nobody came.

TONY: Mr. Plunk!

MR. PLUNK: I called a while ago to tell you to pick up the

sousaphone, but the young lady didn't seem to understand.

SALLY: Sousa . . . sousaphone! Oh, my goodness! I thought you were talking about a girl . . . Susie . . . Susie something or other! Oh, Tony, then there's no Susie after all! Wait till I tell Kim! (*Starts to leave*)

OFFICER RILEY: If you don't mind, miss, I'd rather you stayed here till we write up this whole case. Who is this gentleman?

TONY: This is Mr. Plunk. He has the music store down on Main Street. I bought the sousaphone from him, or I should say, I was going to buy it as soon as I could get the down payment together.

MR. PLUNK: But that's what I came to tell you, son. After reading all about the high school band going to the Thanksgiving Day Parade, I decided I should do something to help. So you may have the horn without the usual hundred-dollar deposit. (*As he places sousaphone on table, he sees old tuba—"Big Bertha."*) Where did you get this magnificent tuba?

TONY: That? Oh, that's Big Bertha.

AUNT ABIGAIL: It belonged to his Great-uncle Joshua. It's a very fine instrument.

MR. PLUNK: I should say it is, and a very rare one, I'm sure. (*Adjusting his glasses*) Do you mind if I examine it?

MRS. HILL: Go right ahead.

MR. PLUNK: Why, this appears to be a genuine Helicon, one of the earliest, in fact. I place it about 1880. (*To* TONY) Why didn't you tell me you had this rare instrument, Tony?

TONY: I never thought it was rare or important, Mr. Plunk. I just thought it was old.

MR. PLUNK: It's both. This is the type of tuba used in John Philip Sousa's concert and marching bands.

AUNT ABIGAIL: For your information, Mr. Plunk, this tuba is not just the *type* that was used in Sousa's bands. It's the real thing. Uncle Joshua inherited it from his father who traveled through Germany and England with the March King.

MR. PLUNK (*Excitedly*): What a find! What a find! Wait till the National Sousa Foundation hears about this! Their publicity committee is planning a TV documentary on Sousa, and we've scoured the country for a horn like this. Tony, I don't think you need to worry any further about paying for your new horn. If you and your mother would agree to rent it to us for the program, I can promise you a generous fee—at least a hundred dollars, maybe more.

TONY: A hundred dollars! What do you say, Mom?

MRS. HILL: Big Bertha belongs to you, Tony.

TONY: But maybe it shouldn't belong to me, Mom. Maybe it belongs in a museum where more people could get to see such a rare and historic instrument.

MR. PLUNK: If you really want to do that, Tony, I am sure I could arrange it.

TONY: Thank you, Mr. Plunk. That's what I'd like to do with Big Bertha—after the TV program, of course.

AUNT ABIGAIL (*Happily*): It's just what your Uncle Joshua would have liked.

MRS. HILL: I'm so proud of you, Tony!

OFFICER RILEY (*Examining sousaphone*): So this is a sousaphone?

MR. PLUNK: That's right, sir. Designed according to instructions from Sousa himself. You will note that the large-sized, upright bell is placed so as to "diffuse the sound over the entire band, like the frosting on a cake." And I might say those are Mr. Sousa's exact words.

OFFICER RILEY: Well, I'll be jiggered. Say, Dugan, isn't this the same kind of horn that fellow from upstate brought into Headquarters yesterday?

OFFICER DUGAN: I believe you're right, Riley. It looks exactly the same to me.

TONY: You mean you have a horn like this at the police station?

OFFICER RILEY: It was there this morning, unless the owner has claimed it by now.

SAM: Jumpin' juniper! How did it get there?

OFFICER RILEY: A funny thing happened. Last Wednesday night this salesman from Erie parked his station wagon in front of the civic auditorium, and when he got home, he found a tuba—I mean—a sousaphone in the back seat.

SAM: So that's what happened!

TONY: I can't believe it! Sam, you lunkhead, you put that horn in the wrong station wagon! This sure saves my neck.

OFFICER DUGAN: Do you know something about it, boy? Do you know who owns it?

TONY: I sure do, officer. It belongs to Brewster High. We played in a concert last Wednesday night, and Sam carried the horn down to the station wagon . . . only he must have put it in the wrong one.

SAM: I told you you should have reported it to the police.

TONY: But I was afraid Mr. Carl would throw me out of the band and I'd miss the trip to New York. Mr. Carl is a real demon when it comes to the school instruments. Of course I planned to tell him about it on Monday—*after* the Thanksgiving Day Parade.

MRS. HILL: So that's why you had to have a new horn on such short notice.

MR. PLUNK: I can see you were in pretty hot water, my lad. But now that the school horn has been found, you won't be needing the sousaphone.

MRS. HILL: Oh, but he will, Mr. Plunk. We're hoping he'll make the band next year at State and he'll want his own instrument.

MR. PLUNK: Good! Then our deal still holds. I have another call to make, so if you can bring the Helicon down to the store this afternoon, I'll give you a receipt for it. You'll be hearing from the TV committee in a few days. This will be great news for them and for the museum as well. It's been a pleasure to see all of you—especially this fine young man. (*Shakes hands with* TONY) Thank you and good day. (MR. PLUNK *exits.*)

TONY: Oh, boy! A hundred dollars! Sam, I'm staking you to that dance tonight. You're a real pal.

SAM: Thanks, Tony. Now the next time you get into a mess like this, you can count me out.

MR. RAMSAY (*To* SAM): I guess I should apologize to you again, young fellow. No hard feelings, I hope.

SAM: No, sir, I guess this is all in a day's work.

OFFICER RILEY: And thanks for being so alert, Mr. Ramsay. We need more conscientious businessmen like you. Keep up the good work.

OFFICER DUGAN: We'll be glad to take you back in the cruise car, Mr. Ramsay.

MR. RAMSAY: Thanks! I've always wanted a ride in one. (*Walks to right exit with policemen.*)

OFFICER RILEY: Good day, ladies. Glad everything is squared away.

AUNT ABIGAIL: I'm sorry I was such a nervous Nelly, gentlemen.

OFFICER DUGAN: Think nothing of it, ma'am. The police are here for your protection and reassurance.

OFFICER RILEY: And it's not a bad idea to keep your doors and windows locked, even in a neighborhood like this.

MRS. HILL: I'm sure this is the last you will hear of my son's friend as a second-story man, officer.

OFFICER RILEY: I'm sure of it, ma'am. It's a funny thing but young people who are tied up in musical activities seldom run afoul of the law.

OFFICER DUGAN (*To* TONY): And don't blow any wrong oom-pah-pahs on that bass horn, young fellow. We'll be watching on TV.

TONY: Thank you, sir. I'll do my best. (*Policemen exit, followed by* MR. RAMSAY.)

MRS. HILL: Well, Abby, if your nerves are settled, I could use some help in the kitchen. We still have this Thanksgiving dinner ahead of us.

AUNT ABIGAIL: A piece of tomfoolery! The idea of having Thanksgiving ahead of time just because of a parade.

MRS. HILL: Thanksgiving isn't a date, Abby. It's a state of mind, and I think this family has a lot to be thankful for.

SALLY: A new sousaphone . . .

TONY: A hundred dollars. . . .

SAM: And Big Bertha! Who would have thought that thing was worth a plugged nickel?

AUNT ABIGAIL: It's turned out to be a real horn of plenty, if you ask me!

MRS. HILL: Sam, will you stay for dinner? It's the least we can do for you after all you've been through.

SAM: Thanks, Mrs. Hill, but I'm warning you— Mom says I eat like a horse.

MRS. HILL (*Laughing*): I think we'll have plenty for two horses. (*As* TONY *moves toward exit*) Tony, where are you going?

TONY: To find Kim. I have some tall explaining to do. (KIM *enters carrying a pie covered with aluminum foil in each hand.* TONY *rushes over to her.*) Kim! Kim! I have something to tell you!

KIM: I don't want to hear it. I didn't come over here for any of your silly excuses. Mrs. Hill, Mother baked these mince pies for your Thanksgiving dinner. I hope you enjoy them. (*Hands pies to* MRS. HILL *and turns to leave.*)

MRS. HILL: How very nice of her. Thank you, dear. I'll call her right away.

TONY (*Putting hand on* KIM'S *arm*): Kim, you've simply got to listen. You're wearing orchids to the Thanksgiving Ball.

KIM: Orchids!

TONY: Orchids! No measly French irises for my girl tonight!

KIM: Who says I'm your girl? And besides, I thought you were broke.

TONY (*Pulling her toward table where tuba is*): That was before Big Bertha came to the rescue. Look! I have something to show you. Tell me—what do you see?

KIM: Tony Hill, you must be out of your mind. I don't see anything at all except that rusty old horn.

TONY: Correction, please! That is no "rusty old horn." That, my dear Kim, is the original Horn of Plenty!

KIM: The horn of plenty?

TONY: Right! And thanks to its bounty, you and I are going to be the happiest couple that ever led the grand march at a Thanksgiving Ball! (*Curtain falls, as* TONY *swings* KIM *around in an impromptu dance.*)

THE END

Production Notes

Horn of Plenty

Characters: 6 male; 4 female.

Playing Time: 35 minutes.

Costumes: Policemen wear regular uniforms; others wear everyday informal clothes. Sally carries a purse.

Properties: Cartons of assorted items; baseball glove; sporting equipment; small radio; tennis racket; alarm clock; portable typewriter; two change or coin purses; sousaphone; metal toy bank; old-fashioned tuba; coins; keys; dress box; two pies, covered with aluminum foil.

Setting: The Hill living room. The room is simply furnished but should have sofa and various chairs, and at least one table with a telephone and a desk with several drawers in it. There is also a large table at one side on which the tuba lies. A door at left leads to the kitchen; another, at right, to the street.

Lighting: No special effects.

Sound: Doorbell, siren.

A Broadway Turkey

Characters

LINDA LAWRENCE, *a Broadway actress*
DIGBY LAWRENCE, *her husband, a Broadway playwright*
MR. WARREN
MRS. WARREN, *his wife*
PEGGY WARREN, *their teen-age daughter*
TED WARREN, *their teen-age son*
GRANDDAD WARREN, *a patriot*

TIME: *Thanksgiving morning.*
SETTING: *The living room of the Warren home in Connecticut.*
AT RISE: DIGBY LAWRENCE *is pacing the floor. He is wearing an overcoat. Two large traveling bags are at center stage. After two or three turns about the stage, he calls impatiently off left.*

DIGBY: Linda! Linda! For heaven's sake, hurry up! (LINDA *enters, carrying two cups of coffee.*)
LINDA: Sh! Not so loud, Digby. You'll wake the whole household.

DIGBY: Good grief, Linda, aren't you ready? I told you I wanted to be out of here by eight o'clock.

LINDA: You know I can't go without my coffee. (*Hands him cup.*) Here's a cup for you. It's good and hot. I just made it in the Jiffy Perk up in our room.

DIGBY: I don't want a cup of coffee. I don't want anything except to get out of here.

LINDA: Drink it. It will do you good. You need something hot in your stomach.

DIGBY: Something hot in my stomach! If I had a sore finger you'd tell me I needed something hot in my stomach.

LINDA: Do sit down and relax for a few minutes. Carrying on like this won't do us a bit of good.

DIGBY: I know. I know. Don't rub it in. Nothing will do us any good. I guess after last night I know that better than anyone else. Digby Lawrence, playwright, author of the biggest flop of the Broadway season! *American Nightmare* . . . a real turkey!

LINDA: Stop saying that, Digby. It's still too soon to tell—for sure. I know we flopped in New Haven, but we don't open in New York until Tuesday. That gives you six days to rewrite your third act.

DIGBY: Oh, sure! It's as simple as that. I rewrite the third act, and presto . . . our turkey is transformed into a golden peacock with a tail in living color!

LINDA: Cut out the sarcasm. I'm only trying to help. You know the critics said the play had possibilities. It's just that lousy third act.

DIGBY: So now *you're* calling it a lousy third act. I thought you were supposed to be an actress—not a critic.

LINDA (*Angrily*): I'm not just *supposed* to be an actress. I *am* an actress and a darned good one—when I have a decent play to act in.

DIGBY: That does it! (*Picks up one of the bags*) I'm going back to New York this minute, and you can get back under your own power. (*Sarcastically*) Maybe one of our esteemed critics will give you a ride. (*He storms toward left.*)

LINDA (*Running after him*): Oh, Digby, I didn't mean it that way. You know I think *American Nightmare* is the greatest thing you've ever done, but I've said from the beginning that third act doesn't click. It's too grim.

DIGBY: How do you want it to end—all sweetness and light? I suppose you want to come on stage dressed as Miss Liberty waving a flag, while the band plays "The Stars and Stripes Forever."

LINDA: You're impossible, Digby. You can't even think straight about the play at this point. Don't you understand I'm just as disappointed and upset by the reviews as you are, but I haven't given up hope. I *know* you can do it if you just give yourself a chance. What you need is a new slant.

DIGBY: What I need is to get back to New York. We'd have made it last night, if you hadn't been such a sissy about a little rain.

LINDA: Whose idea was it to take the short cut that brought us on this back road in the first place? We were lucky to pull in here and find a room. It was very good of these people to take us in—practically in the middle of the night.

DIGBY: That's the first thing you've said this morning that made any sense. Now I'm leaving.

LINDA: O.K., O.K. Just give me a minute to wash these

cups and throw some things into my travel case, and I'll be with you. You can certainly wait that long. (*She exits.*)

DIGBY (*Resuming his pacing*): Wait, wait, wait! That's all you ever do when you travel with a woman. *American Nightmare* . . . even the title is driving me crazy. I should have known from the first line it would be a flop. (MRS. WARREN *enters.*)

MRS. WARREN (*Brightly*): Why, good morning, Mr. Lawrence. Don't tell me you folks are leaving so early and without your breakfast.

DIGBY: We're not breakfast eaters, Mrs. Warren. My wife made some coffee in our room.

MRS. WARREN (*Contemptuously*): That stuff isn't *real* coffee, Mr. Lawrence. Let me get you some that's freshly perked. It won't take a minute. A nice dish of oatmeal and some ham and eggs wouldn't do you any harm either. From the looks of you, you could stand something hot in your stomach.

DIGBY: Oh, for heaven's sake . . . (*Smiling, embarrassed*) Sorry, Mrs. Warren. I appreciate your kindness, but I just don't need anything else that's hot in my stomach. Besides, my wife and I must be getting back to New York.

MRS. WARREN: But it's still raining, Mr. Lawrence, and the last we heard on the radio, they're afraid of a washout on the Powder Mill Road.

DIGBY: After what we came through last night, Mrs. Warren, we won't mind a little thing like a washout.

MRS. WARREN: You must be joking, Mr. Lawrence. Up here a washout isn't a laughing matter, especially if the bridge goes out at Crescent Corners. That really ties up the traffic around here. (LINDA *enters in hat and coat. She carries overnight case.*)

LINDA: Oh, good morning, Mrs. Warren. We had an excellent night's rest, and we do thank you for taking us in last night.

MRS. WARREN: I was really hoping you folks would stay for Thanksgiving dinner.

LINDA: Thank you, Mrs. Warren, but we couldn't think of it.

MRS. WARREN: Always room for a couple of extra places at a Thanksgiving dinner, and we'd be so glad to have you. I was just telling your husband that we might have some real trouble if the bridge washes out. Mr. Warren just went down to the village for the papers, and he'll be able to tell you how the roads are as soon as he gets back.

DIGBY: I'm sure we'll get through, Mrs. Warren. Thanks for everything. (MR. WARREN *and* TED *enter. They carry several newspapers and a grocery bag or two.*)

TED: Wow! What a downpour! They expect the bridge to go out at any minute.

DIGBY: In that case, we'd better move fast.

MR. WARREN: You'd better not move at all, young man. My advice is to stay put. Besides, the barricades are up on the other side of the village . . . no traffic on the New York road at all.

DIGBY: Of all the rotten luck!

TED: You won't think so when you taste Mom's Thanksgiving turkey.

DIGBY: Did you say *turkey?*

TED: I sure did . . . a thirty-pounder this year. Mom could hardly get it into the oven.

LINDA: Thirty pounds! Isn't that a tremendous amount of turkey, Mrs. Warren?

MRS. WARREN: We're all pretty big eaters in this household, and we're expecting a few extra people this year.

DIGBY (*More to himself than to anyone*): There ought to be *some* way to get out of here.

LINDA: Oh, Digby, simmer down, can't you? Let's stay.

MR. WARREN: You're certainly welcome, Mr. Lawrence, and we'll guarantee you a Thanksgiving to remember.

PEGGY (*Calling from offstage*): Mother! Will you please come up here?

MRS. WARREN (*Calling*): Just a minute, dear.

MR. WARREN (*Chuckling*): So our leading lady has decided to rise and shine.

LINDA: Leading lady?

TED: My sister has the lead in the Thanksgiving play tonight at the village, and, boy, does she feel important!

PEGGY (*Desperately, from offstage*): Mother! Mother! I'm stuck!

MRS. WARREN (*As she exits*): Coming.

MR. WARREN: Better let Ted help you upstairs with those bags, Mr. Lawrence, and join us for dinner.

LINDA (*Slipping off her coat and handing it to* DIGBY): You might as well take this along. I won't be needing it.

DIGBY: It looks as if we have voted, Mr. Warren. (*With sarcastic bow to* LINDA) I yield to the majority. (*Picks up one large bag and the overnight case, as* TED *picks up second bag*) Tell Mrs. Warren to save the wishbone of the turkey for me. I'll need it. (TED *and* DIGBY *exit.*)

LINDA: You'll have to excuse my husband for appearing so rude, Mr. Warren. He's really a sweet guy, but he's a bit upset. As a matter of fact, we're both upset. We've just had some pretty bad news.

MR. WARREN: I'm sorry to hear that, Mrs. Lawrence. Maybe if my wife made him some sassafras tea . . . something hot in his stomach, you know.

LINDA (*Laughing*): No, no, thank you. I'm afraid that wouldn't help.

MR. WARREN: Well, anything we can do, ma'am, just say the word. (*Picking up grocery bags*) I'd better take these things out to the kitchen. Emma will be needing them when she comes down. (*He exits.*)

LINDA (*Picking up a newspaper, as* MR. WARREN *exits*): Oh, I see you have the New Haven papers. (*Leafing through papers*) Oh, dear! Here's another bad review. (*Reading*) "*American Nightmare,* by Digby Lawrence, due for short run in New York. Critics pronounce the Thanksgiving week opening of the new Lawrence satire a real turkey, a verdict, which in any man's language is disappointing news for fans of the promising and talented Broadway playwright."

I hope to goodness he doesn't see this. (*Continues reading*) "In spite of the brilliant performance of Linda Lawrence as the First Lady and the valiant efforts of a fine supporting cast, *American Nightmare* proved to be a bad theatrical dream from which New Haven audiences were only too happy to be awakened at the end of a particularly dismal third act." (*Slamming down paper in anger*) How can they think of all those horrible things to say! (MRS. WARREN *and* PEGGY *enter.* MRS. WARREN *is carrying a rumpled Pilgrim costume over her arm.* PEGGY *is in a housecoat, her hair tucked under a scarf.*)

MRS. WARREN: Mrs. Lawrence, you haven't met our daughter, Peggy. She was in bed when you arrived. Peggy, this is Mrs. Lawrence. She and her husband were caught in the cloudburst last night.

LINDA: Hello, Peggy.

PEGGY: How do you do, Mrs. Lawrence. (*With a gasp of surprise*) Mrs. Lawrence. . . . Lawrence . . . could it be possible? Are you by any chance *Linda* Lawrence?

LINDA: Yes, I am.

PEGGY: You mean you're *the* Linda Lawrence, the actress!

LINDA: I'm afraid you're right.

PEGGY: Oh my goodness! Mother, why didn't you tell me it was *Linda Lawrence?*

MRS. WARREN: Now how in the world was I to know . . .

PEGGY: But everybody, just everybody knows Linda Lawrence. Why, Mother, her picture is always in the drama section, and . . .

LINDA: Oh, I wouldn't say "always."

PEGGY: Well, almost always, and you've been in the movies and on television, and, my goodness, this is perfectly fabulous. Imagine having a real star right in our own house.

MRS. WARREN: I'm afraid our daughter is one of those stage-struck teen-agers, Mrs. Lawrence.

LINDA: They tell me you're a star, too, Peggy—or will be after tonight.

PEGGY: I'll never live through it, Mrs. Lawrence, never! I'm so shook up right now I can't remember a single one of my lines, and my hair isn't right, and this hateful costume is ripped, and my face is full of freckles.

LINDA (*Laughing and cupping* PEGGY'S *face in her hand*): I fail to see a single freckle, my dear.

PEGGY: You must—you must see them. They're all over my nose.

LINDA (*Peering closely*): I see . . . one . . . two . . . three freckles. Nothing that a little base make-up won't take care of.

PEGGY: Base make-up? What's that?

LINDA: I'll show you. I have some in my make-up kit.

MRS. WARREN: And I can fix this costume in a few minutes. When it is pressed, it will look ever so much better. (*She exits.*)

LINDA: It isn't every actress who has a wardrobe mistress right under her own roof.

PEGGY: Wardrobe mistress? Oh, you mean Mom. (TED *and* DIGBY *enter.*)

TED: The papers are right here, Mr. Lawrence. Both the New Haven *Register* and the New York *Times*.

DIGBY: I'll take them upstairs if no one is reading them.

LINDA (*Quickly*): Oh, Digby, you haven't met Peggy. She has the leading part in the Thanksgiving play, you know.

DIGBY: Congratulations, Peggy. I hope the play is worthy of your talent.

PEGGY: Oh, it is. It's a wonderful play, Mr. Lawrence. Ted wrote most of it.

DIGBY: Indeed? I didn't know you were a playwright, young man.

TED: I'm not. I'm not a playwright at all. I just sort of fixed up the last scene.

DIGBY: That can very often be the most important part of the play.

PEGGY: And Mr. Lawrence ought to know, Ted. He's a real playwright. He's written all sorts of plays. You know — *Time Is a Beggar* and *Death by Candlelight* and *Meet Mr. Monkeyshine* . . . all big hits.

TED: I didn't realize you were *that* Mr. Lawrence. (*To* LINDA) Then you must be . . .

LINDA: Yes, Ted, I'm Linda Lawrence.

PEGGY: Isn't this just super? I'll bet we're the only family in town who ever had two such celebrities for Thanksgiving dinner.

DIGBY: But we're still not actually sure we're staying, Peggy.

TED: You have to stay, Mr. Lawrence. There's no escape. In fact, if that bridge goes out, you might be marooned here for days.

PEGGY: Bridge? What bridge?

TED: Are you a stranger around here, Peggy? The bridge at Crescent Corners, of course.

PEGGY: Oh, good heavens! If the bridge is out, Sue Hastings won't be able to make it for the performance, and she's my mother in the play.

TED (*With a whistle*): Golly, Peggy, you're right. And that confounded bridge has been closed to traffic since early this morning. What will we do?

PEGGY: We'll have to get Miss Larrabee. (*To* LINDA) Miss Larrabee's our director. She knows all the lines. I'm going to get dressed and run over there right away. (PEGGY *exits.*)

TED: This is a heck of a note. I wish I had never started with this thing in the first place.

DIGBY: That's show business, son. One crisis after another.

LINDA: Don't worry, Ted. Things have a way of turning out all right in the end. What's the name of your play?

TED: It's called *A Modern Thanksgiving*. Corny title, isn't it? I wanted to call it *A Dream Boat Thanksgiving*, but no one would listen to me.

DIGBY: I can't think why.

TED: Neither can I. You see, it's about this family, you know—one of these modern set-ups where nobody has any time for anything except himself. The father's too busy with his business and his golf. The mother is too tied up with committees and bridge parties. The kids don't care. Everybody thinks Thanksgiving is just another day, so why bother?

LINDA: Then somebody falls asleep and dreams about the first Thanksgiving.

DIGBY: And somebody else shows up in a Pilgrim costume and holds forth about the virtues of the real Thanksgiving and what a great country this will be some day.

TED (*Amazed*): How did you know? You haven't even read it.

DIGBY: No, but I've read about nine thousand, nine hundred and ninety-nine other plays just like it.

TED: You mean the idea has been used before, and it isn't any good?

LINDA: Well, yes, Ted, the idea has been used many times, but that doesn't mean it isn't good.

DIGBY: It's the treatment of the idea that really counts—how you handle it.

TED: I sure wish you could have been here when I was writing that last scene. You would have known just what to do.

DIGBY: I doubt it, boy, I doubt it.

TED: But you're a real playwright! (*Suddenly*) Say, will you—could you take a look at the final speeches if I get the script?

DIGBY: I tell you I'm no good at final scenes, Ted, no good at all.

LINDA (*Soothingly, to* TED): Of course he'll read your play, Ted. He'll be glad to. Run along and get it.

TED: Oh, boy! This is great! I'll bring it right down. (*He exits.*)

DIGBY (*Annoyed, to* LINDA): What's the big idea of volunteering for me? You know I have no time for this amateur rot and drivel.

LINDA: Don't you see, Digby. This isn't rot and drivel to them. It's fine and wonderful and they're dead serious about it.

DIGBY: What do you want me to do—pat him on the back and tell him he's another Shakespeare?

LINDA: Just read it and try to be helpful, and if you say one word or make one single crack, I— I'll never forgive you. (PEGGY *enters, dressed in street clothes.*)

PEGGY: Now we're really in the soup! Miss Larrabee went over to spend the night with Sue Hastings, and they're both marooned. Now we don't even have a director.

DIGBY: Well, Peggy, it looks as if your curtain's going down before it even went up.

PEGGY: But that can't happen, Mr. Lawrence, it just can't! The whole town turns out for the annual Thanksgiving play. It's . . . well, it's a tradition, and we simply can't call it off now.

MRS. WARREN (*Entering with freshly pressed costume*): Here's your costume, Peggy. See how fresh it looks? I mended it so you'll never notice the tear under the arm.

PEGGY (*Tearfully*): Oh, Mother, it looks as if I'm not going to need the costume. I'm afraid there isn't even going to be a play.

MR. WARREN (*Entering left in time to hear last line*): Why not? What in the world has happened?

TED (*Entering right with script in his hand*): Here it is, Mr. Lawrence. Now if you'll just look over this last scene, I'd like your honest opinion of the final speeches. (*Hands script to* DIGBY)

PEGGY: It's no use, Ted. Miss Larrabee went over to visit

the Hastingses. Now neither she nor Sue will be able to make it for the play. We're sunk.

TED: But we can't be.

MR. WARREN: This is a pretty kettle of fish!

MRS. WARREN: I hope to goodness Granddad doesn't hear about this. It will ruin his day.

PEGGY: How can he help finding out? Everybody's talking about it.

DIGBY: I must say I don't quite get it. Why all this fuss? What tremendous investment is at stake that the show must go on?

MRS. WARREN: You don't understand, Mr. Lawrence. This play means a lot to the community. It's an important part of our Thanksgiving.

LINDA: I can see that it would mean a lot to the young people.

MR. WARREN: Not only to the young people, Mrs. Lawrence. My father is eighty years old, and the Thanksgiving play means even more to him than it does to Peggy and Ted. (GRANDDAD WARREN *enters.*)

GRANDDAD: What in tarnation's going on around here? What's all this tommyrot about calling off the play for tonight? Folks down in the village are all riled up!

MRS. WARREN: For goodness' sake, Granddad. You shouldn't have come out in this downpour! And without your rubbers!

GRANDDAD: Rubbers, poppycock! That's the trouble with your generation! Want to wrap everybody up in cotton wool! Rubbers, indeed!

MRS. WARREN: But you'll catch your death of cold.

GRANDDAD: That's what they've been telling me ever since I was knee-high to a grasshopper and I'm still here, hale and hearty! What's the matter with you people anyway—can't you even stand up to a little rain? Want to call off the Thanksgiving play just because the bridge is out!

TED: But, Granddad, we have no director.

PEGGY: And one of the main characters can't come.

GRANDDAD: Then find somebody else. Don't just stand there sniveling. That's the trouble with you young people today—always ready to give up. No spunk and spirit! (*Noticing* LINDA *and* DIGBY) Who are these folks? Never saw 'em before.

MR. WARREN: These are our guests from New York, Father. Mr. and Mrs. Lawrence.

LINDA *and* DIGBY: How do you do, Mr. Warren.

GRANDDAD: New York, eh? Well, now, they say New Yorkers always know the answers. What's your suggestion?

LINDA: I'm afraid we're not much help, Mr. Warren.

DIGBY: This play is very important to you, isn't it, sir?

GRANDDAD: Important? Let me tell you, young man, this play is one of the most important events in this town.

MRS. WARREN: Do sit down, Granddad, and let me take your coat. You're wet through. (*She helps him off with coat and hands it to* TED, *steers* GRANDDAD *to sofa and gets him to sit down*) Peggy, run upstairs and get your father's wool jacket. (*As* PEGGY *moves toward exit*) And take that costume along with you. I don't want it cluttering up the living room. (*She kneels beside* GRANDDAD) Now let's have a look at those shoes! Peggy, bring down a pair of slippers. His feet are soaked. (*Over his protests, she removes* GRANDDAD'*s shoes and hands them to* TED *with coat*) Here, Ted, take these wet things out to the kitchen to dry. (TED *and* PEGGY *exit.*)

GRANDDAD: Stop fussing, Emmy. I never could abide a fussy woman!

MRS. WARREN: And I never could abide a crotchety old man! Now you sit there, and I'll go make you a nice cup of tea. (*She goes out.*)

GRANDDAD: I don't want any tea!

DIGBY: It will do you good, Mr. Warren. . . . something hot in your stomach, you know.

LINDA: Pay no attention to him, Mr. Warren.

MR. WARREN: Here are the morning papers, Father. Maybe you'd like to look at them.

GRANDDAD: Papers! Who wants to read the papers any more? Nothing but scandal sheets.

MR. WARREN: At least you can look at the headlines.

GRANDDAD: I'm not interested in a pack of smart aleck reporters trying to scare folks out of their wits.

MR. WARREN: There are some good editorials.

GRANDDAD: Editorials! More young whippersnappers writing nonsense about our country going to the dogs.

MR. WARREN: I give up. (*He goes out.*)

DIGBY: I take it you have a brighter view of our country's future, Mr. Warren.

GRANDDAD: Of course, I do. Why would I want to live to be a hundred if I had no faith in the future?

LINDA: So you want to live to be a hundred, Mr. Warren. I think that's wonderful.

GRANDDAD: What's so wonderful about it, young lady? Everybody wants to live.

LINDA: But it takes courage, Mr. Warren, especially these days. In fact, I think it takes a very special courage to face the strange and uncertain years ahead.

GRANDDAD: Poppycock! What's there to be afraid of? When you take a look at our past and understand what's gone before us, you can certainly face up to the future. That's the whole point of our Thanksgiving celebration, you know.

DIGBY: I'm afraid I *don't* know, Mr. Warren. I don't seem to understand the importance you people attach to Thanksgiving and especially to this Thanksgiving play. (PEGGY *enters with jacket and slippers.*)

PEGGY: Here, Granddad, let me help you into these dry things.

GRANDDAD (*As* PEGGY *helps him*): What are you trying to do, Peggy, make a mollycoddle of your old granddad?

PEGGY: Nobody could do that, you old fire-eater. We're just trying to take care of you.

GRANDDAD: These people from the city can't seem to get the hang of our Thanksgiving celebration, Peggy. They can't understand all the fuss and feathers.

TED (*Entering with cup of tea*): Here's your tea, Granddad, and you'd better drink it if you know what's good for you. Mom's on the warpath.

GRANDDAD: Tea! Bah! I never did like tea.

TED: Mom put some honey in it, just the way you like it. (*To* DIGBY) Have you had a chance to look at the script, Mr. Lawrence?

DIGBY: I've just been telling your grandfather that I'm a little confused by all this Thanksgiving activity. I realize that Thanksgiving is a national holiday, but . . .

GRANDDAD: Thanksgiving is a sight more than just a national holiday, son. Thanksgiving is a personal holiday . . . a personal holiday for every man who calls himself an American.

PEGGY: This is Granddad's favorite topic, Mr. Lawrence.

GRANDDAD: When I was your age, young man, Thanksgiving was just a day to eat too much turkey and maybe go to a ball game in the afternoon. But in 1917 America went to war.

DIGBY: World War I—the war that was to make the world safe for democracy.

GRANDDAD: It didn't much matter to me what the war was about. It just mattered to me that my oldest son was in it and that he was reported missing somewhere over France.

LINDA: I'm sorry, Mr. Warren.

GRANDDAD: So was I, so was the whole town, because a lot of families lost their sons in '17 and '18. A wartime Thanksgiving can be pretty grim. But then some of us got together and decided to have a community Thanksgiving. We put on a pageant down at the Town Hall.

DIGBY: Was it a success?

GRANDDAD: Maybe not according to your way of thinking, but that home talent show did something for all of us—made us feel the war wouldn't last forever and made us determined to give the rest of our boys a better country to come home to.

DIGBY: It must have been a fine play to do that, Mr. Warren.

GRANDDAD: Come to think of it, it wasn't much of a play, but it sure had a powerful story . . . the story of the Pilgrims is hard to beat. It has courage, determination, faith, every quality that has enabled this country to endure.

PEGGY: After that, well, we've had a Thanksgiving play every year.

TED: We've never missed.

GRANDDAD: No, sir, we've never missed. Back in '29, the year of the stock market crash, folks didn't have very much to be thankful for, and there were some Thanksgivings during the Depression when most people were out of work—not even sure where their next meal was coming from. But a good look at our Pilgrim fathers turned the holiday into a day of real thanksgiving.

TED: All through World War II, even when Dad was on Guadalcanal and Mom was worried sick, she and Granddad went right on with the Thanksgiving show just the same.

LINDA: And now these young people want to carry on the same tradition.

GRANDDAD: How can they help it? It's part of them. That is what is so important. How can we keep our American way alive, if we don't plant our great national principles in their minds and hearts? Good heavens! That's what's wrong with some of these scaredy-cats who write for the papers. They're afraid of the future because they don't believe in the past.

DIGBY: Do you really think we learn from the past, Mr. Warren?

GRANDDAD: Sure we do. Now take those fellows who came over here on the Mayflower. They had plenty to be scared of . . . hunger, Indians, sickness, death. They were away from home. They were worried about their women folk and their children, but did they give up and go crawling back home when the Mayflower returned to England? Not a dad-blamed one of 'em. They all stayed right here and kept on fighting. And that's the whole story of Thanksgiving in a nutshell. We can all be thankful that these people were our ancestors, and so long as we stick by their faith and their ideas of freedom for ourselves and for others, we've no cause to be afraid.

DIGBY: But the world of today is so different . . . and the world of tomorrow even more uncertain.

GRANDDAD: Mark my words, mister, if we present-day Americans just take a leaf out of the Pilgrims' book, we'll be more than ready for whatever comes.

DIGBY: I think I see what you mean, Mr. Warren, and I am beginning to understand what Thanksgiving means to you and to your town.

LINDA (*Enthusiastically*): So do I, Mr. Warren, and I can promise you one thing: Your play will go on as scheduled—that is, if you'll let me play Sue Hastings' part.

TED (*Excitedly*): Let you! Wow, Peggy, did you hear what the lady said?

PEGGY (*Overwhelmed*): You don't mean it! You can't mean it!

LINDA: But I do mean it, Peggy. I'd like very much to play the part, if you think I could do it.

TED: Do we think you can do it! You must be kidding.

DIGBY: I don't think she's kidding, Ted. I think she's very much in earnest. And if there's anything I can do backstage in the absence of the director, count me in.

PEGGY (*Ecstatically*): This is too good to be true. (*Running to doorway*) Mother, Dad, come in and hear the good news. We're having the play after all.

GRANDDAD: I can't tell you how much I appreciate the favor you are doing us and the whole town.

DIGBY (*As* MR. *and* MRS. WARREN *enter*): On the contrary, sir, I am really doing myself a favor, a very great favor. You see, Linda and I are theatre people. She is an actress and I am a playwright.

TED: A very famous one, too. He's written a lot of hits, Granddad.

DIGBY: I've also had my share of flops, Ted. When we came here last night, I was really running away from myself as a writer because my new play was a failure—what the critics call a "real turkey."

MRS. WARREN: "Turkey!" That's a funny word for failure.

DIGBY: But today you folks have shown me how I can turn that turkey into a real Thanksgiving turkey after all.

LINDA: Oh, Digby, do you really think you have the new slant you needed?

DIGBY: I'm sure of it, Linda. It's all here, right here in this room. (*Tapping script*) It's in Ted's play. . . .

TED: Do you really like it, Mr. Lawrence?

DIGBY: I like it fine, Ted, and I like what I have found here—a real spirit of thankfulness for our American heritage.

LINDA: Oh, Digby, you *do* have a different slant.

DIGBY: You see, Granddad . . . you don't mind if I call you that, do you, sir?

MR. WARREN: Half the town calls him that now, Mr. Lawrence.

DIGBY: Well, you see, Granddad, I was one of those smart alecks, one of those scaredy-cats you've been talking about.

PEGGY: I don't think you were ever afraid of anything, Mr. Lawrence.

DIGBY: Oh, yes, I was, Peggy. I was afraid of the critics, afraid of myself, and worse than that, I was afraid of the future. Somehow I had forgotten that we can always borrow courage and wisdom from those who have gone before us. Here in this room I have learned that from your grandfather, and now I can finish my play—finish it in such a way that it will teach the same lesson to others who are doubtful and fearful about the future of America.

LINDA: Are you going to keep the same title, Digby—*American Nightmare?*

GRANDDAD: *American Nightmare?* I don't know if I like that, young man.

DIGBY: I think you'll like it when you see it opening night, sir, if you and your family will be our guests.

PEGGY (*Overcome*): A real Broadway opening! I can hardly believe it!

DIGBY: You see, sir, the best part of a nightmare is waking up and knowing it was only a bad dream. I've had my nightmare, sir, and now, thanks to you, I am wide awake. I can see that America has had enough of my kind of thin-blooded loyalty and half-hearted patriotism. Today we need to be reminded of our forefathers who could count their blessings in the face of danger, hardship, and fear.

LINDA: How are you going to end your play, Digby?

DIGBY: In much the same manner that Ted has ended his.

TED: That's a real compliment.

DIGBY: Not in the same words, exactly, but in the same spirit—the true spirit of faith and Thanksgiving. Here, I'll show you.

MRS. WARREN: What do you mean, Mr. Lawrence?

DIGBY: As the new director, I'm taking over. (*Grouping cast as he talks*) Linda, you're over here, right stage. Ted, you're on one side of her, Peggy on the other. Mr. and Mrs. Warren, I'll want you left stage, a bit further downstage, if you please. There, that's right. And now, Granddad, as Governor Bradford, you're right here, center stage. Stage lights dim (*Lights follow spoken cues*), the spotlight is on you, as you lead your people in the Pilgrim's favorite psalm of Thanksgiving. (*Background music of "We Gather Together" as* GRANDDAD *begins the 100th Psalm.*)

GRANDDAD: Make a joyful noise unto the Lord, all ye lands.

LINDA: Serve the Lord with gladness; come before His presence with singing.

MR. WARREN: Know ye that the Lord He is God; it is He that hath made us, and not we ourselves.

PEGGY: We are His people and the sheep of His pasture.

TED: Enter into His gates with thanksgiving and into His courts with praise.

MRS. WARREN: Be thankful unto Him and bless His name.

ALL: For the Lord is good; His mercy is everlasting; and His truth endureth to all generations. (*If desired, audience and cast join in singing "We Gather Together" as the curtains close.*)

THE END

Production Notes

A Broadway Turkey

Characters: 4 male; 3 female.

Playing Time: 30 minutes.

Costumes: Modern dress. Digby, Linda, Mr. Warren, Ted, and Granddad have heavy coats, which they wear as indicated in the text. Linda has a hat. Peggy wears a housecoat and scarf, then wears street clothes. Granddad changes to wool jacket and slippers during the play.

Setting: A comfortably furnished living room.

Properties: Two traveling bags and an overnight case; cups and saucers, newspapers and grocery bags, rumpled Pilgrim costume.

Lighting: If desired, lights may dim and spotlight may be used, as indicated, at the end of the play.

Red Carpet Christmas

Characters

MRS. HITCHCOCK
MR. HITCHCOCK
PAM, CORKY, MARCIA — *their children*
ANITA PAGE, JIMMY HALE — *Marcia's friends*
BESSIE, *the housekeeper*
COUNT CORELLI
MAGGIE CORELLI, *his wife*
TONY, GINA — *their children*

TIME: *The afternoon of the day before Christmas.*

SETTING: *The living room of the Hitchcock family. There is a large window right.*

AT RISE: MARCIA *is kneeling on sofa, looking out of window through binoculars.* ANITA *is beside her.*

ANITA (*Excitedly*): Can you see him, Marcia? Can you see Tony?

MARCIA: I'm not quite sure, but there's somebody moving about in the living room.

ANITA: Is it Tony?

MARCIA: I think so. Yes, I'm almost positive. I can see the back of his neck and one ear.

ANITA (*Grabbing for binoculars*): Let me look! Let me look!

MARCIA: Stop shoving. You'll get him out of focus. Now he's leaning over. He seems to be moving a piece of furniture. I wish he'd come closer.

ANITA: I'll concentrate. (*Shuts her eyes tightly*) Closer, closer, closer! (*Opens eyes and leans over* MARCIA'S *shoulder*) Is he coming any nearer?

MARCIA: A little. He's stopping at the table . . . now . . . now . . . oh, Anita! He's coming toward the window. He's . . . oh, my goodness! He's looking right over here, right at our house. (*Scrambles off sofa and ducks behind curtain*) Do you suppose he can see me?

ANITA: Of course not. The house is too far away. (*Snatching binoculars*) I simply *must* see him! (*Pause*) Wow! He's positively handsome! Oops! Don't do it! Don't do it! Don't you dare do it!

MARCIA: What? What is he doing?

ANITA (*With exaggerated sigh of relief*): It's all right now, but for a minute I almost had heart failure. I thought he was going to pull down the shade.

MARCIA: You've had the binoculars long enough. Let me look.

ANITA (*Holding on to binoculars*): Just a few seconds more, Marcia, please. You can look at him all afternoon after I've gone. Um-m-m! Tall, dark, and handsome—just the way I like 'em!

MARCIA: That's funny. I remember Tony as a blond.

ANITA: Well, his hair is darker now, and he has a marvelous tan—that real Riviera look.

MARCIA: Let me see.

ANITA: Uh-oh! Sorry! He just walked out.

MARCIA: Now I've missed him again. I've been watching for three days, and I've never once had a good look at him.

ANITA: I don't see why you don't ask him over for your Christmas party tonight. After all, you were once engaged to him.

MARCIA: Engaged to him! What on earth are you talking about?

ANITA: You told me so yourself. He gave you a ring and everything.

MARCIA: Oh, Anita, you nitwit! That was ten years ago when he was eight and I was six. The ring came out of a Crackerjack box.

ANITA: But you promised to wait for each other. And I'll bet you still have the ring.

MARCIA (*Crossly*): What if I do? It was only a silly game we played the last summer he was here visiting his grandmother Briggs. He's never been back since she died.

ANITA: But the whole family's here now. (*Digs clipping out of purse*) Did you see this write-up in the Sunday paper? (*Reads*) "Countess Corelli and family to winter in Bakersville. After a twenty-year absence in Italy, the former Margaret Briggs will re-open her childhood home in time for Christmas."

MARCIA: I didn't see that one. Is Tony's picture there? (*Looks at clipping*)

ANITA: No, just the Count, the Countess, and Gina. What are they like?

MARCIA: I've never seen any of them. Tony used to visit his grandmother by himself. Gina is younger—closer to Pam and Corky's age.

ANITA: But your mother knows the Countess. Didn't they grow up together?

MARCIA: Sure. They used to be very close friends. Mother still calls her Maggie Briggs. But there was some sort of quarrel, and Mother never heard from her after she married the Count and went off to Italy. In fact, I don't think Mom's too pleased that they've come back here to live.

ANITA: I think it's marvelous. Imagine living right next door to a count and a countess.

MARCIA: It's stretching a point to say we live right next door. There's a big garden between the Corelli house and ours.

ANITA: But they're still your nearest neighbors. Oh, Marcia, why don't you ask the whole family to your open house? That would be the neighborly thing to do.

MARCIA: I told you Mother doesn't want to be that neighborly. She's already told us she doesn't want us pushing ourselves in. Never let it be said that the Hitchcocks are social climbers.

ANITA: Tony is an old friend. It wouldn't be social climbing to ask him. Besides, you do need an extra boy.

MARCIA: But he's been here three whole days and hasn't called or dropped in. He probably doesn't even remember us.

ANITA: Well, you should certainly be able to think of some way to meet him. (*Handing binoculars to* MARCIA) Here. Take the binoculars and keep up with your homework. I promised to meet Jimmy about four. Anything you want me to pick up downtown?

MARCIA: It would be a help if you could pick up a boy to fill in for Bob Lucas. What a time for him to get tonsillitis!

ANITA: I'll ask Jimmy. He knows everybody.

MARCIA: Thanks a lot. See you tonight. (*As* ANITA *exits left,* MARCIA *resumes her lookout post*) Oh, dear! The room is still empty. I wonder when he'll be back. (PAM *enters right with plate of cookies, one of which she is eating.*)

PAM: At it again, are you? You'd better not let Mom catch you snooping on the new neighbors.

MARCIA: I am *not* snooping, Pamela Hitchcock.

PAM: Then I will. (*Offering cookies to her*) Here, have some of Bessie's hermits while I scan the Corelli horizon for another look at Gina. She's cute as anything. But when I saw her this morning after breakfast she seemed to be crying.

MARCIA: What would a girl who has everything find to cry about?

PAM: Don't ask me. Say, who's been fooling with these binoculars? I can't see a thing.

MARCIA: There's nothing to see. (*Puts cookie plate on coffee table*) Everybody's out.

PAM: I like to look at the room. Did you ever see such gorgeous decorations and such beautiful furniture?

MARCIA: I didn't notice.

PAM: That's because you're too busy looking for Tony.

MARCIA: I haven't seen him, except for one, teeny-weeny glimpse.

PAM: I sure wish Mom would invite the whole family to our open house tonight, but I guess it's just as well. This house is so shabby.

MARCIA: What a thing to say! I like our house just the way it is.

PAM: Oh, sure, but compared to the Corelli house, it's nothing. They must have done over the whole place. They've taken up that ugly old carpeting, and they have the most gorgeous Oriental rugs.

MARCIA: Mom's been talking about getting a new rug in here.

PAM: You ought to see the draperies.

MARCIA: Now who's snooping?

PAM: *I* didn't say it was snooping. That's just what Mother calls it. To me it's just like watching a play—you know, the same as television. You don't actually know the people, but you like to see what they're doing.

MARCIA (*Clapping her hand to her head*): Television! Good grief! I forgot to call the repair shop! Dad told me to call right after breakfast. I hope it's not too late. (*Goes to phone and dials*)

PAM: Dad will have fits if he can't see his Christmas programs tonight. Hey, sis, come and look. Somebody's going into the Corelli house.

MARCIA: Oh, dear! The line is busy. (*Hangs up and runs to window*) Who? Where? Let me see. (*As girls pass binoculars back and forth,* MRS. HITCHCOCK *enters from center.*)

MRS. HITCHCOCK: Marcia! Pam! Put those binoculars down this minute! I will not have you spying on the Corellis.

PAM: But, Mother, they're so fascinating, and it's so exciting, living so close to royalty.

MRS. HITCHCOCK: Royalty, my foot! Counts were a dime a dozen when Maggie Briggs married hers.

MARCIA: Maggie Briggs! Oh, Mother, she's the Countess Margarita now.

MRS. HITCHCOCK: She was just plain Maggie Briggs when I knew her. Now put those binoculars down and get away from that window. Marcia, you go help Bessie with the punch and sandwiches.

MARCIA: I must call the TV repair shop first, Mother.

MRS. HITCHCOCK: Good heavens! Haven't you done that yet?

MARCIA: The line was busy. I'll try again. (*Goes to phone and dials*)

MRS. HITCHCOCK: And you, Pam, you can polish the silver tray. Bessie has so much extra work to do, making her Christmas cookies besides everything else.

PAM: Oh, Mother! Do I have to?

MRS. HITCHCOCK: You most certainly do.

PAM: But she's doling them out to the whole town. She even baked a fresh batch this morning. Can't you stop her?

MRS. HITCHCOCK: That new batch was for our party. I wouldn't stop her, even if I could. Bessie's Christmas cookies are a tradition in this town.

PAM: Maybe that's why they named it Bakersville.

MRS. HITCHCOCK: Don't try to be funny, Pam. You know how much those cookies mean to Bessie. She sends them to neighbors the way other people send Christmas cards. Now get moving.

PAM: What about Corky? What's he doing to help get ready for the party?

MRS. HITCHCOCK: Your brother did his share this morning. Now it's your turn. So git! (*Shoos* PAM *offstage.*)

MARCIA (*At phone*): Oh, I see. Well, I can understand that

you are rushed, but couldn't you possibly? (*Pause*) Well, that would be fine. We certainly would appreciate it. Thank you. Goodbye. (*Hangs up*)

MRS. HITCHCOCK: Any luck?

MARCIA: Mr. Young said his men are working over at the Corellis, putting in two new sets.

MRS. HITCHCOCK: The Corellis! I wish to goodness they had stayed in Europe! They've done nothing but upset this household ever since they came back.

MARCIA: But, Mother, it isn't actually their fault. They haven't really done anything. It's just that . . . well, they're so important, and glamorous . . . and it's exciting to have them as neighbors.

MRS. HITCHCOCK: We're not exactly neighbors just because there are no houses between the old Briggs mansion and 925 Hilltop Road. And, furthermore, I don't want you wasting any more time gawking at the Corelli family with these binoculars. I'm going to take them upstairs and put them under lock and key.

MARCIA: Oh, Mother, don't you understand? I'm dying to see Tony.

MRS. HITCHCOCK: If he stays here all winter and goes to public high school, you'll see him every day.

MARCIA: But I want to see him now, tonight. Please, couldn't I ask him to the party to fill in for Bob Lucas?

MRS. HITCHCOCK: Forget it, Marcia. If Tony wants to see you, he knows where you live. Goodness knows he could always find his way over here when he was a little boy.

MARCIA: And you always liked him then. I don't see why you object to him now.

MRS. HITCHCOCK: Of course I liked him. He was a nice child, and I have no doubt he's grown into a nice young man. But I am not going to have my daughter falling all over herself to cultivate any Corelli. Now do hurry, dear. Bessie needs your help.

MARCIA (*With resignation*): O.K., Mom. I'll go fix the punch and sandwiches. (*Turning at door*) You can tell Dad that Mr. Young said he'd send one of the men over from the Corellis to fix the TV set if they finish before five. (MARCIA *exits.*)

MRS. HITCHCOCK: Humph! I like that! We've been good customers for years, but now the Corellis come first! I'll bet Maggie figures the whole town will come flocking just because she's a countess! Two television sets! I'd love to see what she's done with that old house. (*Picks up binoculars and looks around guiltily*) For two cents, I'd take a peek myself . . . (*Gets into position on sofa*) That front parlor used to be a regular mausoleum, but now I suppose . . . (*Lifts binoculars to her eyes, as* MR. HITCHCOCK *enters left with several packages.*)

MR. HITCHCOCK (*As he drops his parcels on chair*): I think I've got everything on the list. (*He suddenly notices binoculars.*) Ethel! In heaven's name, what are you doing?

MRS. HITCHCOCK (*Startled and embarrassed*): Henry! You scared the life out of me! I didn't hear you come in.

MR. HITCHCOCK: Don't tell me you've succumbed to the family weakness of Corelli-watching!

MRS. HITCHCOCK: Not quite. I admit I was close. But don't you dare tell the children!

MR. HITCHCOCK: What's the fatal fascination? Every time I come in, somebody's glued to those binoculars.

MRS. HITCHCOCK: I know, Henry. It's terrible, simply terrible. But between you and me—and I'll throttle you if you breathe a word—I'm dying to see Maggie Briggs.

MR. HITCHCOCK: It seems only yesterday I heard you vow

that you never wanted to see Maggie Briggs as long as you lived.

MRS. HITCHCOCK (*Ruefully*): I know—that was the time she ruined my Christmas Eve party by giving a bigger and better one on the same night, remember?

MR. HITCHCOCK: How could I forget? That was the night we announced our engagement. You said you'd never forgive her.

MRS. HITCHCOCK: But I did . . . or I almost did. In spite of everything, I always liked Maggie a lot. I guess I still do.

MR. HITCHCOCK: Then why don't you let bygones be bygones and invite the whole family over tonight?

MRS. HITCHCOCK: Henry! We couldn't possibly!

MR. HITCHCOCK: Why not?

MRS. HITCHCOCK: Because . . . well, in the first place, Maggie's a countess now. They have their own friends. The society pages of the papers have been full of their coming back to Bakersville and moving into the Briggs mansion. And anyhow, this house—this room—

MR. HITCHCOCK: What's the matter with this house and this room?

MRS. HITCHCOCK: Oh, it's fine, Henry, and I love every bit of it. But it is—well, it's just plain shabby. Look at this rug, for instance.

MR. HITCHCOCK: I'm looking at it.

MRS. HITCHCOCK: Well, don't you see how worn it's getting, and . . . oh, I know this sounds snobbish and silly, but I just can't see ourselves entertaining the Corellis . . . and besides . . .

MR. HITCHCOCK: And besides, you're still angry at Maggie for standing you up at your Christmas party.

MRS. HITCHCOCK: I guess I am. And you know, Henry, I never could figure out why she did such a nasty thing.

MR. HITCHCOCK: As I remember the story, she always claimed you never invited her, so she decided to beat you at your own game.

MRS. HITCHCOCK: But I *did* invite her. I even wrote her a special little note and told her what I had never told another living soul.

MR. HITCHCOCK: Not even me?

MRS. HITCHCOCK (*Shaking her head in mock exasperation*): You already knew what I wrote her.

MR. HITCHCOCK: I did?

MRS. HITCHCOCK (*Smiling affectionately*): I wrote to tell her we were engaged. Don't you remember? We were going to keep it a secret, but I always told Maggie everything. I took the note over to her house early one morning and slipped it under the door.

MR. HITCHCOCK: I still think it's high time you forgot that schoolgirl quarrel and had the Corellis over here. I understand the Count breaks eighty on the golf course.

MRS. HITCHCOCK: You're as bad as Marcia and Pam. You seem to think we can go barging in on the Corellis as if—as if—

MR. HITCHCOCK: As if they were our neighbors, which is exactly what they are.

MRS. HITCHCOCK: But they're no ordinary neighbors, Henry. Besides, Tony has already high-hatted Marcia. He's been here three days and hasn't come near her. And anyhow, I don't want the children getting big ideas about cars and clothes and fine furniture and . . .

MR. HITCHCOCK: Seems to me you've been getting some of those big ideas yourself. After all, you don't seem to think our living-room rug is socially acceptable.

MRS. HITCHCOCK: But that's different, Henry. You know yourself, we've been talking about this rug for years. (CORKY *enters left, carrying a strip of red carpet in a roll over his shoulder.*)

CORKY: Hi, Mom. Hi, Dad. Look what I've got.

MRS. HITCHCOCK: What on earth is that?

CORKY: It's a strip of hall carpet. It'll be great for the clubhouse the gang's fixing up. (*Drops rug onto floor, but does not unroll it.*)

MR. HITCHCOCK: Where did you get it?

CORKY: I bought it for fifteen cents from Eddie Murphy. Mrs. Corelli asked him to haul their trash away this morning. Want to see it?

MRS. HITCHCOCK: I most certainly do not want to see it. And you can just take it out and put it in our own trash pile, Corky Hitchcock. I will not have any of the Corelli castoffs in this house.

CORKY: For Pete's sake, Mom. It's a perfectly good strip of carpet.

MR. HITCHCOCK: Better take it out to the garage, son. Your mother is anti-Corelli right now.

CORKY: What gives, Mom? I've been thinking of inviting Gina to the New Year's Eve dance.

MR. HITCHCOCK: Aren't you a little ahead of yourself? After all, we haven't met any of the family yet.

CORKY: Speak for yourself, Pop. The Countess and I are already on pretty good terms. She's nice, Mom. You'd like her.

MRS. HITCHCOCK: Indeed! And just when and where, may I ask, did you meet the Countess?

CORKY: In her kitchen this morning, when I went over to borrow the sugar.

MRS. HITCHCOCK: Borrow the sugar? What on earth possessed you?

CORKY: Bessie. You know how she's always running out of things in the middle of her cookie baking.

MRS. HITCHCOCK: Good heavens! What will they think of us?

CORKY: They'll think we ran out of sugar. What else? (*Moves to television set.*) Anything good on television?

MRS. HITCHCOCK: It hasn't been fixed yet. (*Acidly*) Mr. Young's men are busy installing two new sets for the Corellis.

CORKY: That's what we ought to have—two new sets instead of this antique.

MR. HITCHCOCK: That beats everything. Now I'll miss all the Christmas programs!

CORKY: There's a little TV repair shop down on Ninth Street we could try. Maybe if we drove down there, we could bring a guy back with us.

MR. HITCHCOCK: I know the place you mean. Come on, Corky. I'll drive, and you can run in. We'll never find a place to park. (MR. HITCHCOCK *and* CORKY *exit left.*)

MRS. HITCHCOCK: This is too much! Dragging that old carpet in here, and actually running over there to borrow sugar. I certainly have a few things to say to Bessie. (*Calling*) Bessie, Bessie, where are you? I want to talk to you.

MARCIA (*Entering, right*): I can't find Bessie anywhere, Mother, and we don't have enough bread. I've used up every scrap. If you'll finish the punch, I'll go to the grocery for the bread.

MRS. HITCHCOCK: No, I'll go. You might as well finish the punch, now that you've started. What do you suppose has become of Bessie?

MARCIA: Heaven only knows! Nobody can keep track of her at Christmastime!

MRS. HITCHCOCK: I do hope Bessie isn't up to something. Christmas seems to go to her head. She's completely irresponsible. Well, I'll run along to the store. (MARCIA *and* MRS. HITCHCOCK *exit right. After a short pause,* BESSIE *and* TONY *enter from left.* BESSIE *carries a dress over her arm.*)

BESSIE: Come in, Tony, and make yourself at home.

TONY: It's wonderful to be back again, in this house, I mean. Ours is such a complete madhouse—Mother all upset, Gina homesick, Dad wandering around like a lost sheep, and now Carlotta in hysterics over the new electric stove—that was the last straw.

BESSIE: Now don't you worry, Tony. Everything will be all right. I'll just run up to my room and fix this dress of Gina's. And then, if we can't get that stove of yours to work, I'll do your turkey over here.

TONY: I don't know what we'd do without you, Bessie. It's so good of you to go to all this trouble.

BESSIE: Trouble? Since when is it any trouble to be neighborly, especially at Christmas. And Carlotta certainly needs a helping hand.

TONY: When we lived in Italy, Carlotta was the one who helped everyone out.

BESSIE: Poor thing! I can just see myself if somebody plopped me down in a strange country and turned me loose with a contraption like that stove that I'd never seen before. But I'll have Carlotta fixed up in no time. Just wait and see.

TONY (*Looking around room*): Gee, nothing's changed a bit. Same furniture, same rug, even the same old television set. (*Walks over to it*) Remember how you used to drag Marcia and me away from the kiddie shows when it was time for supper?

BESSIE: I sure do. You never did know when to go home.

TONY (*Still at television set*): Is . . . is Marcia here?

BESSIE: Sure. She's probably out in the kitchen making the refreshments for tonight. (*Calling*) Marcia, Marcia, somebody's here to see you. (*To* TONY) I'll just scoot upstairs and fix the dress. (BESSIE *exits center.*)

MARCIA (*Offstage*): Bessie, is that you? I've been waiting for you. (MARCIA *appears in doorway left, holding glass of punch. She pauses briefly, then enters, continuing to address* BESSIE.) I want you to taste the punch. (*Seeing* TONY, *she breaks off.*) Oh, I thought Bessie was here. Did she let you in?

TONY: Yes . . . that is . . . well . . . we came in together.

MARCIA: Well, thank goodness you came so soon. I hope you can fix this stupid TV set. (*She sets down glass of punch.*)

TONY (*Blankly*): Fix it?

MARCIA: Well, don't look so surprised. I know the set is old, but it's worth fixing. The picture's just fuzzy and the sound fades out every now and then. Good grief! Where are your tools? Don't tell me you didn't bring them!

TONY: Well, you see—I—

MARCIA: Don't apologize. Just see what you can do. I'll get you anything you need from Dad's workshop. Shall I turn on the set?

TONY (*Clearing his throat*): I—I guess I should see where it's plugged in.

MARCIA: Back here. We'll have to move it out from the wall.

TONY: Let me do that. (*As they move the set forward, he gets a coughing spell.*)

MARCIA: My goodness, you have a terrible cough.

TONY (*Choking and sputtering*): Yes! I know. I guess it's the climate. (MARCIA *runs to table for glass of punch.*)

MARCIA: Here, take a sip of this. (*As* TONY *drinks, his cough subsides.*) Drink all of it. The fruit juice will be good for you.

TONY: Thanks. This is delicious. Much better than cough medicine. What is it?

MARCIA: Just some fruit punch. Do you think it's sweet enough?

TONY: Perfect.

MARCIA: Maybe you'd better sit down for a few minutes till you catch your breath.

TONY: Thanks, I will. (*Sits and mops face with handkerchief*)

MARCIA (*Offering him plate of cookies*): Here, have some cookies.

TONY: Thanks. I didn't have much lunch.

MARCIA: I guess Mr. Young keeps you repairmen on the jump this time of year. And then when people like the Corellis want two sets installed on the day before Christmas! Well, some people just have no consideration, that's all! (TONY *coughs again.*) Be careful of those cookies—the crumbs may make you start coughing again. Let me get you some more punch.

TONY (*Rising*): No, no, thank you. I'm all right. I'll take a look at that set now and see what I can do. (*Moves television set further from wall and squats down behind it, as* ANITA *and* JIMMY *enter left.*)

ANITA: Yoo-hoo! Marcia! We have good news.

MARCIA: Hi, Anita. Hi, Jimmy. Help yourselves to the cookies.

JIMMY: Thanks, Marcia. Is this a sample of what we're getting tonight?

ANITA: Don't start stuffing yourself before you tell her the news.

JIMMY: I dug up an extra man for you, although I still don't see why you can't capture this divine Tony that Anita keeps raving about. I sure would like to see that guy.

ANITA: Maybe you can. (*Using binoculars*) Maybe he's over there now. (*Looking*) Yes, sir. There he is. Look, Jimmy. (*She hands him binoculars.*)

JIMMY (*As he looks out window using binoculars*): Where? Where? I don't see him.

ANITA: Right there by the window. He's moving a chair or something. Oh, Jimmy, isn't he the most handsome thing you ever saw? (TONY *raises his head above the television set for a second, then ducks back.*)

JIMMY: I still don't see him.

ANITA: How can you miss him? He's the only person in the room.

JIMMY (*Again looking through binoculars*): But that's not Tony Corelli!

ANITA: It most certainly is. And he's a real count!

JIMMY (*Disgustedly, putting binoculars down on table*): "Count," your grandmother! That's Gus Flanders. He works for an interior decorator.

ANITA: It can't be!

MARCIA: Are you sure?

JIMMY: If you don't believe me, you can ask him yourself. He's the guy I invited to your party tonight.

ANITA: I can't believe it!

MARCIA: I *knew* Tony was a blond.

ANITA: And I admired his Riviera tan!

JIMMY: Riviera? Gus has never been out of Wilmington except to work over here on holidays and weekends.

MARCIA: Then I've never seen the real Tony at all.

TONY (*Stepping forward*): I think your set will work now, miss. Shall I turn it on? (*All are startled.*)

MARCIA: Good grief! I forgot you were there. (*To* ANITA) This is the television repairman Mr. Young sent us. (*To* TONY) I'm sorry I don't know your name.

TONY: Just call me Mr. Fix-It!

MARCIA: These are my friends, Anita Page and Jimmy Hale.

TONY (*Bowing with mock courtesy*): Charmed, I'm sure. (*To* MARCIA) If you have any further trouble, just call Mr. Young. (BESSIE *enters, carrying dress on hanger.*)

BESSIE: I'm all set, Tony. The dress is ready to wear, and I've got some aspirin for Carlotta. We'll have her back on her feet in no time. (*Turning to* MARCIA) Doesn't Tony look wonderful, Marcia?

ALL: Tony!

MARCIA: Oh, no! It can't be!

ANITA: Not Tony Corelli!

JIMMY: But he's the repairman!

TONY: Not a very efficient one, I'm afraid. I didn't even bring my tool kit.

MARCIA: Oh, Tony, what must you think of me?

BESSIE: Don't tell me you didn't recognize Tony!

MARCIA: But he's changed so much, Bessie.

TONY: So have you. No more braces on your teeth—no more pigtails.

BESSIE: Well, I must run. (*To* MARCIA) The Corellis' maid, Carlotta, is having hysterics over that new-fangled electric stove. Poor thing, she can't get it to work. I'm going over to see what I can do. Tell your mother I'll be back in plenty of time to start supper. (BESSIE *exits.*)

ANITA: And we'd better go, too. I'm sure you and Tony have lots to say to each other. It's been wonderful to meet you, Tony. Come along, Jimmy.

JIMMY (*Shaking hands with* TONY): Women! They're all a bit whacky, Tony, but I guess we couldn't get along without them. Maybe I'll see you tonight after all.

ANITA: Jimmy Hale! What a thing to say!

TONY: Something tells me Jimmy and I will be friends. So long. (JIMMY *and* ANITA *exit left.*)

MARCIA: Oh, Tony, I'm so ashamed. I wanted to call you, but, well . . . I guess I was waiting for you to call me.

TONY: Gosh, I'd have been over here long ago, but Doc Smith has had me in bed ever since we got here. The sudden change in climate gave me a bad dose of bronchitis. This is my first day out.

MRS. HITCHCOCK (*Calling from offstage*): Marcia, where are you? Is Bessie back yet?

MARCIA: Oh, Mother, come and see who is here. (*As* MRS. HITCHCOCK *enters*) Look, Mother! It's Tony!

TONY (*Shaking hands with* MRS. HITCHCOCK): It's good to see you again, Mrs. Hitchcock.

MARCIA: Oh, Mother, he's been sick in bed, and I thought he was the television repairman, and he caught us all red-handed using those awful binoculars, and . . . oh, Mother, the whole thing is impossible!

MRS. HITCHCOCK: I must say it's impossible for me to understand what you're talking about, but I'm certainly glad to see you, Tony. How's your family?

TONY: Terrible! We all have colds, Mother's upset, Gina

is homesick, and Bessie's over at our house now trying to explain electricity to Carlotta.

MRS. HITCHCOCK: Oh, dear! I'm sorry to hear that. Is there anything we can do? (MR. HITCHCOCK *and* CORKY *enter left*)

CORKY: I'm sure I could fix it, Pop. Just let me try.

MR. HITCHCOCK: What do you want me to do? Buy a whole new set?

MARCIA: Don't worry, Dad. The set has been repaired.

TONY: I think it will be O.K. now, Mr. Hitchcock.

MR. HITCHCOCK (*Beaming*): That's fine, young man. What do I owe you?

TONY: I've already had my pay in punch and cookies, Mr. Hitchcock.

MARCIA: Daddy, this is our neighbor, Tony Corelli.

MR. HITCHCOCK: Not that little shaver who was afraid to jump off the pier! (*Walks over to* TONY *and holds out his right hand.*)

TONY: Glad to see you again, sir. (*They shake hands.*)

MRS. HITCHCOCK: And this is our son, Corky.

CORKY (*Shaking hands with* TONY): Glad to meet you, Tony. I've sure heard a lot about you.

MARCIA: Corky!

CORKY: Well, it's the truth. I'll bet if Marcia had known you were coming, she'd have spread out the red carpet for sure!

MRS. HITCHCOCK: Corky! That's enough.

MR. HITCHCOCK: Speaking of carpets reminds me. I thought your mother told you to take that (*Pointing to rolled-up carpet*) out to the garage.

CORKY: Will do. (*Shoulders roll of carpet*) Excuse me, Tony. (*As he brushes past* TONY, *he drops the carpet which unrolls at his feet.*) Oops! I didn't mean to drop it, Mom.

TONY: That looks familiar.

CORKY: It should. It came out of your house. (PAM *enters left in a dither.*)

PAM (*Excitedly*): Marcia! Mother! Guess who is coming down our walk this very minute. You'll die when I tell you. You'll simply expire.

MRS. HITCHCOCK: I hope not, dear. At least not until I've had the chance to introduce you to Tony. Tony, this is my younger daughter, Pam.

PAM: Tony? Tony Corelli?

TONY: One and the same.

PAM: Why, I just looked out the window and saw your mother and father—

MRS. HITCHCOCK (*Breaking in*): Maggie? Coming here?

PAM: And she's bringing Gina.

CORKY: Gina? If she's coming, we need the red carpet for sure! (MAGGIE CORELLI *runs in, followed by* GINA *and* COUNT CORELLI.)

MAGGIE: Ethel! Ethel! Oh, my dear, how are you?

MRS. HITCHCOCK (*Embracing her*): Oh, Maggie! I'm so glad to see you! All these years, and not a word from you! Why, Maggie Briggs! I believe you're crying!

MAGGIE: Look who's talking! So are you!

MRS. HITCHCOCK (*Wiping her eyes*): Come, I want you to meet my family.

MAGGIE: But I know them—every single one! Henry, of course . . . (*Shakes hands with* MR. HITCHCOCK) And this must be Marcia, and Corky, and little Pam. (*They greet each other.*)

TONY: And this is my Dad, and my sister, Gina.

CORKY: I'm certainly glad to see you, Gina.

COUNT CORELLI: This is a pleasure. Indeed, I think my wife and children would not have survived Christmas without calling on you.

MR. HITCHCOCK: And we've been feeling the same way.

GINA: It's so lonely here.

ALL: Lonely!

MAGGIE: Poor Gina, she's been so homesick. But all of us, all of us are lonely. We felt as if we didn't have a friend in the world until Bessie came over and brought the cookies. Oh, Ethel, I just had to come over and tell you what it meant to me, having you send those cookies over to me! (BESSIE *enters.*)

MRS. HITCHCOCK: Oh, Maggie, it's all Bessie's doing.

MAGGIE (*Putting her arm around* BESSIE): Ah, this blessed Bessie! She's brought Carlotta to her senses, and showed her how to work all our new gadgets, from the electric stove right down to the electric can opener.

BESSIE: Right now Carlotta's like a kid with a lot of new toys. When I left, she was opening cans right and left! Good heavens! Where did that red carpet come from?

GINA: It looks like our old hall carpet.

CORKY: That's just what it is. Gee whiz, I was supposed to get it out of here. (*As he starts to roll it, he finds a note.*) Say, what's this thing stuck underneath? (*He stands up and unfolds letter.*) This looks like an old letter. (*He examines it closely.*) I can hardly make out the writing, but I think it's addressed to Maggie Briggs.

MAGGIE: To me? Let me see it. (CORKY *hands letter to her, and others crowd around as she begins to read it.*) "Dear Maggie, I couldn't go to sleep without telling you my wonderful news . . ."

MRS. HITCHCOCK: Good heavens! That's the note I wrote —the invitation I slipped under your front door . . .

MAGGIE: Only you must have slipped it under the hall carpet instead, and it's been lying there all these years! Oh, Ethel, can you ever forgive me?

MRS. HITCHCOCK: There's nothing to forgive, Maggie. It was all a stupid mistake.

CORKY: Give me a hand, Dad, and we'll get this carpet out of here.

MRS. HITCHCOCK: You'll do nothing of the sort, Corky Hitchcock. I want that red carpet to stay right where it is!

BESSIE: Not right in the middle of the living room floor!

MRS. HITCHCOCK: It looks beautiful there! A red carpet's just right for Christmas and the guests of honor at our open house tonight. (*With a curtsy*) Countess Margarita! Count Corelli, will you do us the honor?

COUNT CORELLI (*Bowing*): We will be delighted.

MAGGIE (*Throwing her arms around* MRS. HITCHCOCK): Oh, Ethel, you silly goose! We'll be thrilled to come.

TONY: Too bad you already have that extra man for tonight, Marcia.

MARCIA: Oh, Tony, please come.

TONY: I wouldn't miss it.

PAM: I guarantee you won't be lonely after tonight, Gina.

GINA: I never thought I'd be going to a party tonight.

CORKY: Just don't go making any dates for the New Year's Eve dance, young lady. I want to continue this red carpet treatment.

BESSIE: You know I always did like a red carpet. There's something so warm and friendly about it. Too bad it's gone out of style.

MRS. HITCHCOCK: Gone out of style! Why, Bessie, it's the height of fashion. The Hitchcocks and the Corellis are just about to celebrate their first Red Carpet Christmas! (*Curtain*)

THE END

Production Notes

RED CARPET CHRISTMAS

Characters: 5 male; 7 female.

Playing Time: 35 minutes.

Costumes: Modern everyday dress. Bessie wears an apron over her clothes. Anita carries a purse.

Properties: Binoculars, newspaper clipping, plate of cookies, packages, strip of red carpet, dress, hanger, glass of punch, handkerchief, folded note.

Setting: The living room of the Hitchcock family. There is a large window at right. The room is furnished with a sofa, coffee table, chairs, television set; other pieces may be added. A rug is on the floor. There is a telephone on one of the tables. Christmas decorations are in evidence. There are exits at right, left, and center.

Lighting: No special effects.

The Mistletoe Mystery

Characters

BOB BLAKE, *a college senior*
ELLEN BLAKE, *a high school senior*
BARNEY BLAKE, *a camera bug*
MR. BLAKE } *their parents*
MRS. BLAKE }
RED FREEMAN, *Bob's roommate*
DICK MORGAN, *Ellen's Christmas date*
CLAIRE
NANCY

TIME: *Christmas afternoon.*
SETTING: *The Blakes' cluttered living room.*
AT RISE: MR. BLAKE, *in shirt sleeves, his face covered with a handkerchief, is taking a nap on the sofa.* MRS. BLAKE *and* ELLEN *are curled up in easy chairs on either side of the fireplace.* BOB *is folded up like an oversized jack-knife in a third chair, one leg dangling over the chair arm, an open book lying face downward on his chest.* BARNEY *is stretched out full length on the floor, his head resting on a football. After a brief pause during which*

loud snores are heard, BARNEY *stirs. After a series of violent, but ineffectual contortions aimed at a more comfortable position, he sits up, yawns, stretches and staggers to his feet. He surveys the scene with amusement, and then turns to the audience.*

BARNEY: A picture no artist could paint! This scene must be preserved for posterity! (*He tiptoes with elaborate care to table near Christmas tree, picks up Polaroid camera, and tries various positions for a shot. Finally he mounts a chair and snaps a picture using a flash bulb.*)

MR. BLAKE (*Sitting bolt upright*): What was that? What was that?

MRS. BLAKE: What's the matter? What happened?

ELLEN: It's not time to get up yet.

BOB: What in blazes is going on? Why can't a guy ever have a little peace and quiet?

BARNEY (*Climbing down from chair*): This should be the picture of the year! Boy, oh boy! Four sleeping beauties at one shot!

MR. BLAKE: I'm afraid that giving you that confounded camera was a mistake.

MRS. BLAKE: Barney, you're just wasting your film with all these crazy pictures. You've been taking them all day.

BARNEY (*Adjusting camera to develop picture*): Nothing's ever wasted, Mom. I just might win a prize in *Photo Magazine* with one of these Polaroid shots.

ELLEN: Barney Blake, you just dare show that picture to anybody, and it will be your last. I know my mouth was open.

BARNEY: At least a foot! Maybe wider! We'll know in a few seconds, as soon as the picture's ready.

BOB: When are you ever going to grow up? Every Christmas you keep things in an uproar. Last Christmas it was that blasted trumpet. Now it's this camera. . . . What time is it anyway?

MRS. BLAKE (*Looking at watch*): Good heavens! It's after three! And just look at this room. (*Fumbles under sofa for shoe*) I told you boys to carry all this trash down to the incinerator before dinner. (*Putting shoes on*) Now get busy.

ELLEN: After three o'clock! Ye gods! Dick will be here before I have time to change my dress. (*Hunts for shoes and scrambles into them*)

BOB: Red Freeman's stopping by for me, and I'm not even ready. I'd better scram.

MRS. BLAKE: Not so fast, you two. I want you to sort out your things and take them upstairs.

ELLEN: But I want to show Dick my gifts.

BOB: Red and I are picking up Claire and Nancy, Mom. Can't we do it later?

MRS. BLAKE: You can take time to clean up some of these papers. (*Starts to pick up some of the litter*)

MR. BLAKE: Let the boys do that, Ruth. They can put all this trash in a carton. There's one on the back porch, Barney.

BARNEY: Just a minute, Dad. (*Removes print from camera*) Take a look at this picture! Boy, oh boy! Wait till Dickie Boy sees his fair Ellen in this one!

ELLEN (*Snatching picture from* BARNEY): Don't you dare show that to Dick. (*Taking a look*) Why, it's ghastly! Absolutely ghastly!

BARNEY: You give that back! (*They fight over picture.*) Look out, you'll tear it. (*In the scuffle they almost back into* RED, *who enters center.*)

RED: Hey, what kind of Merry Christmas is this? What did I walk in on? A family row?

BOB: Hiya, Red.

RED (*Greeting members of family and shaking hands*): Merry Christmas, everybody.

MR. BLAKE: Merry Christmas.

MRS. BLAKE: Merry Christmas, Red.

RED (*To* ELLEN): And how's my second-best girl?

ELLEN: Your second-best girl is about to slay her kid brother with his own camera.

BARNEY (*Avoiding* ELLEN'*s lunges and handing picture to* RED): You can be the judge, Red. How's this for a prize indoor snap?

RED (*Looking at picture*): Hm-m-m! Depends on what your title is. You might call it "The End of a Perfect Day."

BOB (*Looking at picture*): He sure caught us all napping.

MR. BLAKE (*Looking over* BOB'*s shoulder*): It's certainly typical of the After-Christmas-Dinner Collapse.

ELLEN: I'll never go to sleep again if that's how I look. (BOB *puts picture on desk.*)

RED: I must say your camera didn't do justice to your beautiful sister, Barney. (*Takes* ELLEN'*s wrist and drags her under mistletoe*) Why not try for a better one under the mistletoe?

BARNEY: A good idea. But you'll have to go into a clinch. (RED *puts his arm around* ELLEN.)

BOB: You can do better than that, Red. Let's see a real ladies' man in action.

BARNEY: How about a gooey Hollywood fade-out?

RED: Something like this? (*Embraces* ELLEN)

ELLEN (*Giggling*): Stop, you're tickling me!

BARNEY: That's good, now hold it!

RED: With pleasure. (*Holds pose*)

BARNEY: I got it! I got it! If this is any good it should *really* take a prize.

MRS. BLAKE: Break it up, you two. Red, you might as well join the clean-up squad and help take this paper and some of these boxes to the cellar.

RED: At your service, ma'am. (*Scoops up an armload of papers*) Come along, shutterbug. (RED *exits right.*)

BARNEY: Wait till I see how this turns out.

MR. BLAKE: On your way, Barney. I'll take care of your photography.

BARNEY: O.K., Pop. (*Handing camera to* MR. BLAKE) But don't leave it in too long. (*Grabs an armload of papers and follows* RED, *off right.*)

ELLEN: That Red gets cuter every year. If I didn't have Dick . . .

BOB: Now don't go getting ideas, Ellen. Do you want Nancy Nelson scratching your eyes out?

ELLEN: I was only kidding, Bob. Red's just like one of the family. Even if I did get a date with him it would be just like going out with you or Barney.

BOB: Perish the thought!

MRS. BLAKE: I don't think Red looks too well, Bob. Is anything wrong?

MR. BLAKE: Seemed like his old self to me. Just as much of a clown as ever.

BOB: Oh, he still puts on an act . . .

MRS. BLAKE: An act? Then you mean something really *is* wrong?

BOB: Well, not really . . . not exactly. But I know Red's

plenty worried about going back to college next semester. His dad broke his leg and was in the hospital quite a while. With the doctor's bills and his father having to stay out of work for the next few months, Red may not have enough money to stay in college. On the way down from school, he was talking about looking around for a job.

MR. BLAKE: I'd hate to see him leave college with just one more term to go before he graduates.

MRS. BLAKE: That would be a shame. He's such a bright boy.

BOB: You can say that again. He's a real whiz at physics and chemistry. (RED *and* BARNEY *enter with carton.*)

RED: Here we are, ready for the next load! (MRS. BLAKE *and* ELLEN *stuff paper into carton.*)

BARNEY: For Pete's sake, Dad, didn't you take that picture out yet? I'll bet it's ruined.

MR. BLAKE (*Removing print*): No, it isn't. Say, not bad! Not bad at all. Maybe you two kids should go on the stage. (*He shows picture around.*)

ALL (*Ad lib*): Say, that's pretty good. You two look great! Some camera! (*Etc.*)

ELLEN: It's a better picture of Red and the mistletoe than it is of me. (*Puts picture on desk*)

RED: That's a neat camera, Barney. You must have a drag with Santa Claus!

MR. BLAKE: I'm afraid it was a bad investment, Red. Now he'll want more allowance so he can buy more film! (*Phone rings.*)

BOB: I'll get it. (*Exits*)

RED (*To* ELLEN): Let's see your loot. (*Goes to gifts under tree*) Or didn't you get anything this year?

ELLEN: It's been a wonderful Christmas, Red. (*Shows

boxes) Look, Mother and Dad gave me this evening dress and slippers. (*Holds up pocketbook*) Brother Bob crashed through with a bag, and Barney progressed from cologne to real perfume this year. Smell? (*Holds bottle under* RED'*s nose for a sniff.*)

RED: Wow! (BOB *enters.*)

BOB: That was Claire. Nancy is over at her house and from the icicles in her voice, we'd better get over there and fast.

RED: Then what are we waiting for?

BOB: I have to change. (*Tossing him car keys*) Here, you take my car and go bring them over here. I'll be ready when you get back.

RED: O.K., chum. (*Starts to exit, pauses and turns*) Oh, by the way, if there should be a call for me, tell them to call back in an hour, will you, please?

BOB: Will do. Now get on your horse. (RED *exits.*)

BARNEY: This carton's full. I'll take it down and burn it.

MRS. BLAKE: Then come back and get some of these boxes. I'm going to take my things and Dad's upstairs. Christmas can certainly make a terrible mess of a house. (BARNEY *exits.*)

ELLEN: But it's a wonderful mess, Mom. I love every bit of it—even the cleaning up.

BOB (*Picking up water skis*): I might as well take these water skis upstairs. Gee, I can hardly wait to try them at the lake this summer. When Pop and I get that new motor with Aunt Martha's Christmas check, that old boat of ours will really get up some speed.

MRS. BLAKE: New motor? Where did you ever get the idea we're going to use Aunt Martha's Christmas check for a new motor? The little wife and mother in this household has a request in for a washer and dryer.

ELLEN: But, Mom, you promised me last year we'd do over my room with Aunt Martha's check. It hasn't been papered or painted since I was ten.

MR. BLAKE: Seems to me you're all mighty free with Aunt Martha's money. It so happens I have some plans of my own for that check.

BOB: Atta boy, Pop! (*Making noise like a motor*) Put-put, put-put . . . I can hear that little old motor now.

MR. BLAKE: So can I, but the motor I hear is the new power saw down in my workshop!

BOB: But, Dad, you already have a saw!

MRS. BLAKE: I positively can't put up with that washer another year. (BARNEY *enters.*)

BARNEY: Well, I've dumped two loads of paper in the incinerator. Don't you have this stuff cleaned up yet?

MRS. BLAKE (*Ignoring* BARNEY): After all, Aunt Martha sends that check for the whole family, and I can't think of anything that would make a better family present than a washer and dryer.

BARNEY: Good grief, Mom! You're not going to spend Aunt Martha's Christmas money on any old washer and dryer, are you? What about that jalopy I've been looking at?

BOB: A jalopy! When I was in high school I was lucky to get the family car on Saturday night!

ELLEN: But my room is still pink and blue! It looks like a nursery!

MR. BLAKE: We're certainly not going to spend our Christmas afternoon arguing about Aunt Martha's check. After all, it's made out to me, and I'm going to stick it in my wallet right now, and put it in the bank first thing tomorrow morning. It can stay right there till we come to some sensible decision. (*Opens wallet and goes to desk*) Where is it? It was right here on this desk a minute ago. With all this mess of cards, I can't even find it.

MRS. BLAKE: That's because it isn't there, dear. (*Moves to mantelpiece*) Remember, you folded it up and tucked it here under the clock. (*Looks for check*) Well, that's funny. It isn't here.

ELLEN: Of course, it isn't there. *You* opened the envelope, Mom, and laid the check on the television set.

MRS. BLAKE: I did no such thing, Ellen. I never touched it.

MR. BLAKE: Ellen's right, Ruth. I remember distinctly. It was right after you opened the compact Bob gave you. Remember, Bob?

BOB: I was too busy opening my own packages . . . but, yes, I do remember. No! No! It wasn't Mom. It was Ellen.

ELLEN (*Outraged*): Me? I never even saw the check!

BOB: Yes, you did, too, because you put it back in the envelope and handed it to Mom, and she handed it to Dad, and Dad handed it to Barney, and . . . Barney, what did you do with Aunt Martha's check?

BARNEY: How did I get into this? You had the check in your hand when Claire called this morning. You probably laid it on the telephone table. (BOB *dashes off right.*)

MR. BLAKE (*Rummaging through cards on desk*): Maybe it's here with these cards.

MRS. BLAKE: It was in a regular letter-sized envelope.

ELLEN: Oh, no, Mother. The envelope was very long and narrow . . . very modernistic . . . (BOB *re-enters with phone book, which he is holding by the cover and shaking.*)

BOB: It's not on the phone table. (*Gives book another shake*) And it's not here either.

MRS. BLAKE: Start looking through the gift boxes. Maybe one of us slipped it inside a package.

BOB: It's more likely to be in this mess of paper on the floor. (*Searches through papers*)

BARNEY: I only hope . . . (*Clapping hand to head*) Oh, no! No, it couldn't have been!

BOB: What? What couldn't have been? Anything can happen on Christmas.

BARNEY: You don't suppose it could have been in that batch of paper I burned in the incinerator!

ALL: The incinerator!

MR. BLAKE: Well, don't stand there! Do something!

BARNEY: What can I do? If it was in there, it's too late now!

MRS. BLAKE: You can at least go look. If it was on top of the pile, maybe you can still rescue it.

BARNEY: Not a chance, Mom. That stuff blazed up right away. But I'll take a look anyhow. (*He exits.*)

ELLEN: This is terrible.

MR. BLAKE: Well, don't give up. Keep looking.

MRS. BLAKE: We certainly don't have money to burn in this family.

BOB: It's not as if it were *real* money, Mom.

ELLEN: How real can you get?

BOB: Well, after all, it was just a check.

MRS. BLAKE: Just a check!

BOB: I mean it's not as bad as if it were actual cash. Can't Aunt Martha make out another one?

MR. BLAKE: And who's going to tell Aunt Martha that we were so careless with her Christmas present that we threw it in the incinerator?

MRS. BLAKE: We weren't careless, Harvey. It's just . . . well . . . it's just all the excitement that goes with Christmas.

ELLEN: None of us is really to blame. (BARNEY *enters.*)

BARNEY: No luck! If it was ever there, it's gone now!

MR. BLAKE: This really beats the deuce!

MRS. BLAKE: Bob took the empty Christmas-ball boxes to the attic this morning. It just might be in there.

BOB: I'll take a look, Mom.

MRS. BLAKE: You never find anything, even when it's right under your nose. I'll look. (*She exits.*)

ELLEN: We took that box of fruit from California out to the kitchen, and there's a box of candy in the dining room. You don't suppose . . .

BARNEY: It's worth a try. Come on, Dad, you take the kitchen and I'll take the dining room. (MR. BLAKE *and* BARNEY *exit.*)

ELLEN (*Staring around the room*): I have a feeling it simply has to be somewhere in this room. I wonder if it might have blown under the sofa. (*She kneels down and peers under sofa. As* ELLEN *struggles to look under the sofa, doorbell rings, and after a pause,* DICK MORGAN *enters, candy box in hand. He stands under the mistletoe.*)

DICK: Merry Christmas! Hey, where is everybody? (*Louder*) Merry Christmas!

ELLEN (*Rising suddenly and bumping her head*): Ouch! Goodness, you scared me! How did you get in?

DICK: Well, that's a fine greeting for a Christmas caller, especially when he's under the mistletoe.

ELLEN: I'm sorry, Dick. But the most dreadful thing has happened!

DICK: Don't tell me you didn't get any presents in your

stocking. From the looks of this room, you really made a haul.

ELLEN: Oh, yes, we've had a marvelous Christmas, but we've lost Aunt Martha's Christmas check. It's just disappeared.

DICK: Is that why you were trying to crawl into the woodwork when I came in? (*Handing candy to* ELLEN) Here, have some candy. It's the kind you like, and they took all the calories out for Christmas.

ELLEN: Thanks, Dick. Thanks a million. Just make yourself at home, will you? Mother and Dad and the boys are tearing the house apart looking for that check, and I'm a sight. If you'll excuse me, I'll go change. It won't take me a minute.

DICK: Go right ahead. I'll look at the Christmas presents. Wow! Whose Polaroid? This is a dandy.

ELLEN: That's Barney's. It's his pride and joy.

DICK: No wonder. I wouldn't mind having one of these myself. Maybe he'll lend it to me sometime.

ELLEN: Maybe he will, but you can't pry him loose from it today. He's taking pictures every five minutes.

DICK (*Picking up pictures from desk*): Are these some of the masterpieces?

ELLEN: I suppose so. There's one there of me that's perfectly terrible. Don't even look at it.

DICK (*Beginning to glare*): Hm-m-m! I see what you mean.

ELLEN: Isn't it awful? My mouth must be open a foot!

DICK: Not in this one, it isn't. Now I can see why your enthusiasm for mistletoe has worn off a bit.

ELLEN: What do you mean?

DICK (*Holding out picture*): Let's say what do *you* mean? I was under the impression *I* was your Christmas date.

ELLEN: But you are. We're going out tonight, and tomorrow there's the Pen Club party, and Wednesday there's the State Dance, and New Year's Eve . . .

DICK: Hold it, hold it! What do you take me for?

ELLEN: Why, Dick, you're getting angry.

DICK: Of course I'm getting angry, and I'm going to get a lot angrier as soon as I find out the name of this jerk under the mistletoe with you.

ELLEN (*Looking at picture*): Oh, Dick, that's nothing. That's just a crazy picture Barney took of me and Red Freeman. It's nothing at all!

DICK: Nothing at all, is it? I suppose you'd say the same thing if I had my picture taken under the mistletoe with Sally McBride.

ELLEN: But that's different. Sally's in high school and Red Freeman is in college.

DICK: So this Red is in college and Sally's in high school. I fail to see the difference.

ELLEN: I happen to know that Sally McBride would give an eyetooth to have a date with you.

DICK: Well, maybe she'll get one. Who knows?

ELLEN: Now look here, Dick Morgan, if you want to date Sally McBride, you go right ahead. But don't try to pretend it's because of a silly old picture taken with Red Freeman. Why, he's like a brother to me.

DICK: Some brother!

ELLEN: Dick, you're making a mountain out of a molehill. Mother and Dad and Bob and Barney were all here when that picture was taken. It was all in fun.

DICK: Some fun!

ELLEN: Oh, stop talking like that. If I had known you had such a jealous disposition, I'd never have agreed to go to all those parties with you.

DICK: Well, do you want to call it off?

ELLEN: Yes, I do! No, no, I don't! Oh, I hate you, Dick Morgan. Things are upset enough around here without having you start a fight about this miserable picture. (BARNEY *and* MR. BLAKE *enter.*)

BARNEY: It really beats me, Pop. I don't see how a check could get up and walk off like that.

MR. BLAKE: Carelessness, just carelessness, that's all it is. Oh, hello, Dick. Glad to see you. Merry Christmas.

DICK (*In a glum voice*): Merry Christmas, sir.

BARNEY: What's with you, Morgan? You sound like the Friendly Undertaker. Hey, did you see my camera? Isn't it a dandy?

ELLEN: He's seen it all right, and he's seen a lot more. Thanks to your photographic efforts, your sister is without a date for the Christmas parties.

BARNEY: My photographic efforts? What are you talking about? I get blamed for everything around this house.

DICK: She means this, Barney. (*Handing him the picture*) You might be a good photographer, but I sure don't care for your choice of models.

BARNEY: Oh, this. Come off it, Dick. That was only a gag. (*He puts picture in pocket.*)

DICK: Some gag!

MR. BLAKE (*To* DICK): Well now, son, I can see you might be a little upset when you first look at the picture, but when you understand that Red is an old friend of the family . . . and it was only a joke . . .

ELLEN: Don't you dare say it! Don't you dare!

DICK: Say what?

ELLEN (*Imitating* DICK'*s funereal tone*): Some joke!

DICK (*Laughing in spite of himself*): Maybe I have been a little silly about the whole thing, but no guy likes to see his girl in a picture with another fellow like this—

especially when the other guy is as good looking as this Freeman bird!

MR. BLAKE: I can see what you mean. (*To* BARNEY) What do you say we destroy the evidence?

BARNEY: Maybe it's not such a bad idea. I have plenty more.

DICK: You mean you've taken others?

BARNEY: Sure. I've shot a whole roll. Oh, I don't mean a whole roll of Ellen and Red. I mean a whole roll of everybody. (*Taking pictures from shirt pocket*) Look, here's the whole family after dinner. Here are Mom and Dad. I caught them under the mistletoe first thing this morning. See, aren't they the romantic couple? Look at old Pop doing the great lover bit, and Mom playing up to him for all she's worth! (*Suddenly doing a double take as he looks at the picture and bursting into a shout*) Hey, Mom! Come quick! Look, look, Dad! I've found the check! I've found it!

MR. BLAKE: What's got into you? What are you talking about?

BARNEY (*Thrusting picture into* MR. BLAKE'*s hand*): Take a good look. It's all right there! (*Dashes offstage calling*) Mom, Bob! Hurry up! I've found it! I've found it!

ELLEN (*Looking over her father's shoulder*): What's he so excited about, Dad? I don't see a thing in this picture except you and Mother.

DICK (*Also looking*): He must have taken it bright and early. Your mother is still in her housecoat!

MR. BLAKE: By Jove, that's it! That's it!

ELLEN: I still don't see it. (BARNEY *enters doing a war dance and waving the check above his head.* MRS. BLAKE *and* BOB *follow.*)

BOB: He's actually found it.

MRS. BLAKE: Where in the world was it, Barney? We've hunted high and low.

BARNEY: Trust old Barney the Camera Bug to come through with a photo finish. It's all there in that picture.

MRS. BLAKE: What picture?

ELLEN: The one of you and Dad under the mistletoe. You're wearing that awful old housecoat!

BOB: But what does a housecoat have to do with it?

BARNEY: A housecoat has pockets in it, and one of the pockets has a check in it. (*All crowd around picture.*) See? There's a corner of it sticking out.

ELLEN: That's it, all right.

BOB: Well, what do you know!

MRS. BLAKE: I remember now. I stuck that check in my housecoat pocket so it wouldn't get thrown out by mistake.

MR. BLAKE: Barney, you really saved the day. Now give me that check, and I'll put it in my wallet. (*Does so*)

BARNEY: Actually, it was Dick here who gave me the lead. If he hadn't been so burned up over that mistletoe shot of Red and Ellen, I'd never have started showing him the rest of my collection.

DICK: I'm glad something good came of it. I'm afraid I made an awful fool of myself, Ellen.

ELLEN: That's all right, Dick. In a way, I'm sort of flattered. Nobody was ever jealous of me before. But I agree that we should tear up the picture. If you were jealous, it might strike Nancy Nelson the same way.

DICK: Who's Nancy Nelson?

BOB: Nancy is Red's girl, and I don't think she'd be too keen about that mistletoe picture either.

BARNEY (*Taking picture from pocket and tearing it into small pieces*): I'll do the deed myself! (*Flings scraps into the air*) There she goes!

MR. BLAKE (*Taking a five-dollar bill from his wallet*): There was no reward offered for finding the check, Barney, but I think you could use this for some extra film.

BARNEY: Gee, thanks, Dad. But maybe you should save it for gas, just in case I get that jalopy, now that we've found Aunt Martha's check.

MRS. BLAKE: Don't indulge in wishful thinking, son. I'm still voting for the washer and dryer.

ELLEN: Every time I think of that revolting bedroom, I could die!

BOB: When you take a ride in the boat this summer with that new motor, you'll forget all about your bedroom.

MR. BLAKE: Possession is nine points of the law, and that old saw of mine is in bad shape. (*Phone rings and* BOB *runs off right to answer it.*)

ELLEN: Looks like you're in for a family argument, Dick. We're all spending our Christmas check before it's cashed.

DICK: I've had enough arguments for one day. I think I'll sit this one out.

MRS. BLAKE: With the family split five ways, nobody will ever get a majority.

MR. BLAKE: In that case, four of you vote, and I'll get my saw tomorrow morning.

BARNEY: Dictators are out these days, Dad. (BOB *re-enters in a sober mood.*)

ELLEN: Was that call for me, Bob?

BOB: No, it was for Red.

MRS. BLAKE: He said he was expecting a call.

MR. BLAKE: Did you tell them he said to call back in about an hour?

BOB: No, they asked me to take the message.

MRS. BLAKE: You look worried, Bob. Is something wrong?

BOB: All depends on how you look at it. It was Mr. Hastings, president of the Halifax Works. He's spending Christmas with friends of Red's family, and he knew Red wanted a job.

MR. BLAKE: Well, did he get it?

BOB: Yes. He's to report for work the day after this semester ends.

MRS. BLAKE: Then this means the end of college.

BOB: I'm afraid so.

BARNEY: Can't he go back later?

MR. BLAKE: That's easier said than done, Barney. I'd hate to think of Bob leaving right now.

BOB: I'm sure he'd go back later on, but it would mean he couldn't graduate with the class. He's worked so darn hard . . . if only he could just hold out this semester.

MR. BLAKE: He's sure to be a success when he graduates.

MRS. BLAKE: Isn't there somebody who could help him?

BOB: He's too proud to ask for help, Mom. I guess I'm the only person he's ever talked to about how much college means to him.

DICK: But surely a guy like this Red must have a lot of friends who could lend him the money.

BOB: Sure, he has friends, good friends, but right now they're all too busy thinking about new motors for their boats.

MRS. BLAKE: And new washers and dryers.

ELLEN: And new bedroom wallpaper.

BARNEY: And old beat-up jalopies.

MR. BLAKE: And new power saws . . .

BOB: Say, Dad, Mom, Ellen, Barney, how about it?

MR. BLAKE: As president of the Blake Christmas Corporation, I call for a vote!

ELLEN: Oh, Dad, do you really mean it?

MR. BLAKE: Of course, I mean it. And this time, I'll bet we have an overwhelming majority. All those in favor of lending our Christmas check to Red, say . . .

ALL: *Aye!*

DICK: Excuse me, everybody; I forgot I was a non-voter!

ELLEN: That's all right, Dick, your vote is as good as the next fellow's on this issue.

BOB: What if he won't take the money?

MR. BLAKE: I'm sure he will. This is important to him . . . and when he learns that it's important to us, too, he'll take the money. After all, it won't be as if it were charity. He can pay it back after he gets through college, and his father is back at work again.

ELLEN: How are we going to tell him?

MR. BLAKE: We're not going to tell him, Ellen. Tomorrow that boy is going to get a check that will tell him all he needs to know, and a letter that will convince him that he should accept it.

ELLEN: Oh, Dad, you're wonderful!

MRS. BLAKE: Of course, he's wonderful, Ellen. But so are all of you wonderful!

BOB: Maybe we should call ourselves the wonderful, wonderful Blakes.

BARNEY: Don't kid yourselves, wait till this Christmas spirit burns itself out. Then we'll be back to normal.

ELLEN: But that's the most wonderful part of it all,

Barney. If you have the real Christmas spirit, it never burns itself out. It just keeps on blazing brighter and brighter from one year to another. (*Doorbell rings.*)

BOB: It's Red with Claire and Nancy. I'll let them in. (BOB *exits.*)

BARNEY: This should make a great shot—all four of them under the mistletoe. (*He gets set with the camera as* BOB, CLAIRE, RED *and* NANCY *enter.*) Hold it! Hold it! Take your places for the Mistletoe Classic. (*The boys embrace their girls and strike a romantic pose.*) That's it. That's fine. Watch the birdie.

DICK (*Seizing* ELLEN'*s hand*): Come on, Ellen, what are we waiting for? (ELLEN *and* DICK *join the group.*)

MR. BLAKE (*With his arm about* MRS. BLAKE): Hurry up, Barney. Your mother and I are next. We want to bring our Mistletoe Record up to date. (*Curtain*)

THE END

Production Notes

THE MISTLETOE MYSTERY

Characters: 5 male; 4 female.

Playing Time: 30 minutes.

Costumes: Modern everyday dress for the Blakes. Red and Dick wear suits; Claire and Nancy wear attractive dresses. Barney has photographs in his shirt pocket; Bob has car keys in his pants pocket. Mrs. Blake wears a watch, and Mr. Blake has a wallet.

Properties: Handkerchief, book, football, Polaroid camera with flash attachment, photographs, large carton, pocketbook, perfume bottle, keys, water skis, wallet, Christmas cards, phone book, box of candy, check, five-dollar bill.

Setting: The Blake living room. There is a large pile of opened gifts (an evening dress and slippers, pocketbook, perfume, water skis) under the Christmas tree, and the floor is littered with wrapping paper, string, gift cards, etc. A large sprig of mistletoe hangs above the front door, at center. There are three large easy chairs, two of which are on either side of the fireplace. A clock is on the mantelpiece. There is a desk with Christmas cards on it, and, at left, a sofa. A TV set, chairs, tables, and lamps complete the furnishings. A door at right leads to the rest of the house. At rise, Barney's Polaroid is on a table, Mrs. Blake's shoes are under the sofa, and Ellen's are beside an easy chair.

Lighting: No special effects.

The Red Flannel Suit

Characters

HERB PHIPPS, *a moving man*
MAC GREER, *his helper*
MR. PATTERSON, *a newcomer to Hill Haven*
MRS. PATTERSON, *his wife*
MARY ALICE, *their daughter*
RICK, *their teen-age son*
TUCK, *a younger son*
MRS. PHIPPS, *a neighbor*
BLAIR, *her son*
MARJORIE, KIT, SALLY — *Hill Haven residents*

TIME: *The afternoon before Christmas.*

SETTING: *The living room of the Pattersons' new home. The room is empty, except for one or two rickety kitchen chairs.*

AT RISE: *The* PATTERSONS *are standing center stage, in front of the fireplace, talking to two moving men,* HERB *and* MAC, *one of whom has a bill of lading for* MR. PATTERSON *to sign.*

HERB: Well, sir, I guess that's the best we can do for you. I sure am sorry about the rest of the stuff, but you can't fight a blizzard. If you'll just sign here, please.

MR. PATTERSON (*As he signs*): But are you sure there's nothing else? Weren't you able to get more than the beds and mattresses on your truck?

MAC: We *did* bring the springs, you know, and that took quite a bit of doing. The way that moving van's stuck in the ditch down there at the foot of the mountain, we were lucky to get anything.

HERB: That little pick-up truck of mine won't take much of a load, Mr. Patterson, and we couldn't have made the hill with much more.

MR. PATTERSON: I'm sure you did your best, and we appreciate it. At least we won't have to sleep on the floor tonight.

MARY ALICE: How about blankets? We might just as well sleep on the floor and freeze to death entirely as to try to sleep without blankets. At least, that way it would be quicker.

HERB: Now don't you worry about covers, miss. I know the missus can rake up a few extra blankets and maybe a comforter or two. Never let it be said we let any folks freeze in Hill Haven, especially on Christmas Eve.

TUCK: Say, Pop, you don't think my new bike was smashed up, do you?

MR. PATTERSON: We have more to worry about than your bicycle, Tuck.

MAC: It's a pretty safe bet nothing got smashed up, sonny. That whole rig just slid off the road into that ditch as slick as grease . . . not even a scratched fender. She'd be as right as rain, if we could just get her on the road again, but that hill's like glass.

HERB: We'll get your things up here the day after Christmas for sure. The paper says bright and clear tomorrow with no more snow after midnight.

RICK: One thing's sure—we'll have a white Christmas. You ought to go for that, sis. You and Irving Berlin . . . (*Singing slightly off key*) "I'm dreaming of a white Christmas . . ."

MARY ALICE (*Crossly*): Oh, shut up!

MRS. PATTERSON: Be quiet, Ricky. (*To* HERB) I didn't mean to sound ungrateful, Mr. Phipps. I know you've done all you can. But we're really in a spot . . . stuck here with no furniture in this big, empty house, the day before Christmas.

HERB: We understand, ma'am. It sure is tough.

MAC: But at that, you're luckier than some. Your electricity is still on, and you have a telephone. With that electric stove in the kitchen, you won't starve, and I hear the oil burner running, so you won't freeze.

MARY ALICE: We're just not used to your New England winters.

MAC: Oh, you'll get used to them in no time, miss. The young folks around here make a big thing of winter sports—skating, tobogganing—and there's some fine skiing up on old Baldy.

RICK: That's the best news yet.

TUCK: It's not much of a place to ride a bicycle in winter.

MR. PATTERSON: He has bicycles on the brain. I'm sure we'll be fine. Thanks again, boys, and a merry Christmas to you.

HERB *and* MAC: Same to you folks. (*They walk to door right.*)

HERB (*Turning in doorway*): I won't forget that extra bedding, Mrs. Patterson.

MRS. PATTERSON: We'll appreciate anything you can spare.

MARY ALICE: Couldn't we go to a hotel, Daddy?

MAC (*Removing fur cap and scratching his head*): Well, now, miss, the fact is, we don't really have a hotel here in the village. 'Course, there's Mrs. Murphy's boardin' house, but she's full up with her regulars, and the motels are closed for the season.

MARY ALICE: Some town, I must say! Not even a hotel!

MAC: Hill Haven isn't exactly a metropolis, but we have some very nice folks living round here, and I think you'll like it fine, once you get settled.

MRS. PATTERSON: I'm sure my daughter didn't mean to be rude, Mr. Greer.

MAC: Oh, I don't take any offense, ma'am. It takes most outsiders a while to get used to Hill Haven.

HERB (*Suddenly turning in doorway*): Say, Mac, we clean forgot that big packing box in the front end of the truck. Come along and give me a hand.

MAC: Maybe there's some gear in that box you can use, Mrs. Patterson. We'll have it here in a jiffy. (HERB *and* MAC *exit.*)

TUCK: I hope it's my new bike.

RICK: How dumb can you be, Tucker? You know your bike wouldn't be in a packing box.

MRS. PATTERSON: I hope to goodness it's the box of sheets and blankets.

MARY ALICE: I could use a dozen sweaters and a whole bale of coats.

RICK: I'll take pots and pans. I'm starved. How about you, Pop?

MR. PATTERSON: At this point we can use anything we get. Here they come. Out of the way, boys. (*They step aside,* as HERB *and* MAC *carry big wooden box onstage.*)

HERB: We just grabbed this in a hurry, Mr. Patterson.

MRS. PATTERSON: Oh, dear! It's not the bedding box.

MR. PATTERSON: Never mind what it is. Just set it down, fellows, and we'll try to get it open.

MAC (*Taking a screwdriver and a hammer from pockets*): Want us to pry it open for you?

MR. PATTERSON: No, thanks. Don't you bother. You fellows have done a lot for us already, and I'm sure you want to get home for Christmas Eve.

MAC: O.K. I'll leave these tools with you and pick 'em up later.

HERB: One more thing: if you want to buy any groceries, you'd better do it before five o'clock. Everything shuts up here tight as a drum on Christmas Eve.

MRS. PATTERSON: We'll do that, Mr. Phipps. I guess we'll find plenty of stores on Main Street.

MAC: Nope. Only one—the Hill Haven Market. And we're lucky to have that. It's just a miracle it didn't catch fire last night when the Town Hall burned down.

MR. PATTERSON: So that's where the fire was. We noticed it was still smoldering as we drove in.

HERB: Yes, worst fire we've had in years. A shame, too, right before Christmas.

MRS. PATTERSON: Hill Haven Market. We'll get over there right away. And thanks again, for everything.

HERB: Glad to help you, ma'am. Only wish we could do more. Feel free to call on us if there's anything else.

MAC: Same here, Mrs. Patterson, and a merry Christmas to you. (*They exit.*)

MARY ALICE: *Merry Christmas!* I can hardly say the words without choking. How can people keep saying that to us when they can see what a mess we're in!

RICK: Well, what do you expect them to say? "Have a cruel Yule!" They're only trying to be friendly.

MARY ALICE: But I don't feel friendly. I feel terrible. When I think of all the fun the kids are having back home, I could just die!

RICK: Well, go ahead and die, if it will make you feel any better. Only don't expect too much in the way of a funeral! What's in the box, Dad?

MR. PATTERSON (*Working with hammer and screwdriver*): I'll have it open in a minute. I thought your mother said she had labeled all these boxes.

MRS. PATTERSON: I started to label them, but the movers arrived before I'd half finished. Oh, Harry, I hope we never, never, never have to move again.

MARY ALICE: You mean you hope we spend the rest of our lives in this dump?

TUCK: Where you can't even ride a bicycle in December!

RICK: I bleed for both of you! Wow! That does it, Pop! You have it open.

ALL (*Crowding around box, ad libbing complaints*): Oh, no! Look at that! This we need like a hole in the head! (*Etc.*)

TUCK (*Trying to look into box*): What is it? What is it? What's in the box, Dad?

ALL: The Christmas stuff!

TUCK: What Christmas stuff? Is it our presents?

MR. PATTERSON: You know we've already had our presents, Tuck. No, this is the box of Christmas decorations we've used ever since you kids were little—tinsel, angels, stars, lights, tree ornaments—the works. (*He reaches into box and lifts out box of tree ornaments.*) See, here's a box of Christmas tree balls.

RICK (*Reaching into packing box and producing string of lights*): And here are the lights for the outdoor decorations.

MRS. PATTERSON (*Carefully lifting out a punch bowl*): And here's my punch bowl. My beautiful, cut-glass punch bowl!

MARY ALICE: Careful, Mother, careful! Oh, dear! Where can you put it? There's just no place.

RICK (*Lifting out a card table*): Yes, there is. Here's our old card table. I remember packing it in there.

MR. PATTERSON (*As* RICK *sets up card table*): And here are the folding chairs. (*Lifts them out*) At least we can sit down to drink our punch. (MRS. PATTERSON *sets bowl on table and unwraps several cups packed inside bowl.*)

MARY ALICE: They're so pretty, Mom! Remember that hot, spiced fruit punch you used to serve in these every year when we came in from caroling?

MRS. PATTERSON: Oh, yes, and last year, remember we had open house on Christmas Eve? Just think . . . over a hundred people—all our friends!

MARY ALICE (*Half-crying*): Oh, Mother, how can you bear to talk about it? I could just cry my eyes out when I think of all our wonderful holidays with Grandma and Dick, and Bob, and Mr. and Mrs. Evans, and the Kane twins, and . . . and . . .

TUCK: And don't forget Bruce Turner. He's the one you're *really* bawling about!

MARY ALICE: Yes, he is, and I don't care who knows it! I'll never find another boy like Bruce. Never, never, never! I don't see why we had to move way up here in the wilderness where we don't know a living soul and just when Bruce and I had been going steady for a whole week! It's ruined my whole life! Just ruined my whole life!

MRS. PATTERSON: Now, now, honey, don't cry! I know it's especially hard on you youngsters at Christmastime, but you'll get to know people, and there'll be other boys!

MARY ALICE: I don't want any other boys! Oh, Mother, this is the worst Christmas we've ever had!

TUCK (*Reaching into packing box*): Look, look, Pop, there's my electric train. (*Taking it out*) Is the track there? Is it in there, Pop? Can we set it up after supper? Can we, Pop?

MRS. PATTERSON: Oh, Tuck, don't drag all that track out here in the living room. It will just be in the way.

TUCK: In the way of what? Look, Mom, we've never had so much room in all our lives. We can run track clear around the room and not run into any furniture. Zowie! See if you can find my switches and the turntables, Dad.

RICK (*Reaching into box*): Here's the artificial Christmas tree Dad set up in my room the Christmas I had the measles. I can still see Dad in that old red flannel suit and Santa Claus mask, poking his head into the doorway of my room and shouting "Merry Christmas!"

MR. PATTERSON (*Excitedly, taking Santa Claus suit, beard and mask from packing box*): Why here's the old suit I used, packed away in moth balls! (*He holds up various parts of costume as he speaks.*) Here's the coat . . . and the pants . . . and the belt.

RICK (*Holding up pillow*): Here's the pillow for the big, fat stomach.

MR. PATTERSON (*Holding these items up as he speaks*): And the cap, and the muffler . . . even the gloves.

RICK: And here's the mask! (*Putting it on and leaning

toward Tuck) Ho, ho, ho! And what do you want for Christmas, my little man?

Mary Alice: Oh, for heaven's sake! *Must* we drag all that stuff out now when we don't even want to *think* about Christmas?

Tuck: Go ahead, Rick. I like it. What else is in there?

Rick: Old Santa's pack, and boy, it's a whopper.

Mrs. Patterson (*Taking from packing box big green bag with a Merry Christmas label on it*): It's big, all right, but it was never big enough to hold all the things you children wanted.

Mr. Patterson (*Reaching into box again*): And here are my old fishing boots! (*Holds up boots*) They were just the thing for the Santa Claus outfit.

Tuck (*Diving into box*): And here are all the stockings with our names. (*Distributes them*) Mom, Dad, Sister, Brother, Tuck! Say, it's beginning to feel like Christmas with the train and the stockings and the Santa Claus suit, and everything.

Mrs. Patterson (*Taking her stocking to fireplace*): This old house must have seen a lot of Christmas Eves. Here are the stocking hooks right in the mantle. (*Hangs up her stocking*) There! There's mine!

Rick (*Hangs up stocking*): Here goes mine.

Tuck: And mine. (*Hangs up his stocking*)

Mr. Patterson: Guess I'll have to follow suit. (*He does so.*)

Mary Alice (*As she throws hers on the floor*): I think this is downright silly. What's the good of hanging up our stockings when we've already had our presents?

Tuck: You never can tell. I believe in being prepared. It's the Boy Scout in me.

Rick (*At box*): Well, blow me down! Here's my old trumpet. (*Takes it out*) I haven't touched it since I got my new one last Christmas. (*Plays opening measures of "Silent Night."*)

MARY ALICE: Stop it! Stop it! I can't bear that piece.

MRS. PATTERSON: Why, Mary Alice, what a dreadful thing to say about the most beautiful Christmas hymn in the world.

MARY ALICE: I don't care. I hate it! I hate it! It's the saddest music in the world when you haven't any Christmas of your own.

MRS. PATTERSON: But we *do* have a Christmas, Mary Alice. We're all well and we're together, and we have a roof over our heads, and we're snug and warm.

MARY ALICE (*Bitterly*): We're stuck up here in the hills, away from everybody we ever knew! No Christmas parties, no dances, no friends, no fun . . . no nothing!

MR. PATTERSON: I'm sorry, Mary Alice, I really am. I hated to leave Hunt City as much as any of you, but when you work for a big corporation, they call the shots. I hoped you all understood.

RICK: We do, Pop, honest we do. But I know how Mary Alice feels. Just handling this old horn and remembering our carol parties made me homesick for the rest of the gang.

MRS. PATTERSON: I'm homesick, too, Mary Alice . . . and maybe you're right. Looking at all these Christmas reminders makes us feel worse. Let's put them away.

MR. PATTERSON: Yes. We'll put them away and forget about Christmas. No more talking about what we did last year, or the year before that, or the year before that.

RICK: And no more "Silent Night." (*Puts horn back into box*) Come on, Tuck, put that train away.

TUCK: Trains are for year round. Not just Christmas.

MR. PATTERSON: You have a point there, Tuck, but let's put the rest of this stuff out of sight and out of mind.

MRS. PATTERSON: Of all the things we *don't* need, it's this Santa Claus suit.

TUCK: What we need most is something to eat.

MR. PATTERSON: Now you're talking, Tuck. Have you your list, Mother?

MRS. PATTERSON: No need for a list, Harry. We need the works.

TUCK: What about a turkey, Mom?

MRS. PATTERSON: O.K., if it's a TV dinner.

MR. PATTERSON, RICK *and* TUCK: TV dinners! On Christmas!

MRS. PATTERSON: Very well, if you geniuses have any suggestions about roasting a turkey with no utensils, speak up.

TUCK: We could toast hot dogs in the fireplace.

RICK: Not a bad idea, Tuck. I always did say your brains are in your stomach.

MRS. PATTERSON: I'll leave the shopping up to you menfolks. Use your own judgment and your own money.

MR. PATTERSON: It's a deal. Come along, Rick. We'll have to put the chains on the car before we can pull away from the house.

MRS. PATTERSON: Your feet will be soaked. You should be wearing boots.

MR. PATTERSON: No sooner said than done. (*Begins to put on Santa Claus boots*) I've stood in many a trout stream with these, Doris. I guess they can take a little snow. (*Stamps feet several times to get the feel of the boots*) Um-m, they feel good. (*Starts to hum "Jingle Bells," stamping in rhythm*)

MARY ALICE: For heaven's sake, Dad, what are you doing —a song-and-dance act?

MR. PATTERSON (*With rather a faraway stare*): What's that? Oh . . . I didn't realize I was singing. Say, I believe I'll put on this red flannel coat.

MARY ALICE: What are you trying to do—give the natives a laugh?

MR. PATTERSON: Nothing of the sort. I'll just stuff the tails inside my trousers and I'll have a red flannel jacket . . . warm as toast and less cumbersome than an overcoat. (*He does so.*)

MRS. PATTERSON: A good idea, Harry. (*As she hands him a scarf*) You'd better wrap this scarf around your throat, too. You're not used to this climate. (MR. PATTERSON *sings "Jingle Bells" louder and louder.*)

MARY ALICE: If you *must* vocalize, Dad, why not work out on some other tune?

MR. PATTERSON: Sorry, kiddo. I just can't seem to get the tune out of my head.

MRS. PATTERSON: Oh, Mary Alice, stop picking on your father. By the way, Rick, those are your best pants, you know.

RICK: Not quite the thing for putting on chains, are they? O.K. I'll just wear these Santa Claus pants over my own. (*Puts on Santa Claus pants*) A little baggy, I guess, but they'd be a sensation on the ski slopes. (*Suddenly starts singing*) "Ricky, the red-clad reindeer, had some very snazzy clothes. Where in the world he got them, no one ever would suppose!"

MARY ALICE: I'm getting out of here.

RICK: Hardly worth the effort, sis. We'll be gone in a jiffy.

TUCK: Let me go along, Pop. I can carry the market basket.

MR. PATTERSON: What market basket? We'd need a clothes hamper for all of our shopping.

TUCK: How about the Santa Claus bag? That would hold a lot.

MR. PATTERSON: O.K. Bring it along.

TUCK (*Shouldering bag and singing*): "Here comes Santa Claus, here comes Santa Claus, right down Santa Claus Lane!"

MARY ALICE: Maybe you think you're all terribly funny, but I think you are just plain mean!

RICK: Wait till you see the Christmas present I'm buying for you, sister mine. A great big box of Kleenex for your next spell of the weeps. (MR. PATTERSON, RICK *and* TUCK *exit.*)

MARY ALICE: Thank heaven, they've gone. I couldn't take much more of that. What do you suppose got into them —singing all those Christmas songs, after we had agreed to drop the subject completely.

MRS. PATTERSON: I have no idea, but Tuck's suggestion about the hot dogs wasn't a bad idea. Do you suppose we could start a fire in that fireplace?

MARY ALICE: It would certainly be a good chance to burn all this Christmas junk.

MRS. PATTERSON: Talking like that isn't making you feel any better, Mary Alice, and it's hard on the rest of us, especially your father.

MARY ALICE: I'm sorry, Mother, but I just can't help it.

MRS. PATTERSON: Well, let's see what we can do about the fire. At least our predecessors left us a full wood basket, and I noticed more logs in the shed. (*At fireplace*) I guess we should investigate before we start a fire. I hope the chimney isn't clogged up. (*Looks up chimney*)

MARY ALICE (*Pushing her mother away from chimney*):

Here . . . let me look. (*Squats down and peers up chimney*) It doesn't look too bad.

MRS. PATTERSON (*Picking up Santa Claus cap and tossing it to* MARY ALICE): Here, put this on. It will protect your hair.

MARY ALICE (*Puts on cap and crawls further into chimney*): Um-m, looks all right to me. (*Steps back*) Jiggle that damper and see if it's open or shut. (MRS. PATTERSON *shakes damper, as if adjusting it.*) That's it. I think you have it open now. I'm sure it would be all right to start a fire now. Let's try it.

MRS. PATTERSON (*Taking kindling from wood basket*): This bit of kindling should catch in no time, and then we can add bigger logs.

MARY ALICE: I'll bring in some extras from the shed.

MRS. PATTERSON: They're terribly dirty, and rough and scratchy, too. Better wear gloves.

MARY ALICE (*Taking Santa Claus gloves and putting them on*): These will do. At least they'll keep my hands clean. (*Moves to door and turns*) Hey, Mom . . .

MRS. PATTERSON (*Putting logs into fireplace*): Yes?

MARY ALICE: I—I was just going to say . . .

MRS. PATTERSON: Say what?

MARY ALICE: I was just going to say . . . oh, nothing.

MRS. PATTERSON: What's the matter?

MARY ALICE: Nothing's the matter, only . . .

MRS. PATTERSON: Only what? (*Turns to look at* MARY ALICE *who is staring strangely at her gloved hands*) What's wrong, Mary Alice? You look so strange.

MARY ALICE: Nothing's wrong, Mom . . . only suddenly . . . well, you'll think I'm crazy, but suddenly I feel as if I could say *Merry Christmas* without choking.

MRS. PATTERSON: Well, that's a relief. Maybe you're snapping out of it.

MARY ALICE: I don't know. Mom, I know this sounds idiotic, but I have the strangest feeling . . .

MRS. PATTERSON (*Looking at her more anxiously*): Mary Alice, are you sick?

MARY ALICE: No, of course not . . . I just have the funniest feeling that I want to hang up my stocking.

MRS. PATTERSON (*Laughing*): Is that all? Well, go ahead and hang it up if it will make you feel any better, although just a while ago . . .

MARY ALICE: Yes, I know. A while ago I didn't even want to hear the word *Christmas,* and now, all of a sudden, without any reason, I want to hang up my stocking (*She does so*), and my fingers positively itch to do something like writing a Christmas card, or trimming a Christmas tree, or hanging up mistletoe, or . . . well . . . anything like that.

MRS. PATTERSON: Mary Alice, what's wrong with you?

MARY ALICE: I haven't the faintest idea . . . I just feel Christmasy all over . . . inside and out. (*Snatches up Santa mask and puts it on, shouting*) Merry Christmas! Merry Christmas, Mom! (*Grabs her mother in a wild hug and continues to shout*) Merry Christmas, Merry Christmas, Merry Christmas!

MRS. PATTERSON (*As* MARY ALICE *whirls her about*): Mary Alice, stop it, stop it! (*Doorbell rings.*)

MARY ALICE: That must be Dad. I'll bet he forgot his key. (*Runs to door calling "Merry Christmas" and runs into* BLAIR PHIPPS, *entering with an armload of blankets.*)

BLAIR: Well, well, well! Merry Christmas to you, Lady Santa Claus!

MARY ALICE (*Removing mask*): Oh! my goodness! I thought it was my father at the door.

BLAIR: Sorry. I'm Blair Phipps. Dad sent Mother and me over with some extra bedding to help you folks out. Mom's just coming up the steps now. (*He puts blankets down.*)

MRS. PATTERSON: How good of you to come! (*As* MRS. PHIPPS *enters*) Good afternoon, Mrs. Phipps, this is certainly kind of you.

MRS. PHIPPS: Nothing at all, Mrs. Patterson, nothing at all. We're so sorry your introduction to Hill Haven had to be by blizzard. But I see the snow isn't dampening your Christmas spirit.

BLAIR: I never expected to have a lady Santa Claus for a neighbor.

MARY ALICE: And I never expected to *be* a lady Santa Claus either. We just found all of these things in that box we were unpacking.

BLAIR: Do you have the rest of the suit that goes with the cap and mask?

MARY ALICE: Oh yes . . . we have the works. Dad was always playing Santa Claus back home.

BLAIR: Say, Mom, this might be the very thing . . .

MRS. PHIPPS (*Sharply*): Blair! Where are your manners? These people have just moved in, remember? They have a million things to do.

MRS. PATTERSON: That's our trouble, Mrs. Phipps. We *should* have a million things to do, only we don't. When my husband and the boys get back with the groceries, maybe we'll have more action. Won't you sit down and chat for a bit? Mary Alice, you and Blair might take these blankets upstairs.

BLAIR: Sure thing, Mrs. Patterson. (*Picking up armload of blankets, etc.*) Lead on, Lady Santa Claus.

MARY ALICE: Wait till I take off this ridiculous cap and gloves.

BLAIR: Leave the cap on. I like it.

MARY ALICE: Even Lady Santa Claus doesn't wear a hat in the house.

BLAIR: On you it looks good. In fact, any part of a Santa Claus suit looks good to me at the moment. (BLAIR *and* MARY ALICE *exit.*)

MRS. PHIPPS: I'm sure you're going to enjoy this house, Mrs. Patterson. The Lawrences, who used to live here, just loved it. (*Sighing*) Oh, dear! The good times we used to have in this old house. I've been coming here for Christmas Eve ever since I was a child.

MRS. PATTERSON: I'm afraid we don't have much Christmas cheer to offer you, but I'm certainly glad you came. We're feeling a bit low ourselves. It's a strange sort of Christmas for us.

MRS. PHIPPS: Actually, it's a strange sort of Christmas for the whole town, Mrs. Patterson. You heard about our terrible fire last night, I suppose.

MRS. PATTERSON: It must have been dreadful.

MRS. PHIPPS: The worst disaster we've ever had here in Hill Haven, and the most terrible part of it is . . . (MR. PATTERSON, RICK, *and* TUCK *enter, all carrying bundles.* MR. PATTERSON *has Santa's bag slung over his shoulder. He and the boys are singing lustily.*)

TUCK: Hey, Mom, look what we have!

RICK: They really gave us the red-carpet treatment in that store, Mom. (*They set bag and other bundles down.*)

MR. PATTERSON: Doris, your cooking problems are over.

Wait till you see . . . Oh, excuse me. I didn't see we had company.

MRS. PATTERSON: Mrs. Phipps, this is my husband, and these are my sons, Ricky and Tuck. (MARY ALICE *enters with* BLAIR.)

MRS. PHIPPS: Welcome to Hill Haven. This is my son, Blair. (*All exchange greetings.*)

TUCK: Mom, wait till you see the turkey! It's already cooked. And we have cranberries and even a mince pie.

BLAIR: So they treated you all right, did they?

RICK: More than all right. Boy, oh boy, you folks in Hill Haven really have the Christmas spirit.

MR. PATTERSON: When we walked into that grocery store, you'd have thought we were visiting royalty the way folks treated us.

TUCK: No wonder, the way Dad was wishing everybody a merry Christmas right and left. I never saw him so jolly.

RICK: And the food! Bushels of it. We'll have a bang-up Christmas dinner for sure.

MARY ALICE: It looks as if we might have a merry Christmas after all!

RICK (*Amused, to* MARY ALICE): Strike me pink! What's happened to Weeping Winnie?

TUCK: Did you hear that, Pop? Mary Alice actually said *Merry Christmas.* (*Turning to* BLAIR) Say, did they tell me your name was *Bruce?*

BLAIR: No, it's *Blair.* Why?

MARY ALICE: Tuck, will you be quiet?

MRS. PATTERSON: That will do, Tucker Patterson. (*To* BLAIR) Excuse him, Blair. It's just sort of a family joke.

MARY ALICE: And not a very funny one either. (*Doorbell rings.*)

TUCK: Oh, boy! More company! (*Runs to door*)

MRS. PATTERSON (*Puzzled*): I can't understand how you could get all that ready-cooked food in a small grocery store.

MRS. PHIPPS: It's not much of a mystery, Mrs. Patterson. You see, every year we have a big community Christmas party, and some of the best cooks in town prepare the food, but this year . . . (MARJORIE, KIT, *and* SALLY *enter.*)

TUCK: Some people to see you, Dad.

MARJORIE: Excuse us for barging in like this, but . . . well . . . this is an emergency.

SALLY: When I saw you walk into that grocery store, Mr. Patterson, I rushed right over and told Marjorie and Kit.

KIT: You'll probably think we're crazy, Mr. Patterson. Your name *is* Patterson, isn't it?

MR. PATTERSON: That's right. This is Mrs. Patterson, my daughter, Mary Alice, and my sons, Rick and Tucker. I suppose you know our neighbors.

KIT: Oh, sure, we know Mrs. Phipps and Blair. I'm Kit Roberts and these are my friends, Marjorie Minter and Sally King. We've come to ask you a tremendous favor, Mr. Patterson.

MR. PATTERSON: I hope I can oblige.

MARJORIE: Oh, I'm sure you can. You see, we'd like to borrow your suit . . . your Santa Claus suit, I mean.

SALLY (*Speaking rapidly*): It's the only one in town. This would be the first year that Hill Haven didn't have a Santa Claus, and the children would be so disappointed!

MR. PATTERSON: You want to borrow this old Santa Claus suit?

BLAIR: These girls are making an awful mess of telling a fairly simple story, Mr. Patterson. You know, our Town Hall burned to the ground last night.

SALLY: And all our Christmas decorations and the Santa Claus suit burned with it.

MARJORIE: It's bad enough that we won't be able to have our regular Christmas Eve party, but if we could just produce a Santa Claus suit, at least the little children wouldn't be disappointed.

MR. PATTERSON: I'm sure I'd be very happy to lend you the suit.

MARY ALICE (*Taking off the cap*): Here's the cap, and you may have the gloves. (*Hands things to* MARJORIE)

TUCK: Here's the bag for the presents. I hope they didn't burn up, too. (*Empties bag and hands it to* SALLY)

KIT: No, thank goodness the presents are safe.

RICK (*Pulling off Santa suit trousers and handing them to* BLAIR): And here are the pants. I hope they fit.

MARJORIE: Oh, that's no problem. We'll just get a Santa Claus who fits the pants, instead of the other way around. Poor Mr. Sullivan, who always played Santa Claus, caught such a cold at the fire last night that he's sick in bed, so we have to get a new Santa Claus.

RICK: Hey, Pop! What about you? You're an old hand at that game.

MRS. PATTERSON: Quiet, Ricky. We're strangers here. Your father wouldn't want to intrude.

BLAIR: He wouldn't be intruding, Mrs. Patterson, he'd be just swell. (*To* MRS. PHIPPS) Wouldn't he, Mom? (*Puts Santa trousers on chair*)

MRS. PHIPPS: It would really be better to have a stranger. Then none of the children would recognize him.

SALLY: Oh, would you, Mr. Patterson? Would you, please?

MR. PATTERSON: Well, I believe I'd enjoy it . . . if you think it would be all right.

SALLY: All right? I think it would be wonderful.

MRS. PATTERSON: But where are you having your party, with your hall burned down?

KIT: We have to skip our regular party, Mrs. Patterson, because there's no other place in town that's big enough. We'll just have to have the treat for the children in the church basement. The rest of us will have to forget about a party this year.

MARY ALICE: Forget about a Christmas party?

BLAIR: It's too bad, but it can't be helped. I wish you folks could have had a real Hill Haven Christmas. We have a wonderful time. The whole town gets into the act. We trim the community tree and go caroling and have a real old-fashioned Christmas get-together.

MRS. PHIPPS: It's like one big open house for the whole town.

MARY ALICE: Oh, Mother . . . *open house!* It was nothing for us to have a hundred people at our open house.

RICK (*Suddenly, looking around*): Say, we could fit *two* hundred people in this place right now. There's no furniture to get in our way. Why don't we have the town Christmas party right here?

MARY ALICE: That's a wonderful idea, Rick!

MRS. PATTERSON: You mean have the Christmas party here . . . in this house?

MR. PATTERSON: It seems like a perfect answer, and we'd have Christmas in our new house after all.

MARY ALICE: Oh, could we, Mother, could we, please? These floors would be great for dancing, and we have no rugs to roll up.

RICK: How about it, Mom? It would be just like old times.

TUCK: I'd even put my train away.

MRS. PATTERSON: It would be a wonderful chance for me to use the cut-glass punch bowl, wouldn't it?

MARY ALICE (*Hugging her mother*): You'll do it! You'll do it! Oh, Mother, you're an angel!

MRS. PHIPPS: You're a brave woman, Mrs. Patterson. Imagine having a party on moving day!

MARJORIE: It's a marvelous idea, Mrs. Patterson, and it won't be any work at all, really. Wait till you see those women on the refreshment committee go into action.

MRS. PHIPPS: That means I'd better go home and start calling them this very minute. Come along, Blair.

BLAIR: Right, Mom! I have to start rounding up the boys in the band.

RICK: If you need an extra trumpet player, count me in.

BLAIR: You're in, boy, and how! We'll be over early for a practice session. (*To* MRS. PATTERSON) You're great, Mrs. Patterson. In fact, I think this family is just what Hill Haven needs.

MRS. PHIPPS: As soon as I've made my phone calls, I'll come right over to help, Mrs. Patterson.

BLAIR (*To* MARY ALICE): And remember, Lady Santa Claus, I get the first dance. I stake first claim. (BLAIR *and* MRS. PHIPPS *exit.*)

MARJORIE: You have no idea what this party means to our town, Mrs. Patterson.

MRS. PATTERSON: You have no idea what this party means to us, Marjorie. We were feeling pretty sorry for ourselves.

KIT: Thanks again, Mr. Patterson. The kids will just love you.

SALLY: We'll go spread the news and be back in time to help. (*They put Santa suit down*)

GIRLS: So long, Santa Claus. (*Girls exit.*)

MR. PATTERSON (*Putting on pants of Santa suit*): I might as well put on the rest of this rig and practice doing my act.

MARY ALICE: Careful, Dad. Let me help you. I wouldn't want anything to happen to this old suit.

RICK: It's really brought us luck, hasn't it?

MARY ALICE: It's brought us more than luck, Ricky. This old red flannel suit has brought our Christmas back again. I don't understand it exactly, but I think there's some sort of magic about it.

RICK: Magic? What kind of magic?

MARY ALICE: I told you I don't understand it, but there's magic just the same . . . a Christmas magic. I felt it as soon as I put on the cap and gloves, and so did you, and Dad, and Tuck. You began breaking out in Christmas spirit the minute you wore any part of the Santa costume.

MR. PATTERSON: Maybe you're right, Mary Alice, maybe you're right. And you know, I think I know what the magic really is.

MARY ALICE: You do?

MR. PATTERSON: Yes, I do. We were all so busy feeling sorry for ourselves that we forgot the real magic of Christmas—you know, the magic of doing something for others.

MRS. PATTERSON: And the red flannel suit helped to remind us. The Santa Claus suit is the spirit of giving, isn't it?

MR. PATTERSON: That's right, Doris. It's just as simple as that. Now that we're all busy thinking about somebody else and making Christmas happy for others, we're happy ourselves.

RICK: That's a good thought, Dad. Be sure to put it in your Santa speech tonight.

MR. PATTERSON: I will, son. (*Reaching into pocket of suit*) And here's something else I'll put into my speech, too. Remember the little verse I used last year? Well, here it is . . . still in my pocket . . . listen:

You can't relive the fun you had
On Christmas Day last year.
Next Christmas is too far away
To bring you any cheer.
But there is one thing you can do
If you'd be truly glad,
Be sure to make *this* Christmas
The best you ever had.

ALL (*Applauding as curtains close*): We will! We will!

THE END

Production Notes

THE RED FLANNEL SUIT

Characters: 6 male; 6 female.

Playing Time: 30 minutes.

Costumes: The Pattersons wear ordinary winter clothing; Rick and Tuck put on winter jackets during play. Other characters wear warm overcoats, hats, boots, etc., when they enter. Mac also wears a fur cap.

Properties: Wood for kindling; screwdriver and hammer; sheet of paper; pen; blankets; bundles; big wooden box containing a Santa Claus suit, a large green sack, pillow, boots, trumpet, and artificial Christmas tree, tree ornaments, string of lights, a punch bowl, glass cups, card table and chairs, parts of an electric train, and five Christmas stockings with names on them—Mom, Dad, Sister, Brother, and Tuck.

Setting: The living room of the Pattersons' new home. The stage is bare except for a couple of old chairs and a wood basket with logs in it, which sits near the fireplace, center. Exits on left and right lead to the rest of the house and to the outdoors.

Lighting: No special effects.

Sound: Doorbell.

A Man Like Lincoln

Characters

ERIC GIFFORD, *a prospective candidate for Governor*
BILL CUMMINGS, *his campaign manager*
CRAIG GIFFORD, *his son*
MRS. ANDREWS, *his secretary*
MARCIA, *her daughter*
PEGGY HARRIS
LOUISE EDWARDS
KEN NOLAN
DEAN KING
} *Junior Historians*

TIME: *Morning, the present.*
SETTING: *The private law office of Attorney Eric Gifford.*
AT RISE: MRS. ANDREWS *is at her desk, sorting mail as* MR. GIFFORD *talks on the telephone.*

MR. GIFFORD: O.K., O.K., I'll do it if you say so, but I'm warning you I'm no TV personality. (*Pause*) So thousands will be watching—that's what bothers me. They can see me, but I can't see them. (*Pause*) Sure, sure, I trust you. I know you're a fine campaign manager, but I can't see for the life of me how my appearance on a

Lincoln's Birthday show is going to do anything for the campaign. (*Pause*) My what? My image? Now, you listen here, Bill, enough is enough. If I'm going to be Governor of this state, I'm going in on my own merit—not on Mr. Lincoln's coattails! (*Pause*) No, nothing's wrong with Lincoln, and I admit I quote him a lot, but as for being like him . . . I'm no more like Lincoln than any other small-town, self-made lawyer. The fact that I collect Lincoln lore is no grounds for a comparison. That slogan you cooked up—"A Man Like Lincoln"—it's downright presumptuous. Next thing you'll want me to wear a shawl and a high beaver hat on television! (*Pause. Using a milder tone*) No, of course I'm not sore, but take it easy, can't you?

Yes, yes, I will. Mrs. Andrews has the invitation on her desk, and she'll write the acceptance this morning. (*Pause*) O.K., and I'll knock the spots off you on the golf course this afternoon. You just wait and see. Right! I'll meet you at one-thirty. So long. (*Hangs up. To* MRS. ANDREWS) Mrs. Andrews, do you have that letter from WCAV?

MRS. ANDREWS: Right here, Mr. Gifford.

MR. GIFFORD: I've just been sold down the river, so you might as well tell them I'll be happy to oblige.

MRS. ANDREWS: You'll be wonderful on TV, sir.

MR. GIFFORD: Wonderful, my foot! That Bill Cummings is a publicity hound! Did you see that baloney in the morning paper?

MRS. ANDREWS: I don't think it's baloney, Mr. Gifford. All it says is that this state could use a man like Lincoln in in the Governor's mansion, and if you don't mind my saying so, sir, you are a good bit like Lincoln in many ways.

MR. GIFFORD: Oh, sure. I was born in a log cabin, I split rails by the hundred, I tended a country store, and I read my way through Blackstone all by myself.

MRS. ANDREWS: You can laugh, Mr. Gifford, but you *are* honest, and you do stick to your principles.

MR. GIFFORD: I should hope so. By the way, is Marcia coming in this morning?

MRS. ANDREWS: I'm expecting her any minute and I have a note on my calendar that she's having a meeting of the Junior Historians here in the office. I hope she cleared it with you.

MR. GIFFORD: Yes, she did. I'm always happy to have the young people go through my collection and use my Lincoln Library.

MRS. ANDREWS: Working here on Saturdays has done a lot for Marcia, Mr. Gifford. We both appreciate it.

MR. GIFFORD: She's a fine girl. She's done an excellent job of filing, and I want to give her a bit of experience in research.

MRS. ANDREWS: Is there anything special you want her to do today?

MR. GIFFORD: You might ask her to dig out some material on Lincoln's Cooper Union speech. Since I have to be on that blasted TV show, I might as well show my copy of the address and compare Lincoln's views on the federal government versus states' rights with current opinions. I'll leave her a note so she'll know what to look for. (*He writes on a memo pad at desk.*)

MRS. ANDREWS: I'm sure she'll be glad to do it for you.

MR. GIFFORD (*Consulting watch*): Oh, boy! It's later than I thought. I have an appointment with Judge Morgan. By the way, Mrs. Andrews, if you see Craig, ask him to phone me if he hears anything on those college applications. Confound it! I'm worried about that boy.

MRS. ANDREWS: He's not in any trouble, is he?

MR. GIFFORD: Not that I know of, but something's eating him lately. He's just not himself.

MRS. ANDREWS: It's probably this uncertainty about college. Marcia died a thousand deaths before she finally got her acceptance at State.

MR. GIFFORD: That's what puzzles me. Why don't we hear, one way or the other? Out of three applications, you'd think we'd hear something by this time.

MRS. ANDREWS: Lots of youngsters don't hear before April or May.

MR. GIFFORD: Maybe I'm too anxious to change my shingle to *Gifford and Gifford.* That boy has the makings of a darned good lawyer, and I want to see him get into the right school.

MRS. ANDREWS: But Craig has so many talents—music—painting. He's really a wonderful artist.

MR. GIFFORD: I know he has a lot of interests and hobbies, but he's never considered anything else but law, and for that, he must have a good solid foundation. I guess I'm just a worrywart. If his mother had only lived . . .

MRS. ANDREWS: You're doing a wonderful job, sir.

MR. GIFFORD: I'm not so sure of that, Mrs. Andrews. I've never had time to get mixed up in the P.T.A., or visit the schools, or do half of the things that mothers seem to take care of. For example, that Mr. Ames at the high school—the one who does something about guidance—he's called me three or four times, and I've never yet managed to have a conference with him. I haven't even . . . holy smoke! Tomorrow is Craig's birthday.

Would it be asking too much of you to stop in at the Sports Shop and pick up something for him?

MRS. ANDREWS: No trouble at all. What did you have in mind?

MR. GIFFORD: Anything you think he'd like. You have his shirt size and he can always use another sweater. Honestly, I don't know what Craig and I would do without you, Mrs. Andrews. Well, I must go. Leave me a memo of any calls, and I'll stop back here later and sign that letter for WCAV.

MRS. ANDREWS: I'll have it ready for you. Good luck with your golf game.

MR. GIFFORD: Thanks. I'll need it. That Bill is a real tornado! (*Exits*)

MRS. ANDREWS: Poor man! He really does have his hands full! (*Sitting at desk*) Well, I might as well get this letter out. (*Types until* MARCIA *enters*)

MARCIA: Hi, Mom. I know I'm late, but this Saturday morning traffic is murder! I stopped to get those Japanese brushes Craig has been dying for. His birthday's tomorrow.

MRS. ANDREWS: Yes, I know. Mr. Gifford asked me to get something for him at the Sports Shop.

MARCIA: Oh, no! Not more clothes! That boy has more shirts and sweaters now than any two people could possibly wear. Couldn't you drop a hint that what he really wants is an easel and a set of good oil paints?

MRS. ANDREWS: You know Mr. Gifford. With this campaign, he doesn't know if he's coming or going.

MARCIA: Well, he'd better start a "Know-Craig-Better Campaign" soon, if you ask me.

MRS. ANDREWS: Marcia! You know Craig's father is devoted to him.

MARCIA: Maybe he needs less devotion and more understanding.

MRS. ANDREWS: And I suppose you do understand Craig.

MARCIA: Sure, I do. At least I understand he's all torn apart trying to make himself into something he isn't.

MRS. ANDREWS: This seems to be your day for talking in riddles.

MARCIA: Take college, for example. Craig doesn't stand a chance of being accepted at any of those schools his father picked out. What's more, he doesn't even want to get in. He wants to go to art school.

MRS. ANDREWS: Art school? Then why didn't he apply?

MARCIA: Because he's so crazy about his dad that he'd jump through a hoop to please him. All he's ever heard is law, law, law, so he's trying to force himself in that direction. Somebody's going to get hurt.

MRS. ANDREWS: Oh, come now, Marcia, aren't you being a bit overdramatic?

MARCIA: You ask Mr. Ames, if you don't believe me. He knows the score, and if only Mr. Gifford would have a talk with him, I think it would help.

MRS. ANDREWS: He mentioned Mr. Ames this morning. If you think it's so important, I'll try to set up an appointment.

MARCIA: Don't bother. Mr. Ames is going to catch Mr. Gifford when he speaks at school on Lincoln's Birthday.

MRS. ANDREWS: Lincoln's Birthday?

MARCIA: Yes, we're having Parents' Night and the Junior Historians are in charge of the program. Craig promised to get his father as the main speaker. You know all about it. You're coming.

MRS. ANDREWS: But that's at 7:30 in the evening, and Mr. Gifford didn't say anything about a speaking engagement. In fact, he has a television appearance at that time.

MARCIA: But that's impossible.

MRS. ANDREWS (*Picking up typed letter and placing it on* MR. GIFFORD'*s desk*): I just finished typing his acceptance.

MARCIA: But Craig promised. We're counting on Mr. Gifford.

MRS. ANDREWS: Mr. Cummings thinks the TV show is very important to his campaign.

MARCIA: That campaign isn't nearly as important as Craig. Mother, I have to do something about this.

MRS. ANDREWS: There's nothing you can do, dear, and I'd advise you to stay out of it. Besides, you have work to do and so have I. Mr. Gifford wants you to get out all his material on Lincoln's address at Cooper Union. There's a note on the desk telling you what to look for. He wants to show his original copy and do a commentary on the speech itself, so you had better get busy.

MARCIA: The Cooper Union speech! Good heavens! That means going through stacks of books. Maybe I can get the committee to help me.

MRS. ANDREWS: Try to do a good job, dear. Mr. Gifford is delighted with your work. I'll have to rush if I'm to get all my errands done. I have to stop at the post office with these (*Picks up envelopes*), and there's some material he wants from the Law Library and the Historical Society. Before I do all that and get Craig's birthday present, it will be lunchtime. (*Gets hat and coat*) Be sure to make a memo of any phone calls. If Craig calls, you can give him Judge Morgan's number. Mr. Gifford is coming back some time later to sign this letter. 'Bye, dear, and try not to get so emotionally involved in Craig's problems. You have all you can do to handle your own and Mr. Lincoln's. (*Exits*)

MARCIA (*To herself*): I still can't understand why his father would turn him down. (*At files*) Lincoln—autographs, biographies, candidacy, Cooper—here it is—Cooper Union, New York City, February 27, 1860. See *The Lincoln Papers,* edited by David C. Mears. See *Lincoln's Sons* by Ruth Painter Randall. Now what would a book about Lincoln's sons have to do with a political speech? Maybe I can dig up a new angle for Mr. Gifford. (*As she is stooping over a low shelf in the bookcase,* CRAIG *enters.*)

CRAIG: Hi, Marcia. Do you know where my father is?

MARCIA (*Startled, she drops book*): Great Hannah! You scared the life out of me. Your father's with Judge Morgan right now, but what's a lot more important, Craig Gifford, is where will your father be at 7:30 on February 12th. Just answer that one.

CRAIG: Oh, boy! I knew you'd jump me about that. Marcia, I know you'll be sore, but . . . well . . . I just couldn't ask him.

MARCIA: For heaven's sake, why not? What's so terrible about asking your very own father to speak at a high school meeting on a subject that happens to be his lifetime hobby?

CRAIG: I know—it sounds silly, but, I just can't afford to.

MARCIA: Afford to? What's that supposed to mean?

CRAIG: I can't afford to have my father anywhere near that high school right now. You know as well as I do that Mr. Ames would corner him, right off the bat.

MARCIA: I thought you liked Mr. Ames.

CRAIG: I do, but not with my father. Don't you see, Marcia, Mr. Ames would spill the beans!

MARCIA: What beans? Just what beans are there to spill?

CRAIG: Plenty. Mr. Ames knows perfectly well I'll never get into a big-name college.

MARCIA: Nobody really knows that for sure until the colleges notify you.

CRAIG: But they already have.

MARCIA: You mean you've heard from them?

CRAIG: All three of them . . . and not one of them will have Craig W. Gifford in their sacred halls.

MARCIA: But then your father already knows the worst. What more can Mr. Ames tell him?

CRAIG: That's just it. My father doesn't know. I haven't told him.

MARCIA: But he'll have to know sooner or later. You can't keep a thing like that to yourself.

CRAIG: I can't keep anything to myself these days. Everywhere my dad goes, everything he does—there's a reporter on the spot. I'm not just an ordinary guy with a college problem . . . I'm copy. Can't you just see the headlines— "Potential Governor's Son Turned Down By Three Major Colleges."

MARCIA: You're exaggerating.

CRAIG: I wish I thought so.

MARCIA: But what are you going to do?

CRAIG: Tell him myself as soon as I get the chance. I know, I should have told him in the first place, but each time I heard from one college, I kept hoping for better news next time. Today I really struck out.

MARCIA: You really are in a mess, and so are we. Where are we going to get a speaker for the twelfth?

CRAIG: Don't ask me. Maybe the committee will have some ideas. (KEN, LOUISE, DEAN, *and* PEGGY *enter.*)

KEN: Ideas about what? You two seem to be having a secret confab. Going to let us in on it?

MARCIA: Thank goodness you're here. Craig has just been telling me we'll have to get another speaker for Parents' Night.

DEAN: What's the matter? I thought we were going to have the "Man Like Lincoln."

MARCIA: If you're making a crack about that article in the morning paper, I can inform you that Craig's father is scheduled for a TV program that night.

DEAN: I didn't mean it as a crack, Marcia. As a matter of fact, I do think that Mr. Gifford is a lot like Lincoln.

LOUISE: So do I, and I hope he's elected.

CRAIG: He has to be nominated first, you know.

PEGGY: Oh, that's in the bag. Everybody says he'll make it. I should think you'd be terribly proud of your father, Craig.

CRAIG: I am.

KEN: Hey, we have to start treating old Craig with a little more respect. If his dad is going to be a "Man Like Lincoln" that makes our friend "The Prince of Rails."

CRAIG: Cut it out, will you?

KEN: That's what they called Lincoln's son—the "Prince of Rails."

CRAIG: Well, I'm no prince . . . far from it.

DEAN: No kidding, isn't your dad going to be the speaker?

MARCIA: I told you—he's booked for a television program.

LOUISE: But, I thought . . .

CRAIG: Thanks, Marcia, but there's no use trying to pretend. I never asked Dad to speak. I didn't ask him because I've been turned down by every college on my list, and I didn't want him to get a blow-by-blow description of my scholastic standing from Mr. Ames.

PEGGY: That's too bad, Craig.

LOUISE: But maybe if your father talked to Mr. Ames, you could apply somewhere else. After all, Mr. Ames is always talking about selecting the right school for the right person. Maybe you didn't pick the right ones.

DEAN: What about art school? You didn't apply to any.

CRAIG: That's out. Dad wants me to be a lawyer.

KEN: But you have real talent. Look at your art work on the yearbook.

LOUISE: And all the poster contests you've won.

PEGGY: I'll bet Mr. Ames could sell your dad on the idea.

CRAIG: I could sell him myself, if it came to that. The point is, I know he's set his heart on my being a lawyer, and I'm not going to let him down.

KEN: I still don't see what harm it would do to get him up to school to talk to Mr. Ames. He helped straighten me out on my college applications.

CRAIG: Look! I don't want to hear any more of this talk. If you're all friends of mine, you'll drop the whole subject.

MARCIA: Craig doesn't want the press to get wind of the fact that he's a three-time loser.

DEAN: Wow! I never thought of that. Thank heavens my dad runs a butcher shop. I hope he never goes in for politics.

LOUISE: I have an idea . . . an idea for a speaker, I mean.

ALL: Who?

LOUISE: Mr. Briggs! He's going to be there anyway to talk about the Briggs Foundation. We could just juggle the program around, put him first instead of last, and he could be the keynote speaker.

DEAN: That's not a bad idea, Louise. The Briggs Foundation is an important outfit and to have Calvin Briggs himself listed as the main speaker might work out nicely. Let's do it.

MARCIA: I don't see how we can do anything else. It's too short notice to go scouting for another speaker.

PEGGY: I still think your father would be better. In my opinion, he's really going to be a great man.

CRAIG: He's already a great man as far as I'm concerned, and you know something—he is like Lincoln in a lot of ways.

LOUISE: Maybe it comes from all the reading and studying he's done about Lincoln. My father says he's always quoting Lincoln.

KEN: And it's great the way he lets us come up here and use his books. He has stuff here you'd never find in an ordinary library. I've learned a lot from his material.

MARCIA: And you can learn a lot more this very morning. I have a big job and I need help.

DEAN: What's the angle?

MARCIA: I'm supposed to dig up some material for him on Lincoln's Cooper Union speech. (*Pointing*) That whole folder is full of references. I hardly know where to begin. How about you all giving me a hand?

KEN: The Cooper Union speech? Did he make that before or after he was President?

CRAIG: Before, you idiot. Even I know that. It was the speech that really won him the nomination in 1860. (*Group moves to table to look at books.*)

MARCIA: There's some material in the two books I pulled out, and plenty more in these others. (*She picks up file, consults it and pulls several more books from the shelves.*)

LOUISE: How do we know what we're looking for?

DEAN (*Looking at book*): This is a long speech—pages and pages.

MARCIA: See if you can organize the points he made on the powers of the federal government versus states' rights.

CRAIG: That's a tall order.

KEN: Here's one that's new to me— *Lincoln's Sons.*

MARCIA: I doubt if you'll find very much about the Cooper Union speech in that.

KEN (*Leafing through book*): It's listed twice in the index.

PEGGY: This book is called *The Lincoln Papers*—they're the papers that belonged to his son, Robert.

KEN: Well, I'll be doggoned.

MARCIA: Did you make a find?

KEN: Listen to this. (*Reads from book*) "Years afterward Robert often said with a smile that he was mainly responsible for his father's first nomination for President—that if he had not flunked his examinations at Harvard, and if his father had not in consequence been so much worried about him that he wanted to come East to see him, it might not have happened. For both Robert and Mr. Lincoln, that flunking proved remarkably beneficial."

CRAIG: Let me see that. You're making it up!

KEN: I am not. It's right here in black and white!

LOUISE: You mean Abraham Lincoln's son flunked out of Harvard? (*Group gathers around* KEN.)

KEN: Wait a minute. Let me go back to the beginning of the chapter.

PEGGY: There's something about it in *this* book. I don't think it means he flunked out of Harvard. It means he couldn't get in. Here's what Robert himself has to say about it. (*Reads*) "I resolved to enter Harvard College, imagining that there would be no trouble in doing so, in which idea, it is unnecessary to say, I was very much mistaken." Then it goes on to say that when he took his college examinations, he flunked fifteen out of sixteen subjects!

DEAN: Now there's a record that's hard to beat.

LOUISE: What did he do?

KEN: In this book it says: (*Reads*) "On being examined I had the honor to receive a fabulous number of conditions which precluded my admission. However, I was resolved not to retire beaten, so, acting under the advice of President Walker, I entered the well-known Academy of Exeter, New Hampshire."

CRAIG: And all this time his father was on the verge of being nominated for the Presidency of the United States!

KEN: That's not all. (*Reads*) "I went to Exeter hoping to enter the class preparing to enter college, the next July, as Sophomores. The worthy Principal, Dr. Soule, soon convinced me of the vanity of my aspirations, and I was obliged to enter the Subfreshman Class."

DEAN: Subfreshman! How low can you get?

MARCIA: How does all this fit in with the Cooper Union speech?

KEN: Well, according to this book, Robert's parents were worried about him.

LOUISE: No wonder.

KEN: Lincoln apparently wanted to visit Robert but didn't have the money. Then Robert got a letter saying some men in New York had asked Lincoln to speak to them and had offered the money for the trip.

MARCIA: And that speech turned out to be the famous Cooper Union address.

PEGGY: The one that got him the nomination.

KEN: And two days later he went to Exeter, visited his son, and made practically the same speech at the school.

CRAIG: You mean he wasn't ashamed of his son's record?

KEN: Apparently not. According to this, they had a fine visit, and everything was great.

CRAIG: But the reporters . . . the press was plenty rough, even in those days.

DEAN: Well, it certainly didn't hurt his chances or damage his campaign.

MARCIA: This is a terrific story, but I'm not so sure it's what Mr. Gifford needs.

CRAIG: Maybe not, Marcia, but I think it's something I need. A man like Lincoln wasn't ashamed of a son who flunked fifteen out of sixteen subjects—Lincoln crossed half of this country just to visit Robert—to see how he was doing—and all this in the midst of a Presidential campaign. Wow! What a guy!

MARCIA: Craig, do you really think your father is a "Man Like Lincoln"?

CRAIG: You know I do.

MARCIA: Then haven't you sold him short by not giving him the straight facts and leaving the rest up to him?

CRAIG: I never thought of it that way. I wish now I had asked him to speak at our meeting.

PEGGY: It's not too late.

LOUISE: You could still do it.

CRAIG: But he's already made this TV commitment.

MARCIA: The letter hasn't gone out yet. He hasn't even signed it. (MR. CUMMINGS *enters.*)

MR. CUMMINGS: Good morning. Does anybody here know where I could find a good lawyer?

CRAIG: Hello, Mr. Cummings. Dad had an appointment

with Judge Morgan this morning. These are some of my friends—Marcia Andrews, Peggy Harris, Louise Edwards, Ken Nolan and Dean King. This is my father's campaign manager, Mr. Cummings.

MR. CUMMINGS: Glad to know you. I'm anxious to get hold of your father before lunch. Are you expecting him back in the office?

MARCIA: He said he'd drop in to sign some letters, Mr. Cummings.

MR. CUMMINGS: Good. I think I'll wait, if you don't mind.

CRAIG: Not at all. Make yourself comfortable.

DEAN: I think our committee had better adjourn. If you have any news for us, Craig, let us know.

KEN: We can wait a few days to have the program printed.

CRAIG: I'll call you this afternoon.

LOUISE (*Handing papers to* MARCIA): Here's the rough draft of the program, Marcia. We'll leave it with you, and you can make any necessary changes.

MARCIA: I'll take care of it, Louise.

PEGGY: Good luck, Craig . . . nice to have met you, Mr. Cummings. (*Committee exits.*)

MARCIA: If you'll excuse me, I'll go ahead with my work. (*Seats herself at table with books and makes notes*)

MR. CUMMINGS: Glad to see you have such nice friends, Craig. I hope you realize you'll be pretty much in the limelight when your dad's campaign really gets rolling. A candidate's personal life is always important.

CRAIG: I think I understand, sir.

MR. CUMMINGS: Your father's a big man, Craig, but a tough one to handle, politically speaking. I had a rough time signing him up for a television appearance.

CRAIG: Is it so terribly important to his campaign, Mr. Cummings?

MR. CUMMINGS: Everything's important to his campaign, son. We've got to keep his image before the public, and see that he meets the right people, makes the right contacts with the right organizations. (MR. GIFFORD *enters.*)

MR. GIFFORD: Well! Well! Looks as if we have a full house. Hello, Craig. Morning, Marcia. Hi, Bill. What's on your mind that won't keep till after lunch?

MR. CUMMINGS: Just wanted to make sure you're on the ball with the TV commitment, Eric, and I've some new press releases for you to O.K.

MR. GIFFORD: The TV letter should be on my desk. Yes, here it is. But save those releases for a bit. I can't bear to look at them on an empty stomach. How's the boy, Craig? Got any news for me?

CRAIG: Yes, and no, Dad. I have news, but I'm afraid it's not what you want to hear.

MR. GIFFORD: Is it about one of your college applications?

CRAIG: It's all of them, Dad. I didn't make it—not any place.

MR. GIFFORD: You mean you've heard?

CRAIG (*Giving him letters from his pocket*): The last one came this morning. I know I should have told you the minute the first one came, but I kept hoping for better news, and, well . . . I just couldn't bear to disappoint you.

MR. GIFFORD: So that's why you've been going around with such a long face. You should know by this time, son, I can take a few disappointments.

MARCIA: Excuse me, sir. I have compiled some references on the Cooper Union speech. (*Handing him sheaf of papers*) Perhaps it's not exactly the material you wanted, but . . .

MR. GIFFORD (*Absently*): I'm sure you've done a good job,

Marcia. (*Glancing at papers*) Wait a minute, child. I think you've made a mistake. This seems to be some sort of program. "Parents' Night—A Lincoln's Birthday Get-Together at Hamilton High School." What's this . . . "Keynote Speaker, Attorney Eric C. Gifford"?

CRAIG: Look, Dad, Marcia didn't make a mistake. I did. I promised the committee I would ask you to make the keynote speech, but I lost my nerve.

MR. GIFFORD: You lost your nerve? What nerve? What nerve does it take to ask me to do something for you and for your school?

CRAIG: It's hard to explain, Dad, but, to be honest, I just didn't want you to come to school.

MR. GIFFORD: You mean you're ashamed of me—ashamed of your father?

CRAIG: Gosh, no, Dad—it's the other way around. I didn't want you to be ashamed of me. I didn't want Mr. Ames to corner you and tell you what a flop I am.

MR. GIFFORD: Just what sort of flop are you?

CRAIG: Those letters should tell you. Mr. Ames has told me all along to try for a good art school.

MR. GIFFORD: Art school! But I thought you wanted to be a lawyer!

CRAIG: I thought *you* wanted me to be a lawyer, Dad.

MR. GIFFORD: Something tells me we haven't been operating on the same wave length, Craig. Bill, you'd better find yourself another partner for that golf match this afternoon. Just put those releases on my desk. I'm taking my son to lunch.

MR. CUMMINGS: I'll call you tonight, Eric. Meanwhile don't forget that letter.

MR. GIFFORD: I've already forgotten it. Haven't you heard, Cummings? I'm going to be the keynote speaker at

Hamilton High that same evening. Marcia, how's your typing?

MARCIA: Not as good as my mother's.

MR. GIFFORD: It should be good enough to send my regrets to WCAV—sorry a previous engagement—et cetera, et cetera. (MARCIA *moves to typewriter.*)

CRAIG: But, Dad, you can't do that!

MR. CUMMINGS: Think of your campaign!

MR. GIFFORD: Look, Bill, you're a fine fellow! You work hard, you're clever, you have my best interests at heart, and I like you. Most of the time I even listen to you. But you have one big weakness—you don't know very much about Abe Lincoln.

MR. CUMMINGS: What does Abe Lincoln have to do with your campaign?

MR. GIFFORD: You seemed to think he had a lot to do with it, when you coined that phrase, "A Man Like Lincoln."

MR. CUMMINGS: And it's a mighty good slogan, even if you don't like it.

MR. GIFFORD: But I *do* like it, Bill. I like it so much that I'm going to do my level best to *be* like Lincoln. Tell me —what do you know about his Cooper Union address?

MR. CUMMINGS: Well, I know it won him the Presidential nomination.

MR. GIFFORD: But do you know how and why he agreed to travel all the way from Springfield, Illinois, to New York City to make that speech?

MR. CUMMINGS: What is this? An exam in American history?

MR. GIFFORD: Not exactly. But you can find the answer in these notes Marcia has made for me. Maybe you'd like to sit down and read them. The main reason Lincoln agreed to make that journey was the two-hundred-dollar fee attached to the invitation. He needed that money to go to see his son at prep school in New Hampshire. He was concerned. He wanted to find out how his son was doing in his uphill battle to prepare for a college which had once turned him down. He wanted to make sure he had not fallen victim to discouragement and fear.

MR. CUMMINGS: What are you getting at?

MR. GIFFORD: I'm getting at the fact that my own son's school is within walking distance of my office and I haven't been inside it for over a year. I'm getting at the fact that Robert Lincoln had a problem very much like Craig's, and he had his father's support in solving it. I'm getting at the fact that a man who seeks to be like Lincoln must do more than follow his example as an honest man, an able politician and a good lawyer. He must also learn to be a good father. And that's what I'm going to do, Bill, campaign or no campaign. Do you get the message?

MR. CUMMINGS: It's coming through loud and clear.

CRAIG: Dad, I just don't know what to say.

MR. GIFFORD: We have lots to talk about, Craig. You'll find me a good listener. (*Phone rings*) Hello—(*Pause*) yes, Mrs. Andrews. (*Pause*) Don't worry about the size. I think my son has outgrown the boys' department without my realizing it. Come to think of it, you might as well skip the shopping entirely. Craig and I will have more fun doing it together. I'm very sure now he knows what he wants. Thanks anyhow. See you Monday. 'Bye. (*As* MR. GIFFORD *hangs up,* MARCIA *rises and brings him the typed letter.*)

MARCIA: I've finished your letter, sir. Will you sign it?

MR. GIFFORD: With pleasure. (*Signs*) And now I suggest we all go out for lunch. I'm starved.

MR. CUMMINGS: I think maybe you and Craig have had enough of me for one day, Eric. I'll stay here and brush up on my history.

CRAIG: Come along, Mr. Cummings. It isn't every day you have the chance to eat lunch with "A Man Like Lincoln." (*Curtain*)

THE END

Production Notes

A MAN LIKE LINCOLN

Characters: 5 male; 4 female.

Playing Time: 30 minutes.

Costumes: Appropriate modern dress. Watch for Mr. Gifford.

Properties: Telephone, typewriter, typed letters, envelopes, hat and coat for Mrs. Andrews, books, letters for Craig's pocket, file folder, draft of Parents' Night program, press releases, papers, pencils.

Setting: Mr. Gifford's combined library and law office. Center stage is a large desk with swivel chair above which is a painting of Lincoln. Other furnishings include bookcases, filing cabinets, a long conference table with six chairs, a secretary's desk and chair, a typewriter on desk or on separate stand and a pedestal on which there is a bust of Lincoln.

Lighting: No special effects.

A Valentine for Kate

Characters

BOB TORRENCE
MRS. TORRENCE, *his mother*
DICK ARMSTRONG
MAC MASTERS
PETE NAYLOR, *new boy at school*
GLADYS KING
MARIAN MARCH
BARBIE SHERIDAN
KATHLEEN SHERIDAN, *her spirited sister*

SETTING: *The Torrence living room.*
AT RISE: BOB TORRENCE *and his friends,* DICK *and* MAC, *are seated around a table.*

DICK: Cheer up, Bob. It's not the end of the world!
MAC: There are still plenty of fish in the sea.
BOB: So who wants to take a fish to the Valentine Dance?
DICK: You have a point there!
MAC: But I don't get it. Why did Barbie turn you down? Does she have another date?
BOB: Nope.

DICK: Do her parents disapprove of you?

BOB: Nope.

MAC: Have you had a fight?

BOB: Nope.

DICK: Have you been using "that greasy kid stuff" again?

BOB: Knock it off, will you?

MAC: But there must be some reason.

DICK: We're only trying to help.

BOB: There's nothing you can do, Dick, so get off my back!

DICK: Never underestimate the power of a pal! Right, Mac?

MAC: Right!

DICK: There must be something we could do.

BOB: If I thought you really meant that—

DICK: But I do.

MAC: So do I. After all, we can't have the chairman of the dance committee sitting at home chewing his fingernails or reading a good book.

BOB: Well, there is something you could do, but—no—you'd never do it in a thousand years!

MAC: Just name it, old boy!

DICK: Anything for a pal, that's my slogan.

BOB: O.K. Do you happen to know Barbie's sister?

MAC: Kathleen?

DICK: Kathleen Sheridan? That sourpuss!

BOB: You *do* know her. Now which one of you big noble buddies will volunteer to take her to the dance?

MAC: Are you crazy? Do we look like a couple of lion-tamers?

DICK: My name is Dick Armstrong—not Clyde Beatty!

BOB: I thought you'd do anything for a friend—anything!

DICK: But who'd ever figure on anything like this . . . a real sacrifice.

MAC: A useless sacrifice. How would it help you?

BOB: But that's my whole problem. Barbie won't go to the dance unless I get a date for her sister!

MAC: She can't be serious!

BOB: She's making a crusade of it!

MAC: Frankly, I'd just as soon go dancing with a man-eating shark!

DICK: Make it a tigress, Mac. Sharks just bite. They don't have claws!

BOB: But you have to admit she's pretty—a real knockout.

DICK: "Knockout" is right. Ed Simpson had a date with her once and came home limping from a kick in the shins.

BOB: She has lots of brains.

MAC: I'll say. She's a one-man debating team!

DICK: How did a nice girl like Barbie ever manage to draw Kathleen for a sister?

BOB: Barbie claims she wasn't like this when they lived in Milford, but some joker there stood her up, or walked out on her or something, and she's been taking it out on the male population ever since.

MAC: If she's so down on men, what's the point of trying to get her a date?

BOB: Therapy! It's Barbie's idea that Kathleen will thaw out and turn into a normal human being once she gets back into circulation.

DICK: That I'd like to see.

BOB: Then ask her to the dance and find out. It would be an experiment.

DICK: Too dangerous! Besides, I'm not the scientific type.

MAC: But there must be somebody who wants to live dangerously. Doesn't she have any friends in the dramatic club?

BOB: She quit the dramatic club. According to her it was too lowbrow! (*Doorbell rings.*)

DICK: Your committee must be arriving.

BOB: I guess I should have warned you. Barbie is bringing Kathleen to the meeting.

MAC: But she's not on the committee.

BOB: She is now. Barbie insisted on making her a member.

DICK: Oh, boy! Now we'll see the fireworks! Nothing will suit her—the hall, the band, the decorations—everything will have to be done her way or we'll have a free-for-all. (*Enter* MRS. TORRENCE *with* PETE NAYLOR.)

MRS. TORRENCE: The boys are in here, Pete. I'm sure Bob will have what you need.

BOB: Hiya, Pete. Come in and join us. Do you know Mac Masters and Dick Armstrong? (*As boys shake hands*) Pete is in my English class. Just moved to town a few weeks ago from Spring City.

MRS. TORRENCE: Let me know when the rest of your committee arrives, Bob, and I'll bring in the refreshments.

BOB: Thanks, Mom. They'll be along shortly. (*Exit* MRS. TORRENCE.)

PETE: Sorry, I didn't know you were having a meeting. I just dropped in to borrow your Shakespeare notes from the beginning of the course. I hear there's a big test coming up.

BOB: There sure is, but a brain like you will blast right through it. (*To others*) This guy is a real Shakespeare bug.

PETE: Just the same, your notes should be a big help.

BOB: Come along upstairs and take a look. You're welcome to anything I have.

PETE: Thanks a lot. I'll need the works. (*Exit* BOB *and* PETE)

DICK: Mac, are you thinking the same thing that I'm thinking?

MAC: I'd say our two great minds are in the same channel.

DICK: There's our pigeon, if ever I saw one.

MAC: A stranger, yea, verily, a stranger!

DICK: An innocent lamb, ready for the shearing!

MAC: If he's just never heard of dear Kathleen!

DICK: We'll soon find out. Now here's how we'll operate. I'll make the opening pitch, and you follow my lead. Got it?

MAC (*Making an "O.K." sign with his finger and thumb*): Got it!

DICK (*Pacing up and down*): Here's hoping our female committee members run true to form by arriving late.

MAC: They will. That's one thing you can always count on. (*Re-enter* BOB *and* PETE.)

PETE: Thanks a lot, Bob. This is just what I needed.

DICK: Don't rush off, Pete. We could use another brain on our dance committee.

PETE: Dance committee?

MAC: Yes, the Valentine Dance. We want to make this a bang-up affair, and I've heard the school dances at Spring City are really something. Maybe we could pick your brains for some new ideas.

PETE (*Intrigued*): I sure would be glad to help. We've always had a King and Queen of Hearts at our Valentine shindig.

DICK: That's a great idea. How about that, Bob? Isn't that a great idea?

BOB: Well, sure . . . but. . . .

DICK: Sit down, Pete. (*Pushing a notebook into his hands*) Now, jot down any suggestions you may have for special entertainment.

PETE: We had a great idea last year. We put on a skit at intermission. . . .

MAC: What about tickets? If you haven't bought yours, we can fix you up.

PETE: But I haven't decided to go to the dance.

DICK: Not go? But you can't miss it. This is the biggest "do" of the whole year.

PETE: Well, you see, I've been here such a short time, I haven't met too many people . . . that is . . . girls.

MAC: Don't let that worry you, Pete.

DICK: As a matter of fact, there's a girl coming here this afternoon—a real knockout. Just wait till you see her.

BOB: Yes, that's right! He just might be able to get a date with Kathleen.

PETE: Kathleen?

BOB: Kathleen Sheridan. I'm planning to take her sister, Barbie. How would you like to make it a double date?

MAC: Wait a minute, Bob. We don't want to get his hopes up. Maybe Kathleen already has a date.

BOB (*In amazement*): Already has a date?

DICK: I see what you mean, Mac. A girl as pretty as Kathleen must have plenty of offers.

MAC: We'll just have to keep our fingers crossed.

DICK (*Clapping* PETE *on shoulder*): You're really lucky that she's coming here this afternoon; it sort of gives you an edge.

PETE: Kathleen Sheridan? I don't think she's in any of my classes.

BOB: Good! (*Catching himself*) I mean goodness! Imagine not knowing one of the most popular girls in school!

PETE: But the name is familiar. Does she belong to the Dramatic Club?

BOB: Not any more!

PETE: But I've heard that name somewhere—Sheridan—Kate Sheridan!

BOB: *Kathleen* Sheridan! Whatever you do, don't call her "Kate"!

PETE (*Surprised*): Why not? I happen to like that name.

BOB: But she hates it! Oh, brother!

DICK: As Shakespeare would say, "What's in a name?" (*Doorbell rings*)

MAC: You'd better answer the door, Bob. (*Practically shoving him offstage*) Don't pay any attention to him, Pete. Bob has a lot on his mind these days. He's apt to exaggerate.

DICK: And you know how girls are about names! Kathleen is such a romantic type.

MAC: And "Kate" just doesn't suit her winsome personality.

PETE (*Stubbornly*): But I like the name "Kate." (BOB *ushers in* MARIAN MARCH *and* GLADYS KING.)

BOB: Girls, I want you to meet our new committee member, Pete Naylor. Pete—Marian March and Gladys King.

PETE: I'm glad to meet you.

MARIAN: I'm so pleased that we have another boy on the committee.

GLADYS: So am I, and I do hope you're strong-minded and outspoken, Pete.

MARIAN: We're going to need steam-roller tactics to keep that Sheridan female in line. (MAC *and* BOB *make signs for her to stop, but* PETE *can't see this.*)

DICK (*Forcing a laugh*): Don't worry about Barbie. Old Bob here knows how to keep her under control.

MARIAN (*Ignoring boys' frantic signals*): Who's talking about Barbie? It's that opinionated Kathleen who will try to run the whole show! (*Boys show signs of despair.*)

GLADYS: Whose idea was it to put *her* on the dance committee. She'll try to take over, just the way she did in the Dramatic Club.

PETE: I *thought* I'd heard of her through Dramatic Club!

MARIAN: Sure, she thought she was the big cheese. But when she couldn't talk them into putting on Shakespeare, she quit!

GLADYS: Imagine! Shakespeare!

DICK: You girls are just jealous!

BOTH: Jealous!

MAC: That's right—*jealous!* You know Kathleen Sheridan is the best-looking girl in school.

DICK: And the smartest, and the most talented. . . .

GLADYS: *And* the most obnoxious!

PETE: Do you happen to be speaking about the popular young lady who is my prospective date for the Valentine Dance?

MARIAN: Are you kidding?

PETE: These good friends of mine have led me to believe I'll be the luckiest guy alive, if I can persuade her to go with me.

GLADYS: You'll be lucky all right—lucky to get home alive.

MARIAN: She'll be the lucky one. That girl hasn't had a date all year.

PETE: Well, she has one now.

BOB (*Incredulously*): You mean it?

PETE: I sure do. There's something about this Kate Sheridan that appeals to me.

MAC: In spite of all these two blabbermouths have said?

PETE: Maybe it's *because* of what they've said. If there's anything I go for, it's a challenge.

DICK: Well, you've got it, pal. You've got it! I know you must think we're a bunch of heels, but when you hear the whole story. . . .

BOB: Pete, if you pull this off, I'm your friend for life.

GLADYS: Maybe I'm beginning to see the light. Are you, by any chance, doing all this for Barbie?

BOB: I sure am—for Barbie and for myself.

MARIAN: You mean she won't go to the dance unless Kathleen has a date.

BOB: That's it!

MARIAN: Oh, dear! Why didn't somebody tell me?

GLADYS: Maybe, after all, we've been a bit rough on the girl. She *is* a very good dancer.

DICK: It's too late now for the soft soap. You might as well give Pete the whole picture.

PETE (*Calmly*): I think I've got the whole picture.

MAC: But this is no ordinary girl, Pete. You could use a few pointers on how to handle the situation.

PETE: Just let me handle it my own way, will you?

DICK: But the right approach might help.

MAC: You don't want to get off on the wrong foot.

BOB: This "Kate" business, for example. That could ruin everything before you got off the ground.

PETE: Now look . . . you fellows want me to take this girl to the Valentine Dance, right?

BOYS: Right!

PETE: O.K. I'll take her, and without any help from the grandstand.

MARIAN: Suppose she won't go?

PETE: She'll go.

GLADYS: Want to bet?

PETE: What do you have in mind?

BOB: You name the stakes.

PETE: Do you mean that?

BOB: I sure do.

PETE: O.K. I'll think about it, but in the meantime, there's one condition.

BOB: Name it.

PETE: I can do with less audience. Can't you girls find something to do, some place to go?

BOB: Sure, they can. They can help Mom with the refreshments. Come on, girls. This way out. (*Steers them to door, and follows them off*)

PETE: And stay out of sight till I give Bob the all clear.

DICK: Do you want us to scram too?

PETE: If you can fade into the woodwork after the introductions, I'll appreciate it.

MAC: We'll be the original Vanishing Americans. (*Doorbell rings*)

DICK: Start the countdown. Here they come.

BOB (*Offstage*): Hi, girls. Come in. Glad you could make it, Kathleen. (BOB *re-enters with* BARBIE *and* KATHLEEN SHERIDAN.)

BARBIE: Hello, Dick. How are you, Mac?

KATHLEEN (*To* BARBIE): I thought you said there were girls on the committee. I might have known, if you had anything to do with it, it would be all boys.

BOB: Marian March and Gladys King are here, but they're out in the kitchen helping Mom.

KATHLEEN: You mean they're actually working for a change?

BARBIE: Now, Kathleen, you promised . . .

BOB: Let me take your coats. (*Helps* BARBIE *with hers.*)

KATHLEEN: Don't bother with mine. I'm not sure how long I'll be staying. (*Looks* PETE *up and down*) And who is the handsome stranger?

BOB (*Laughing*): How about that? I'm forgetting my manners. Barbie, Kathleen, I'd like you to meet Pete Naylor. He's new in town. Pete, these are the Sheridan sisters, Barbie and Kathleen.

PETE: Hello, Barbie. Delighted to meet you, Kate.

KATHLEEN (*Coldly*): The name is Kathleen.

PETE: But I like "Kate." Kathleen is so formal.

KATHLEEN: Good. Let's keep it that way—formal.

PETE (*Laughing heartily*): Say, that's a good one!

KATHLEEN: Just what are you laughing at?

PETE: At you, Kate. (*Laughing louder*) Formal! Let's keep it formal! Boy, that's rich!

KATHLEEN (*To the others who are staring in amazement*): Is this character out of his mind?

PETE (*Absolutely convulsed*): Out of my mind, she says! Oh, brother!

KATHLEEN: Is this some sort of silly joke or do you get hysterical every time you meet a girl?

PETE: Excuse me, please, I'll explain when I can stop laughing. (*Trying to control his laughter*) It's just that the whole idea struck me so funny.

KATHLEEN: What idea?

PETE: The idea of being so formal on my first date.

KATHLEEN (*To others*): Well, don't stand there like idiots! What's wrong with this character? What is he talking about?

PETE: I'm talking about the Valentine Dance. You and I are going together.

BARBIE: How marvelous!

BOB: Congratulations, Pete, old boy!

DICK: We told him you were the best dancer in school, Kate—er—I mean Kathleen.

PETE (*Blandly*): Oh, it's all right to call her Kate. After all, you've known her longer than I have.

KATHLEEN: Will you stop this nonsense!

MAC: Come on, Dick, let's tell Gladys and Marian. (*Exit* MAC *and* DICK)

KATHLEEN: You'll do nothing of the sort! You come back here!

PETE: Why not, Kate? I want everybody to know I've snagged the prettiest girl in Burton High.

KATHLEEN: Is that so? Well, for your information, I am not going to the Valentine Dance or any place else with you.

PETE: I know it's pretty sudden, but this is the first chance I've had to meet you. . . .

KATHLEEN: And it's your last! Bob, you'll either get this nitwit out of here, or I'm leaving.

PETE: Good! I've been wanting to be alone with you ever since the minute we met. So long, folks! (*Takes her arm*) Kate and I have a lot of getting acquainted to do.

KATHLEEN (*Trying to pull away*): You let go of me, you—you—

PETE: Now, now, Kate! I have a million things to say to you.

KATHLEEN: You call me "Kate" just once more, and I'll—I'll—

PETE (*Holding both her arms*): Kate, did anybody ever tell you your eyes have little green and yellow sparks in them when you're angry?

KATHLEEN (*Struggling*): I said, let go of me!

PETE: I will, if you'll sit down over here on the sofa. . . . (*Steers her in direction of sofa*)

KATHLEEN (*Trying vainly to kick him*): I will not sit on any sofa. . . .

PETE: Of course not! Not with all those cushions! Bob, what on earth does your mother mean by cluttering up a perfectly good sofa with those miserable cushions. Get them out of here before I kick them on the floor. (BOB *pulls cushions off sofa.*)

KATHLEEN: Of all the ill-mannered boors I have ever seen. . . .

PETE: I just wanted to make it more comfortable for you, Kate. Frankly, I feel the same way about sofa cushions. (*Pulling her down on sofa beside him*) There! Isn't that better? Now tell me the color of your evening dress so I can send you the right flowers. Flowers are terribly important on a first date, don't you think so?

BARBIE: Her dress is pink.

PETE: I knew it! I knew it would be pink. Which do you want, Kate, carnations or roses?

BARBIE: She adores roses.

KATHLEEN: Barbie Sheridan, you keep out of this!

PETE: We'll make it carnations. They're cheaper and they hold up longer.

KATHLEEN: You're not only mad, you are insulting! Of all the impossible boys I've met in my whole life, you are the most utterly reprehensible!

PETE (*Beaming*): And I'm a good dancer, too. (*Suddenly pulling her to her feet*) Let's give it a whirl. Bob, what kind of host are you? Let's have some music. (BOB, *as if in a daze, puts on a record*)

KATHLEEN (*Trying to push* PETE *away*): Get away from me! I wouldn't dance with you, if you were the last boy on earth.

PETE: Of course not! Who could dance in that silly coat? Let's take it off! (*Succeeds in getting her coat off and tosses it to* BARBIE) Here, take this moth-eaten dry goods!

KATHLEEN (*With a shriek*): I'll have you know that's my brand-new Harris tweed.

PETE: It's not worthy of you, Kate. And what's that thing on your head? (*Pulls off her scarf*) There! That's much better. Now I can see your beautiful hair. (*Dancing her around the room*) When you learn to follow, and let me do the leading, we'll be the best dancers at the hop.

KATHLEEN: I refuse to dance another step. Bob, make him let go of me.

PETE: Oh, my poor darling! You're completely out of breath. Take my advice and lose a couple of pounds before the 14th, will you?

KATHLEEN: Lose a couple of pounds! Look here, you big ape, I'll have you know I'm five pounds underweight now! (*They stop dancing.* PETE *turns off record.*)

PETE: Just goes to show you—it's all in the mind. But, do sit down, Kate. You're completely winded. Bob, how about a nice cool drink for the lady? You and Barbie tell our friends in the kitchen we're about ready for those refreshments.

KATHLEEN: Of all the unmitigated nerve!

BOB: Come along, Barbie, you heard what the man said.

BARBIE: But, Bob, he really is impossible!

BOB (*Firmly*): Come along, Barbie. (BOB *leads* BARBIE *to door left, stopping briefly in the doorway to make "OK." sign to* PETE. *They exit.*)

KATHLEEN: You come back here, Bob. You can't leave me alone with this maniac.

PETE: Maniac! That's an ugly word, Kate, but somehow it sounds beautiful when you say it—maniac—maniac—

KATHLEEN: Please, please, let me go . . . I can't take any more of this. . . .

PETE (*With warning gesture*): Sh! (*He tiptoes to exit, looks around*) It's O.K.; they're out of earshot. (*Taking a different tone as he returns to sofa and holds out his hand*) Congratulations, Kate! You're a real trouper!

KATHLEEN: Now what are you talking about?

PETE (*Again looking around*): Sh! Not so loud. I don't want them to hear us. I know I must seem crazy, Kate, and I apologize, but I just had to see if you've got what it takes.

KATHLEEN: If I've got what it takes for what? You have me going around in circles.

PETE: I had to make sure you have the fire, and by jingo, you do! You were marvellous! Absolutely marvellous! Wait till they see us do our stuff at the Valentine Dance!

KATHLEEN: How many times must I tell you, I am not going to that dance with you?

PETE: But you've got to go, Kate—that is, if you really are the actress I think you are.

KATHLEEN (*Bewildered*): Actress!

PETE: Wait till they see our performance at intermission. They wanted entertainment, and, boy, are they going to get it!

KATHLEEN: What performance? What entertainment?

PETE: You and I are going to do the fastest, funniest, zaniest version of Shakespeare these creeps have ever seen!

KATHLEEN: Shakespeare? What does Shakespeare have to do with it?

PETE: Oh, come now, Kate. Don't pretend you haven't caught on to our little act here this afternoon!

KATHLEEN: What act? What are you talking about?

PETE: *The Taming of the Shrew!* Surely you've recognized yourself as "Kate—the prettiest Kate in Christendom"!

KATHLEEN: So that's it. I'm a shrew, am I? And I suppose you think you are Petruchio come to tame me?

PETE: Come to woo you, Kate. But then, the two go together, don't they?

KATHLEEN: I've never been so insulted in all my life! Never!

PETE: But you should be flattered! Do you think I would have bothered with you for one single minute, if I hadn't seen in you all the earmarks of a fine actress?

KATHLEEN (*Flattered in spite of herself*): Do you really mean it?

PETE: Of course I do. Now listen, and listen hard. We have only a few minutes. Bob and the rest of them think this is a gag, and in a way, it is. . . .

KATHLEEN: All those things you said—about the dance . . . about me—it was all a gag?

PETE: Well, yes—and no. It's a gag that's going to backfire on our jolly little committee and give you and me the leading roles in the senior play.

KATHLEEN: The senior play! But they haven't even selected it yet.

PETE: They will after they see our *Taming of the Shrew* skit at intermission and realize what a riot Shakespeare can be.

KATHLEEN: You're too much for me, Pete. I though I was smart, but I just can't keep up with you.

PETE: It's simple as ABC. You left the Dramatic Club because you wanted to do Shakespeare, and they were all for the kid stuff. Right?

KATHLEEN: That's about it.

PETE: Well, I happen to feel the same way you do. Back home in Spring City, I played every Shakespearean lead they had, but nobody knows me here, so I don't carry any weight. Besides, that Dramatic Club is a lost cause.

KATHLEEN: For the first time, I agree with you.

PETE: But with the senior play coming up, I can call the shots.

KATHLEEN: How?

PETE: Because I happen to have a little bet on with the big wheels in the senior class.

KATHLEEN: A bet? Pete Naylor, you asked me to this dance on a bet?

PETE: On a sure bet, my bonny Kate. Figure it out for yourself. Bob is president of the senior class; Marian is chairman of the social committee; Dick and Mac are officers. Your own sister has a lot of influence. So if you go to that dance with me, and we put on our skit, we can write our own ticket.

KATHLEEN: And the ticket will be . . .

PETE: *The Taming of the Shrew!*

KATHLEEN (*Chuckling*): Pete, you're a great man.

PETE: You mean you'll go?

KATHLEEN: I wouldn't miss it.

PETE: That's my Kate! (*Pulling paperback out of his pocket*) Now how are you as a quick study?

KATHLEEN: The best.

PETE: Then look over Act IV, Scene 5. When I throw you

a line, come back at me with your own version of Kate's response. Think you can do it?

KATE: I can do it. But there's just one thing, Pete.

PETE: What?

KATE: Do you really think I am a shrew?

PETE: Don't you want to be?

KATE: Not really. I know I have a bad temper, and a quick tongue, but . . . well . . . most of it, at least lately, most of it has been a cover-up. I never realized I was in the shrew class.

PETE: In my book, Kate, you're in a class all by yourself.

KATE: Is that a gag?

PETE: It's no gag, Kate. I've had my eye on you ever since I saw you flounce out of that Dramatic Club meeting.

KATE: And you meant some of those things you said—about my eyes, and my hair—and my voice . . .

PETE: Every word. I don't need Shakespeare to tell me you're the prettiest Kate in Christendom!

KATE: I like that. It sounds almost like a valentine.

PETE: There's another line—a better one that I'm saving till I say good night after the dance. Do you know what it is?

KATE: I—I think so.

PETE: Good. Then be sure you have your answer ready. Now, we're ready for the fray! (*Calling offstage*) Hey, you, out there! Kate and I are famished.

BOB (*From offstage*): Refreshments, coming right up. (BOB *enters, followed by others. They carry in trays which they place on small tables around room.*)

MARIAN: Potato chips!

BOB: Ginger ale!

DICK: Pepsi!

MAC: Cheese!

BARBIE: Crackers!

MRS. TORRENCE: And homemade cookies. (*To* KATHLEEN) Hello, Kathleen. How pretty you look!

KATHLEEN: Thank you, Mrs. Torrence. It was so nice of you to bake all these lovely cookies.

MRS. TORRENCE: I hope you enjoy them.

KATHLEEN (*Taking one*): I adore chocolate.

PETE: Chocolate? These are coconut.

KATHLEEN: Why, Pete, they're chocolate . . . with nuts.

PETE (*Loudly*): I say they are coconut . . . with raisins!

KATHLEEN (*Smiling*): How could I be so stupid! Of course, they're coconut!

PETE: Did I say coconut? I mean chocolate. They are chocolate, aren't they, Kate?

KATHLEEN (*Shrugging her shoulders*): Chocolate or coconut, whatever you say, Pete.

MRS. TORRENCE: Are you feeling all right, Pete?

PETE: I feel fine, Mrs. Torrence, but you'll have to excuse me. Sometimes my taste buds go out on me! Just like that!

MRS. TORRENCE: Dear me! Maybe you should see a doctor.

BOB: It's nothing to worry about, Mom.

MRS. TORRENCE: If you need me, just call.

ALL (*Ad lib*): Everything's just great, fine! Thanks a lot! (*Etc.*)

MRS. TORRENCE (*As she exits*): Imagine! Confusing chocolate with coconut! I never heard of such a thing.

DICK (*To* PETE): Is everything settled?

PETE: Certainly.

BOB: That's great. Do you hear that, Barbie? We can all go in my car.

KATHLEEN: Thanks, Bob.

PETE: Sorry, Bob, Kate and I are walking.

BARBIE: Walking!

KATHLEEN: But, Pete, I'll be wearing evening slippers, with high heels.

PETE: I say we're walking.

KATHLEEN (*Smiling*): It's all right with me. We're walking.

MAC: Say, what is this?

KATHLEEN: What's what?

DICK: Who ever heard of walking to a dance?

KATHLEEN: It's up to Pete. If he wants to walk, we'll walk!

MARIAN: Well, don't ever let me hear of you getting such a crazy notion, Dick.

GLADYS: And that goes for you too, Mac.

BARBIE: Kathleen, what's come over you?

PETE: From now on, her friends call her Kate.

KATHLEEN: That's right. And that goes for you, too, Barbie. Pete prefers "Kate."

BOB: What are you, man, a hypnotist?

PETE: I don't know what you're talking about. Come along, Kate. We have to be going. (*Holds her coat*)

DICK: But what about the committee meeting?

MARIAN: We haven't even started.

MAC: I thought you were going to help us with some entertainment for intermission.

PETE: Don't worry about that. It's all taken care of.

BOB: But what is it? What are you planning?

PETE: I'll tell you about it later, when I collect that little bet I made you. Right now I want to take Kate downtown and buy her a Christmas card for Valentine's Day.

ALL (*Ad lib*): A Christmas card! Valentine's Day! (*Etc.*)

KATE: And whatever Pete selects will be the most beautiful valentine any girl ever had! (*Curtain falls*)

THE END

Production Notes

A VALENTINE FOR KATE

Characters: 4 male; 5 female.

Playing Time: 35 minutes.

Costumes: All characters wear everyday modern clothes. Barbie and Kathleen wear coats and head scarves when they first enter.

Properties: Notebook; paperback book; trays with refreshments—ginger ale, potato chips, cheese and crackers, plate of cookies, etc.

Setting: The Torrence living room. There are several comfortable chairs and small tables around the room. At right there is a large sofa with loose cushions on it. There is a record player on a table.

Lighting: No special effects.

Call Washington 1776

Characters

TED GRIFFIN
HILDA MATTHEWS
BILL RYAN
DON BROWN
KAREN SHERMAN
SUSAN BLAIR
PEGGY MILLS
MISS GARDNER, *high school history teacher*
MISS HOPE CONRAD, *member of the State Historical Society*
CLARK BURTON, *reporter*
MAYOR FRANKLIN
JUDGE EMERSON
MR. MIDDLETON, *Chief City Planner*
MISS HATTIE POWELL

TIME: *Morning, Washington's Birthday.*
SETTING: *An old carriage house, the office of "Youth on Call." The room is furnished with a desk, tables, chairs, a filing cabinet, etc. On a large table downstage right there is a collection of bric-a-brac, old books, and odds*

and ends of china and glassware. Propped against the table is a large framed painting. Above the table is a sign reading WHITE ELEPHANT SALE.

AT RISE: BILL RYAN *is looking through card index on desk, and* HILDA MATTHEWS *is writing in bookkeeping ledger at desk, while* TED GRIFFIN *sits on corner of desk and looks over* HILDA'*s shoulder as she writes. Telephone rings and* TED *picks up receiver.*

TED (*Into phone*): Good morning, Youth on Call. (*Pause*) What is the name, please? (*Making notes on a card as he continues on phone*) Montgomery. And the address? (*Pause*) 227 Oakdale Road. (*Writes*) O.K., Mrs. Montgomery, we'll have someone over there in ten minutes. (*Pause, then in a reassuring tone*) Oh, sure, sure, he'll be able to get it open. Don't worry. (*Pause*) Yes, I have it. Thanks for calling. 'Bye. (*Hangs up phone and turns to* BILL) Hey, Bill, this one's for you. Some kid on Oakdale Road has locked himself in the bathroom and turned on all the faucets. The mother is alone in the house with him and hitting the panic button. Do you think you can manage to get the bathroom door open?

BILL (*Saluting smartly*): Youth on Call at your service! No job too big—no task too small! I might have to take the door off the hinges, but I'll get Junior out.

TED: Here's the address. (*Hands him a card*) And hurry, will you, before Mrs. Montgomery has a flood.

BILL (*Putting on his jacket*): I'm on my way. (*To* HILDA) Good luck with those accounts, Hilda. (*Exits*)

HILDA: Youth on Call is really catching on. People know that WASHINGTON 1 7 7 6 is the number to dial for anything from baby sitters to zebras.

TED: Yes. Getting that phone number was the luckiest

break we've had in this whole campaign. (*Phone rings, and* TED *answers it.*) Good morning, Youth on Call, Ted Griffin speaking. (*Pause*) One moment, please, Mrs. Kane. I'll check. (*To* HILDA) Mrs. Kane needs someone to wash dishes tonight after a dinner party. Who's free on our list?

HILDA (*Consulting list*): Most of the girls signed up for today are baking cherry pies for the Washington Tea this afternoon. But I'll go to Mrs. Kane's myself, if we're caught short.

TED (*Into phone*): You can count on us, Mrs. Kane. (*Laughing*) That's one address we don't even need to write down. You're one of our best customers. (*Pause*) Thank you. It's great to know you're so interested in saving the old carriage house. (*Pause*) Yes, this is the last day all right, but we think we still have a fighting change to raise enough money to suit the Mayor. Thanks again. 'Bye. (*Hangs up*)

HILDA: Mrs. Kane is a real Youth on Call booster.

TED: If we only had more like her. Tell me, Hilda, do you really think we'll make it?

HILDA: We've got to make it, Ted. We simply can't lose this building now, after all the work we've put into raising money to save it. When I think of all the baby sitting I've done, the dishes I've washed, the errands I've run, not to mention all the back-breaking work you boys have done.

TED: I'll bet I've personally shoveled twenty-five miles of pavement and dug out fifty cars! But seriously, Hilda, where do we stand?

HILDA (*Studying the ledger*): Well, with the people we have out on jobs now, plus some donations that were promised but not collected, we still need around—let me see—a hundred and fifty or two hundred dollars.

TED: Wow! That's a lot of money to raise in one day!

HILDA: Maybe Miss Gardner can talk the Mayor into extending our drive till the end of the month.

TED: Not a chance! The City Planning Board is pushing him hard.

HILDA: It doesn't seem possible that anyone in his right mind would tear down a building with the tradition and historical importance of this carriage house just to make room for a parking lot!

TED: You just don't understand progress, Hilda. And besides, not everyone believes that history was made here. (*Phone rings.*) Youth on Call! Ted Griffin speaking. Oh, hello, Miss Gardner, what's the good word? (*Pause*) Um-m-m! So that's the pitch? Well, it's just what I expected. (*Pause*) One minute, please, I'll ask her. (*To* HILDA) Miss Gardner is bringing the Mayor and members of the Planning Board down here. She wants to know if you can round up some refreshments.

HILDA: Oh, no! Let me talk to her. (*Takes phone*) Hello, Miss Gardner? I can make some tea, and I think we have some cookies, if the boys haven't eaten them. (*Pause*) Miss Hattie Powell? I don't know. I can try to get her, but you know how she is about publicity of any sort. O.K. I'll try to reach her. Maybe Karen Sherman can talk her into coming. 'Bye. (*Hangs up phone*)

TED: This may be George Washington's Birthday on the calendar but it's D day for us.

HILDA: Will you try to get Miss Hattie Powell on the phone, Ted? Miss Gardner thinks it's important for her to be here.

TED: That will take some doing, if I know Miss Hattie. (*Picks up phone and dials*)

HILDA: Karen Sherman should be over there now. Maybe she can persuade Miss Hattie to come.

TED (*At phone*): Line's busy. (DONALD BROWN *enters*) Hiya, Don. Did you take Siegfried for a nice walk?

DON: In case you're interested, Siegfried turned out to be a Great Dane as big as a calf! He practically tore my arm off.

TED: Well, you said you'd give your right arm to save the Powell Carriage House.

DON: But Siegfried didn't know that! Anyhow, I'm not going back there again.

TED: You have to go back, even if it takes both arms. Mrs. Moberg paid us three-fifty in advance, and we need every dime.

DON: Are they foreclosing on the old homestead?

TED: We don't know for sure, but we're still about two hundred dollars short of our goal.

DON: Whew! But the day's not over till the clock on the wall strikes midnight.

HILDA: Tell that to the Mayor. He's due here any minute with his hatchet men from the Planning Board.

DON: Well, don't just stand there! Worry! We have to think of something we can do.

HILDA: There's one thing you can do, Don. Run over to Miss Hattie Powell's and help Karen talk her into coming down here.

DON: Miss Hattie! You know she never goes out if she can help it.

HILDA: But this is important, and you know how interested she is in saving what's left of this old place.

DON: Will do. (*Grabbing cookie and biting into it*) Ouch!

Don't serve these to the Mayor. He'll sue us for bridge-work! (*He exits.* TED *walks over to white elephant table, takes vase and holds it up.*)

TED: Maybe we should clear away the stuff on this white elephant table. We'll never sell any more today.

HILDA: There's no time. Oh, Ted, I'm so nervous. Miss Gardner sounded so grim on the phone—the way she does in class when everything goes wrong. (*Enter* SUSAN BLAIR *with* BILL RYAN, *each carrying a tray covered with a napkin*)

SUSAN: Look what we have!

BILL: Where do you want these pies?

TED: Pies?

SUSAN: Fresh out of the Women's Club oven. We baked them for the club luncheon. Mrs. Greer gave us some of the extras to sell here for the cause. (*Sets her tray down on table*)

BILL: I'll put them here on the white elephant table. Bet we can get a dollar apiece for them. (*As he sets down his tray, he knocks over a large framed picture propped up against the table.*) Oops! (*Grabs at picture*) I almost ruined Miss Hattie's contribution, the painting by her colonial ancestor!

HILDA (*Rescuing picture and placing it to better advantage*): Anything but that, Bill! Poor dear Miss Hattie thinks it's worth its weight in gold.

SUSAN: Wait till you hear my good news.

TED: We could stand some.

SUSAN: Miss Hope Conrad from the State Historical Society is the speaker at the Washington tea this afternoon.

HILDA: So?

SUSAN: So, when she heard how Youth on Call is working

to raise money to save this old carriage house, she wanted to see it. Peggy Mills is bringing her down.

BILL: Lots of people drop in to poke around, but they never seem to notice our baking powder can for contributions—which reminds me—Mrs. Montgomery gave me five dollars for rescuing Junior. (*Takes bill from pocket and puts it into can.*)

SUSAN: But you haven't heard the best part. It seems that the State sometimes makes contributions to funds like ours. If Miss Conrad thinks this place is of real historic interest . . .

HILDA: Wait till she sees the historic fact sheet we've prepared.

TED: And wait till she talks to Miss Hattie.

BILL: Miss Hattie never talks to strangers.

HILDA: Don't be too sure of that, Bill. We're trying to get her over here to talk to the Mayor and the City Planning Board.

TED: They're descending upon us any minute.

SUSAN: Good grief!

HILDA: Fortunately we can serve a couple of the cherry pies instead of those stale cookies. It'll be worth the investment if we can win the Planning Board over. But we've got to rush.

SUSAN: Let me help. (*Girls move two of the pies to rear table and begin to cut them up to prepare for serving.* CLARK BURTON, *a reporter, enters, carrying camera equipment and a notebook.*)

BURTON: Hello, everybody. I'm Clark Burton, reporter for the *Herald.* I understand you're having some visitors from City Hall.

TED: Welcome to the Powell Carriage House, Mr. Burton. (*Shakes hands with* BURTON) All of us here are working with Youth on Call for the Restoration Fund. I'm Ted Griffin—and this is Hilda Matthews, Susan Blair, and Bill Ryan.

BURTON: You kids are really doing a great job. Have you reached your goal?

TED: Not quite, Mr. Burton, but we're still in there pitching.

BURTON: That's the spirit. (*Looking around*) Wow! This place is really falling apart, isn't it?

SUSAN: The architects tell us the foundation is in wonderful condition for a two-hundred-year-old building.

BURTON: I understand the city fathers are giving you a rough time, especially the City Planning Board.

HILDA: But the Mayor will have to keep his word to us, if we raise enough money for the restoration.

BURTON: What got you so steamed up over this project in the first place? I thought all teen-agers were interested in was hot rods and hootenannies.

TED: I guess it was Miss Gardner, our history teacher, who first got us interested in the place, and then, most of us have known Miss Hattie Powell since we were in first grade.

SUSAN: She was always telling us stories about this old building.

BURTON: Miss Hattie! Why, I remember her from my school days. But she retired ages ago, didn't she? I never see her any more.

HILDA: She doesn't go out very much, but you may see her this afternoon. Miss Gardner wants her to talk to the Planning Board.

BURTON: She can certainly tell them all there is to tell about the Powell family in the good old days. (*Enter* PEGGY *with* MISS HOPE CONRAD.)

PEGGY (*As she walks over to table*): Do come in, Miss Conrad. You already know Susie Blair, and this is Hilda Matthews, Ted Griffin, and Bill Ryan.

MISS CONRAD: How do you do?

TED: So glad you could come, Miss Conrad. (*Indicating* BURTON) This is Mr. Burton, from the *Herald*.

BURTON: I'm happy to meet you, Miss Conrad. I'm planning to cover your lecture on our state folk artists at the Women's Club.

MISS CONRAD (*Smiling, as she walks center and shakes hands with* BURTON): I hope you give it a good review, Mr. Burton. There were some very interesting early painters in this area. (*Looking around*) What a perfectly marvelous old building! And I do believe that these are the original beams and walls. You young people certainly deserve a lot of credit for trying to preserve it.

SUSAN: We hope to make the Powell Carriage House one of the most interesting historic shrines in the East.

MISS CONRAD: I don't mean to discourage you, my dear, but it's one thing to preserve an old building, and quite another to set up an historic shrine. I'm afraid I've never heard of the Powell Carriage House in connection with any specific historical incident or person.

HILDA: Perhaps you would like to look over our historic fact sheet, Miss Conrad. I'd hate to think we've made any errors. And here's a copy for you, Mr. Burton. (*Gives each of them a typed sheet. Enter* MISS GARDNER *with* MAYOR FRANKLIN, JUDGE EMERSON, *and* MR. MIDDLETON.)

MISS GARDNER (*As she enters*): Please come in, gentlemen. I think you will find our Youth on Call staff has everything organized for you. Hello, there, Mr. Burton. Is everything set?

BURTON: I'm already taking notes, Miss Gardner.

PEGGY: Miss Gardner, I'm sure you will want to introduce Miss Hope Conrad to your guests.

MISS GARDNER: Miss Conrad! This *is* a surprise! I am hoping to go to your lecture this afternoon. (*Indicating three men*) May I present Mayor Franklin, Judge Emerson, and Mr. Middleton, our Chief City Planner.

MISS CONRAD: How do you do. (*Pointedly*) I certainly want to congratulate you, Mr. Mayor, on *your* efforts to preserve this fine old building.

MAYOR: Thank you, Miss Conrad, but I'm afraid your congratulations are a bit premature.

JUDGE: The matter has not yet been entirely settled.

MR. MIDDLETON (*Pompously*): As a matter of fact, the Planning Board is not at all in favor of this project. As is the case in most towns, we need this downtown space most desperately for a parking lot.

MISS CONRAD (*Appalled*): A parking lot!

MR. MIDDLETON (*Smiling*): I'm afraid the Powell Carriage House has not accommodated any vehicles of any kind for many a long year.

JUDGE: But we've gone along with these young folks in their worthy ambition to preserve the building—if they can offer us a practical solution.

MAYOR (*To* JUDGE *and* MR. MIDDLETON): Miss Gardner has promised us a financial statement this afternoon. (*Turning to* MISS GARDNER *and young people*) But I might as well tell you that unless we can be assured of adequate funds for restoration, the Planning Board has decided that the carriage house will have to go!

BURTON: May I quote you on that, Mr. Mayor?

MAYOR: You may.

MR. MIDDLETON: Now how about that financial statement, Miss Gardner?

MISS GARDNER: Ted, will you please give the report?

TED: But, Miss Gardner, we still have until midnight.

MR. MIDDLETON: Now look here, young man. We've dilly-dallied around with you young people long enough. A few hours won't make that much difference.

HILDA: Come on, girls, I think we'd better serve the refreshments. (*During this scene girls serve and pass tea and plates with pieces of pie.* BURTON *sits at desk busily taking notes.* MISS CONRAD *examines items on the white elephant table.*)

TED: But there are still a lot of our people out on jobs for Youth on Call.

BILL: And there's a lot of stuff on that white elephant table we are still hoping to sell.

MR. MIDDLETON (*Examining report*): Mm-m-m! Just as I expected . . . two or three hundred dollars short.

MISS GARDNER: Surely, you wouldn't refuse to save the building for such a paltry amount.

JUDGE: It may seem harsh and arbitrary to you, Miss Gardner, but a bargain's a bargain.

SUSAN: The Women's Club has promised us at least twenty-five dollars for the cherry pies we baked for them.

JUDGE: You mean to say you baked these pies, young lady?

PEGGY: We had a pie-baking committee, Judge Emerson. These are some of the extras we brought back to serve and sell.

JUDGE: I must say they are delicious.

MAYOR: I didn't know your Youth on Call jobs included pie baking.

BILL: We've done almost everything, sir, from taking care

of children and pets to moving furniture and washing cars.

MAYOR: I see by your report you cleared thirty-nine dollars on what you call white elephants.

BILL: And I'll bet we could take in another ten or fifteen on what's left.

MISS CONRAD (*Holding framed picture which she has been examining*): Excuse me. I don't wish to interrupt, but may I ask where this particular white elephant came from?

HILDA: That came from Miss Hattie Powell. One of her ancestors painted it.

MR. MIDDLETON (*Inspecting it closely*): Indeed! I must say it's very crude. . . . Whoever painted it certainly wasn't much of an artist.

MISS CONRAD: On the contrary, Mr. Middleton, if I'm right in my supposition, this painting was done by one of the foremost folk artists in this area, Henry Fletcher.

MISS GARDNER: Are you really serious, Miss Conrad?

MISS CONRAD: The State Museum has just one painting by Henry Fletcher. The curator would pay a handsome price to get another.

MR. MIDDLETON: You mean this . . . this daub is actually worth something?

MISS CONRAD: I'm not sure. I would have to have it examined or obtain documentary proof of its origin, but if it's a Henry Fletcher, this one white elephant would more than make up the shortage for restoring this carriage house.

ALL (*Ad lib surprise and excitement.*): Oh, really? What luck! Who can tell us if it's genuine? (*Etc.*)

BURTON: Will you let me have that name again, please, Miss Conrad?

MISS CONRAD: Fletcher, Henry W. Fletcher. He was an itinerant portrait painter of colonial times. We don't know too much about him, but we do know that he worked for a time in this area.

BURTON: Say, this will really be a scoop for the *Herald.*

MAYOR: Now hold your horses, Clark Burton. After all, the lady says we need proof.

HILDA: But Miss Hattie will know. Miss Hattie knows just about everything and everybody in this town.

JUDGE: You're speaking of Miss Hattie Powell, I presume?

HILDA: Of course.

JUDGE: But poor Miss Hattie doesn't have much of a memory these days. After all, she's way along in years and getting more eccentric by the minute.

MAYOR: Hardly goes out at all any more—refuses to see people.

MISS GARDNER: She never refuses to see our Youth on Call workers.

PEGGY: Last week when I dropped by to do her shopping, I could hardly get away. She had one story to tell after the other. I thought her mind was clear as a bell.

SUSAN: And as for her memory, my goodness! She can remember everything she ever heard or read about the early history of this town—especially about this building.

MAYOR: Well, Miss Hattie has always been very proud and very sentimental about this old place. After all, it was part of the original Powell estate.

BURTON: Yes, I see by this fact sheet the young lady gave me that the Powell Plantation House was taken over by the city immediately after the Civil War and was used for municipal offices until it was destroyed by fire in 1900.

HILDA: That's one reason Miss Hattie's so keen on saving this carriage house. It's all that remains of the Powell estate.

MR. MIDDLETON: Surely you can't expect us to keep a ramshackle old place like this in the center of the city just to satisfy the whim of an old lady.

MISS GARDNER: But if Miss Conrad is right about the painting, Mr. Middleton, we'll have enough to start a restoration project. Think what it would mean to the Tourist Bureau to have a spot of historic interest right in the center of town.

MR. MIDDLETON: Mayor Franklin, I believe you have something to say on this matter of historic interest.

MAYOR: Well—er—this is a bit awkward, Miss Gardner, but the fact is, even though you may be able to give us the financial support you promised, the City Council still has some grave reservations about your—er—proposed restoration.

MISS GARDNER: For mercy's sake—why?

MAYOR: Well—er—just what is it that you would restore? A two-hundred-year-old carriage house—restored or not restored—is still only a two-hundred-year-old carriage house. The City Council feels, after talking with Mr. Middleton and the Planning Board, that we would still have—I hesitate to use this expression—but we would still have a white elephant on our hands. Just what would the city do with a two-hundred-year-old carriage house?

MISS GARDNER: What do you *do* with any historic shrine?

MAYOR: But that's just the point, Miss Gardner. We know the building is old, but we don't know that it is actually historic.

HILDA: But Miss Hattie says that George Washington often stopped here.

MR. MIDDLETON: And I suppose he slept here too, curled up somewhere nice and cozy on a bed of hay.

MAYOR: We have never found any sort of records connecting George Washington or any other great figure with this building.

TED: But Miss Hattie says. . . .

MAYOR (*Interrupting, impatiently*): I don't care what Miss Hattie says! She was a fine teacher in her day and quite an authority on local history, but let's face it, Miss Hattie is in her dotage. (*Enter* DON, KAREN, *and* MISS HATTIE, *who is carrying an umbrella and a package wrapped in newspaper.*)

MISS HATTIE (*Brandishing her umbrella at* MAYOR): Is that so, Charles Franklin? Is that so?

ALL: Miss Hattie!!

MAYOR: Now, now, Miss Hattie. I didn't mean to offend you.

MISS HATTIE: Then watch your language and mind your manners. I recall the time you would have stood in the corner with your face to the wall for talking about your elders like that. (*Turning and pointing to others with her umbrella*) Karen, who are all these people?

KAREN: Do sit down, Miss Hattie, and I'll introduce them. (MISS GARDNER *and* DON *place a chair for* MISS HATTIE *center stage, and she sits down.*) This is Miss Gardner, our wonderful history teacher I've told you so much about.

MISS HATTIE (*Pointing umbrella at* MISS GARDNER): Did I have you in the first grade, young woman?

MISS GARDNER: I'm afraid not, Miss Powell. I'm not originally from Washington Borough. Do let me have your umbrella.

MISS HATTIE: No, thank you. I'll keep it right here beside me. (*Puts it on the floor at her feet*) Well, I must say, Miss Gardner, for an outsider you're really quite a local history scholar. This town will be forever indebted to you if you save this historic building from these City Hall vultures, (*Turns toward* MAYOR) and that includes you, Charles Franklin. As Mayor of the city, you are the worst of the lot.

MAYOR (*Placatingly*): Now, Miss Hattie. You mustn't be too hard on your old pupil. You remember Judge Emerson, don't you?

MISS HATTIE (*Looking at* JUDGE *with contempt*): Of course. He sat in the third seat in the row next to the windows and never once finished his number work on time.

JUDGE: I'm afraid I'm still not very good at figures, Miss Hattie. But here's a gentleman I want you to meet who seems to have been born with the multiplication tables on the tip of his tongue. Harvey Middleton, our Chief City Planner.

MR. MIDDLETON (*Bowing*): This is indeed a pleasure, Miss Powell.

MISS HATTIE: Humph! We'll see how much of a pleasure it is after I find out what you intend to do with this carriage house. (*Looking around room*) Karen, who is that pretty young woman holding Cousin Henry's painting? Is she going to buy it?

MISS GARDNER (*Indicating* MISS CONRAD): This is Miss Hope Conrad from the State Historical Society, Miss Hattie. (*Turns to* KAREN) And I don't believe you've met Miss Conrad either, Karen. Miss Conrad, Karen Sherman.

MISS CONRAD: I'm delighted to meet both of you. (*Walks over to* MISS HATTIE) To answer your question, Miss Powell—yes, I'm thinking seriously of purchasing this lovely old painting if it is an authentic Henry Fletcher. You say the artist was your cousin?

MISS HATTIE: Well, of course, Henry's my cousin, even though we were separated by several generations. The Fletchers and the Powells were related on the distaff side of our family.

MAYOR: Distaff side? That means female side, doesn't it?

MISS HATTIE: No need to show off your learning, Charles Franklin.

MISS CONRAD: Then this really is an original painting by Henry Fletcher?

MISS HATTIE: Of course. Luckily it was saved in the great fire that destroyed the plantation house at the beginning of this century. It's never been out of our family.

TED *and* BILL: Oh boy, oh boy.

HILDA *and* KITTY (*Hugging each other*): Isn't it wonderful!

PEGGY (*Passing tray with refreshments*): Won't you have a cup of tea, Miss Hattie, and some of the cherry pie we baked for the Women's Club?

MISS HATTIE: No, thank you, child. I've always made it a rule never to eat between meals. But I must say that pie looks good. If you'll just wrap a piece up in a napkin, I'll eat it with my supper.

PEGGY: Certainly, Miss Hattie.

MISS HATTIE: Well, now that this young man (*Pointing to* DON) and Karen have dragged me down here, what do you want with me?

BURTON: I'm very much interested in your stories about this old building, Miss Powell.

MISS HATTIE: Are you a reporter, young man?

BURTON: Yes, ma'am. I'm from the *Herald.*

MISS HATTIE: I've always made it a rule never to talk to reporters. No good ever comes of it. They always twist what you say one way or another.

MISS CONRAD: But you have a very rare painting here, Miss Powell. If the Historical Society buys it for the state museum, I'm sure the public would be interested in its history.

MISS HATTIE: History! Who cares about history any more except a few old ladies like me and maybe a handful of young ones such as you and Miss Gardner here.

MAYOR: But history is very important to us at the moment, Miss Hattie, if we are to preserve this building for future generations.

JUDGE: The fact is, Miss Hattie, that we're a bit doubtful about the historic associations of this carriage house.

MR. MIDDLETON: An *old* house is one thing; but a landmark of history—that's something else again.

MISS HATTIE: Indeed? Well, how much history do you want? Isn't it enough for you that George Washington stopped here at least a half dozen times on his trips to and from Mount Vernon?

MISS CONRAD: But there are no records of any such visits, Miss Powell, not even in our state archives.

MISS HATTIE: Archives, poppycock! (*Indicating package*) I have the whole story right here in my book.

MR. MIDDLETON: Book? What book?

DON: Miss Hattie is writing the history of our town, sir.

MISS HATTIE: I decided it was high time that Washington Borough should take its proper place in the history of our state and nation. (*Opening package*) So I've written it all down.

MISS CONRAD: I'm sure the Historical Society will be very much interested in your manuscript, Miss Powell, although I'm afraid Washington Corners is much better known in colonial history.

MISS HATTIE: Washington Corners, indeed! Can't hold a candle to Washington Borough. The Powell Tavern put Washington Borough on the map.

MAYOR: But I've never heard of a Powell Tavern here—only the Powell Plantation.

MISS HATTIE: Since when do you know so much about history, Charles Franklin? Here, William. (*Handing manuscript to* JUDGE, *but keeping the package on her lap.*) I forgot to bring my magnifying glass, and you were always a pretty fair reader. You read what it says right there in the foreword.

JUDGE (*Reading*): "Although the village now known as Washington Corners takes credit for Washington's many visits, the fact is that the General's favorite stopping place was the crossroads now known as Washington Borough."

MR. MIDDLETON: If this were true, surely the Historical Society would have the records.

MISS HATTIE: Please be quiet, young man! Everything or just about everything in the Powell Plantation House was destroyed by fire. (*Pausing, expectantly*) Well, what are you waiting for, Harvey? Continue, please.

JUDGE (*Reading*): "The facts have been sadly obscured by my ancestors' misguided ambition to preserve the myth that the Powell Plantation House had always been a private dwelling, the American prototype of an English country house. The truth is, however, that for the first thirty years of its existence, it served as a Publick House of which the Powells were the innkeepers. Because of the disastrous fire of 1900, the old carriage house is now the sole reminder of Washington's visits here."

MR. MIDDLETON: You still persist in this Washington legend!

MISS HATTIE: It is *not* a legend, young man. It is an historical fact. (*To* JUDGE) Please go on, William.

JUDGE: "It was in this carriage house, located at the rear of the present City Hall, that Washington's horses were stabled and groomed. It was here that his coach was twice repaired, and tradition has it that Washington once quartered some of his troops in this historic building."

MISS HATTIE: Well, are you satisfied?

MR. MIDDLETON: Who is to say that this whole story is not a sentimental fabrication?

MISS HATTIE (*Brandishing umbrella*): Young man, if I hear another word out of you! (*Rising*) Karen, Donald, please take me home. I did not come here to be insulted by an ignoramus!

MISS GARDNER: Please, please, Miss Hattie, do sit down. I'm sure Mr. Middleton will apologize. (*Gets her seated*)

MISS CONRAD (*Taking manuscript from* JUDGE): Miss Powell, I will consider it an honor if you will permit me to present your findings to the Historical Society. This manuscript should shed new light on historic events in this area. But, you must understand, we will need documentary proof.

MISS HATTIE: What kind of historian do you think I am, Miss? Naturally I have proof of my statements.

MISS CONRAD: May I come to see you sometime next week when you can show it to me?

MISS HATTIE: I've always made it a rule never to put off until next week what can be done at the moment. I have it with me . . . right here in my lap. (*Handing her a sketchbook*) Here, see for yourself. Somebody managed to save Henry Fletcher's sketchbook when the house burned.

MISS CONRAD (*Excitedly, as she turns pages of sketchbook*): I can't believe my eyes—a whole sketchbook of Henry Fletcher's drawings.

MISS HATTIE: And all drawn from life. Cousin Henry Fletcher worked here as a stableboy before he became a painter. You'll find any number of sketches of George Washington mounting and dismounting in the stable yard.

MISS CONRAD (*As others gather round*): And here's a sketch of the interior. It's still recognizable.

TED: Look there! A blacksmith shoeing a horse. I'll bet it was Washington's horse.

JUDGE: And a wheelwright mending Washington's coach.

MAYOR: Well, Middleton, are you convinced?

MR. MIDDLETON: Convinced? I'm overwhelmed. Miss Powell, I beg your pardon a hundred times. Nobody can deny the eye-witness sketches of a contemporary artist. They are the equivalent of photographs.

HILDA: Does that mean you agree not to tear down the building?

MR. MIDDLETON: Tear it down? We'll restore it according to these sketches—complete in every detail. Tourists will come from miles around to see this.

MISS CONRAD: And I am pretty sure you can count on some financial backing from the Museum.

TED: Don't forget to call WASHINGTON—1 7 7 6 for odd jobs.

HILDA: And guide service!

JUDGE: We'll launch our publicity at once.

BURTON: It's already launched, Your Honor. Wow! What a story! Mayor Franklin, do you plan now to make the official announcement this evening at the annual Washington dinner?

MAYOR: That is my idea, and you can also put down in that notebook that our guest of honor will be Miss Hattie Powell. How about that, Miss Hattie? Will you sit beside your former pupil?

MISS HATTIE: I always make it a rule never to eat a heavy meal in the evening. Bad for my digestion. But if these boys and girls from Youth on Call are going to be present, I'll make an exception—just this once.

MAYOR: Of course, they'll be there! And at the head table, too.

MISS GARDNER: As a matter of fact, they're part of the entertainment. We were so sure of meeting our goal that we've been practicing for weeks. Ted, will you line up your troops? (*Members of Youth on Call group themselves around* MISS HATTIE. BURTON *moves to one side to take a photograph.*)

TED: Ladies and gentlemen, in honor of this great occasion, I propose a toast—a tribute to George Washington, whose birthday we are celebrating here tonight. As you hear the words from an inscription at Mount Vernon, please remember that the young people of this community are dedicated to preserving the ideals and principles as well as the historic landmarks of the Father of our Country.

DON: Washington . . . the brave, the wise, the good . . .

PEGGY: Supreme in war, in council, and in peace . . .

TED: Valiant without ambition . . .

HILDA: Discreet without fear . . .

BILL: Confident without presumption . . .

SUSAN: In disaster calm, in success moderate, in all—himself.

TED: The hero . . .

HILDA: The patriot . . .

DON: The father of the nation . . .

KAREN: The friend of all mankind . . .

BILL: Who, when he had won all . . .

SUSAN: Renounced all . . .

TED: And sought in the bosom of his family and of nature, retirement . . .

DON: And in religion, the hope of immortality. (*Curtain falls*)

THE END

Production Notes

CALL WASHINGTON 1776

Characters: 7 male; 7 female.

Playing Time: 30 minutes.

Costumes: Modern everyday dress. Miss Hattie wears old-fashioned clothes.

Properties: Cards, pencils, papers, cookies, two trays of pies (covered with napkins), painting, money for Bill, camera equipment and notebook for Burton, fact sheets, tea cups and saucers, plates, umbrella and package wrapped in newspaper for Miss Hattie (the package should contain a manuscript and a sketchbook).

Setting: An old carriage house, office of "Youth on Call." There are a few tables and chairs, left and right, and downstage center there is a desk with a telephone and pencils and papers on it. Next to the desk stand a filing cabinet and a bench. On a large table downstage right there is a collection of bric-a-brac, old books and odds and ends of china and glassware. Propped against the table is a large framed painting. Above the table is a sign reading WHITE ELEPHANT SALE.

Lighting: No special effects.

The General Returns

Characters

MISS KELLY, *the General's secretary*
RED, *the General's office boy*
MR. SHARP, *a publicity man*
MRS. EDWARDS, *a business woman*
MISS PERRY, *a reporter*
MR. CRANE, *a real estate agent*
MR. BUSH, *a salesman*
BILLY, RUTH } *teen-agers*
THE GENERAL

SETTING: *The General's outer office.*

AT RISE: MRS. EDWARDS, MISS PERRY, MR. CRANE, MR. BUSH, BILLY *and* RUTH *are seated, waiting to see the* GENERAL. MR. BUSH *holds a bag of golf clubs.* MISS KELLY *is talking on the phone, ignoring* MR. SHARP, *an angry and persistent young man who is standing before her desk.*

MISS KELLY (*Speaking in a businesslike manner*): I'm sorry! The General cannot be disturbed. (*Pause*) Yes, sir, I'll tell him. I can't promise that he will call you, but I'll deliver the message. (*Pause*) Yes, sir. I know that it's very important. I'll tell him. (*Pause*) Thank you. Goodbye. (*Hangs up and turns to* MR. SHARP) Now, sir, what can I do for you, in addition to telling you, for the forty-ninth time, that the General is too busy to see you.

MR. SHARP: But I *must* see him. It's important. Our state is dedicating the longest bridge in the country next Tuesday, and I must have some assurance from the General that he will be at the ceremony.

MISS KELLY: I've told you he is too busy.

MR. SHARP: But the bridge is being named for him.

MISS KELLY: He's had bridges named for him before this —bridges, mountains, rivers, babies, schools, universities, stadiums, hospitals, towns. You can't expect him to attend all of those christenings, can you?

MR. SHARP: That's no concern of mine, young woman. My business is to have the General at that dedication next Tuesday. I tell you I must see him.

MISS KELLY: Then you'll have to wait, along with all those other people. (*Points to people in office*)

MR. SHARP: This is ridiculous. My time is valuable.

MISS KELLY: I'm sorry, Mr. Sharp. But that's the best I can do for you. (RED *enters from center door marked* "PRIVATE," *carrying several letters. All look up expectantly, but seeing him alone, resume former expressions.*)

RED (*Putting letters on* MISS KELLY'*s desk*): Here are the letters, Miss Kelly.

MISS KELLY: Did he sign them?

RED: Not a one. I don't know what's wrong with the old man today.

MISS KELLY (*With a warning look at the waiting public*): Sh! Oh, dear, these people will be so disappointed.

MR. SHARP (*Taking money from pocket*): See here, Bud, here's a fiver for you if you'll tell the General that I want to see him, and give him my card. (*Starts to reach for card*)

RED: It's no use, mister. The General just isn't at home to anybody today. Even for a fiver, I couldn't go in there again.

MR. SHARP: What kind of man is this General anyhow? Who does he think he is?

RED: I wouldn't talk like that, mister. The General is a great believer in courtesy. He wouldn't like it.

MISS KELLY: Please sit down, Mr. Sharp, or better yet, come back tomorrow. I promise you I'll give the General your message and call you the minute I get his answer.

MR. SHARP (*Angry but defeated*): Very well. And there'll be a handsome tip for both of you, if the answer is yes.

MISS KELLY: Tips don't matter when you're working for the General, Mr. Sharp. But thank you very much. Good day. (MR. SHARP *exits.*)

RED: He wouldn't take no for an answer, would he? What did he want?

MISS KELLY: Oh, another bridge dedication. Let me see . . . that must be the seventy-fifth we've had this week. And the General has refused them all.

RED: They'll just have to think up some new names for bridges, that's all. (*Looks through card file on* MISS KELLY'*s desk*)

MISS KELLY: Well, now for this crop of letters. (*Rising*) Mrs. Edwards, please. (MRS. EDWARDS *rises and comes to the desk.*) Mrs. Edwards, I'm awfully sorry, but the General has refused to honor your request for his wife's cookie recipe. He thanks you for your interest and your beautiful compliments on his wife's cooking, but says it is quite impossible to locate the recipe.

MRS. EDWARDS: Oh, dear, I'm so disappointed. I had planned to open a chain of shops all over the country, and we were also going to pack the dry ingredients in package form and market it in all the better grocery stores.

MISS KELLY: I'm sure it was a wonderful idea, Mrs. Edwards, but when the General says No, there's nothing more we can do.

MRS. EDWARDS: Oh, dear. I wish he had signed his name somewhere. At least that would have given me his autograph.

MISS KELLY: I'm afraid the General isn't very autograph-conscious. He doesn't seem to realize how much people appreciate his signature, even on letters of refusal.

MRS. EDWARDS: Well, young lady, I certainly appreciate your kindness to me. I know it wasn't your fault that he refused.

MISS KELLY: Thank you. I wish there were more people like you. And you mustn't think ill of the General, either. You have no idea how many requests he receives in a day.

MRS. EDWARDS: Yes, I can imagine. Well, good day to you.

MISS KELLY: Good day, Mrs. Edwards, and good luck to you in your cookie business. (MRS. EDWARDS *turns and smiles at* MISS KELLY, *then exits.*)

RED: Now there's a nice woman. Too bad the General wouldn't help her out. (*In a whisper*) Say, that girl reporter with the briefcase is beginning to look pretty impatient. You'd better take her next.

MISS KELLY: O.K., I will. (*Calling*) Oh, Miss Perry. (MISS PERRY *rises and hurries to the desk.*)

MISS PERRY: Did he answer my questions? Did he agree to the interview? When can I see him?

RED: Not so fast. One thing at a time.

MISS KELLY: I'm sorry, Miss Perry, but the General gives no interviews to the press. As to your questions, here they are . . . unanswered. (*Hands her paper*)

MISS PERRY: But, but . . . didn't he say anything at all? Surely he must have said something.

RED: Well, as a matter of fact, er . . . he did . . . but . . . er . . . it wasn't very complimentary.

MISS PERRY: Surely my questions were in good taste. They were approved by my editor and represent information that every American woman is interested in. Please tell me exactly what he said.

RED: Well. . . er . . . he said . . . you'll have to pardon me, Miss Perry; remember, I'm only quoting. But he said that it wasn't any woman's business what he ate for breakfast, and as for the new hem lines, he threw back his head and laughed and said, as a military expert, he would not dare to venture an opinion. Oh, the General has a sense of humor, but today he's not like himself.

MISS PERRY: I should hope not! The very idea! Didn't he answer a single one of my questions?

RED: Nope, not one. I don't think he likes reporters, especially lady reporters. I heard him call one a "Meddlesome Mattie" one time.

MISS PERRY: Well, in that case, I might just as well leave, and you can be sure that neither I nor the *Woman's Times* will ever trouble your precious General again.

MISS KELLY: Oh, please don't be offended, Miss Perry,

it's just that the General has so much on his mind that these other things seem trivial to him.

MISS PERRY: Humph! Trivial indeed. Since when is the opinion of one hundred thousand women a trivial matter? (MISS PERRY *exits.*)

MISS KELLY: Oh, dear! What a day! What a day! Here it is, almost closing time and look at all these people still waiting.

RED: Well, let's up and at it. Between us, we can make short work of them. Here's the next refusal . . . a request from the American Real Estate Company.

MR. CRANE (*Rising from chair*): Did I hear someone mention the American Real Estate Company?

MISS KELLY: Yes, you did, Mr. Crane, but I am afraid we have some bad news for you. The General will not consent to having his house photographed for your new real estate folders. He says he loves his home too much to have it used for advertising purposes.

MR. CRANE (*Indignantly*): Well! Really! I assure you that the American Real Estate Company is a reputable concern. The reputation of the General's house would come to no harm through us.

MISS KELLY: Oh, I am sure of that, Mr. Crane, but I guess the General is overly sentimental about his home. He loves to spend all his spare time there, but poor man, he hardly knows what spare time is.

MR. CRANE: Perhaps if our president, Mr. Williams, came to see him . . .

MISS KELLY: I am afraid it would not do any good, Mr. Crane. The General seldom changes his mind once a decision is made. I am sorry to disappoint you.

MR. CRANE: Well, I guess it can't be helped. Thank you

very much, and in the meantime if you are ever thinking of buying a house, just look me up. Here's my card. (*Hands card to* MISS KELLY)

MISS KELLY: Thank you, Mr. Crane. I'll remember you. Goodbye. (MR. CRANE *exits.* MR. BUSH *rises and approaches desk. He carries a bag of golf clubs.*)

MR. BUSH: Excuse me, miss, but I have been waiting for more than an hour.

MISS KELLY: I'm sorry, sir. This is a very busy time for us.

MR. BUSH: I'm Harry Bush, salesman for the Scotch Golf Club Company. I have here a complete set of golf clubs. Our company wishes to present them to the General with our compliments.

MISS KELLY: Oh, thank you, Mr. Bush . . . but . . .

MR. BUSH: Oh, it's nothing, nothing at all. It is an honor to have such a distinguished man use our product. Please let him understand that he is under no obligation, but if he should happen to find that his game improves while using our clubs, we would greatly appreciate a signed statement from him to that effect.

MISS KELLY: Oh, dear, I'm sorry, Mr. Bush, but the General does not accept presents of this sort. He has refused carloads of cereals and cigarettes and other merchandise that various firms have wanted him to endorse.

MR. BUSH: Please, young lady, do not be so commercial. We ask the General to endorse nothing. We just want to give him a present, that's all. Of course, if he cares to write us a note, that would be . . .

RED: Oh, sure . . . sure . . . that would just be pure advertising glory, wouldn't it? Well, it just so happens, Mr. Bush, that this particular General doesn't play golf.

MR. BUSH: Doesn't play golf? A man in his position?

MISS KELLY: No, sir. He has never had a club in his hand,

and I am sure he doesn't know the first thing about the game. So, really, I think you would be just as well off without his endorsement.

MR. BUSH: Very well. If that is the case, I suppose you are right. But I am sorry I have wasted so much of my valuable time.

MISS KELLY: Yes, it's too bad, Mr. Bush. (*As he starts to go*) Here, you're forgetting your clubs, sir. (MR. BUSH *snatches up clubs and exits.*)

RED: Gee whiz! I wish people would give me some of these products for a free trial. I'd be glad to endorse an automobile or a radio-phonograph or a custom-built speedboat or something. How about it, Miss Kelly?

MISS KELLY: You and me, both. I'd be willing to try out some new evening dresses and fur coats and diamond bracelets and things like that. But not the General. No, sir. He won't even let his picture be used on a box of peanut crunch.

RED: I don't blame him, though. It must be sort of sickening to have all these people hounding you day after day. (*Sifting through papers on desk*) Well, Miss Kelly, we're weeding them out. Here's the radio contract . . . still unsigned.

MISS KELLY: Oh, yes. I'll mail that back to the Coastline Network. What about the movie contracts?

RED: I have them here, too . . . all without the necessary John Hancock on the dotted line.

MISS KELLY: I was expecting that, so I have the envelopes all ready for mailing. (*Handing envelopes to* RED) Just stick them in, will you, while I get rid of the rest of these people. (RED *folds letters and puts them in envelopes.* MISS KELLY *surveys office.*) Well, only two left! This should be easy. (*To* BILLY *and* RUTH) I'm sorry, children, but I'm afraid it's too late for the General to see you this evening. Perhaps if you stated your business I could advise you when to return.

BILLY (*To* RUTH): What did I tell you? She's giving us the brush-off.

MISS KELLY (*Laughing*): Oh, no, not quite that bad, but the General has had a long day, and it's too late for any more appointments. What can I do for you?

BILLY: Nothing, unless you let us see the General.

RED: The lady just told you that's out.

BILLY: I know. I heard her.

RED: What are you two selling, anyhow?

RUTH: We're not selling anything.

BILLY: We're working on a history project.

RED (*Laughing*): Say, that's a new one, Miss Kelly. Now I've heard everything. A history project! What next?

RUTH: It's no laughing matter. If you knew our history teacher, you wouldn't even crack a smile. Please, can't you let us in to see him? It's practically a matter of life and death.

MISS KELLY: Sorry. It's closing time, and besides, the General is in no humor to see any more people today.

BILLY: But, history is his business. It's his patriotic duty to see us.

RED: Of all the nerve! Small fry like you trying to tell the General what to do.

BILLY: I know he'd see us, if you'd just ask him.

RED: Well, we're not asking him, not tonight. Go on, Miss Kelly, go get your coat and hat. I'll take care of these two.

MISS KELLY: Thanks, Red. I am in a hurry and this has been an awful day. (MISS KELLY *exits.*)

RED: Now, go on, you two. Beat it! The General is a busy man. He can't be bothered with kids your size.

RUTH: Size has nothing to do with it. It's being a citizen that counts.

RED: Not with me! It's quitting time that counts, and my watch says three minutes after five. (*Sound of buzzer is heard.*) There goes the buzzer. That's for me. And if you kids know what's good for you, you'll be out of here by the time I get back. Go on, now, peddle your papers. (*Buzzer sounds again.*) Go on, I can't keep the big boss waiting.

BILLY: O.K. We'll go, don't worry. But I still have a notion to report you to the General for being impolite to visitors. (RED *exits center.*)

RUTH: Oh, Billy, I'm so disappointed. We might have prevailed on the secretary to let us in, but that fresh office boy was the last straw.

BILLY: Don't worry, Ruth. I know how to fix that office boy.

RUTH: How?

BILLY: All he thinks about is quitting time, isn't it? Well, then, that means he won't be very alert for anything else. He'll be so set on leaving that maybe he won't notice if these filing cabinets aren't pushed so close against the wall. (*Pushes filing cabinet to one side leaving enough room for* RUTH *to get behind it*) Do you think you can squeeze in there?

RUTH: Gee, Billy, you're smart. If we hide there, we can catch the General when he comes out.

BILLY: Right. Go on, hurry. I'll get behind the other one. (RUTH *and* BILLY *hide.* MISS KELLY *re-enters, wearing hat and coat and carrying handbag. She goes to desk and straightens it up.*)

MISS KELLY: Well, I see Red was as good as his word. He got rid of the children. Poor kids! They waited so long to see the General. I feel sorry for them. (RED *enters from center.*)

RED: Very well, sir. Yes, sir. We're leaving right away, sir. Miss Kelly has taken care of all the outgoing mail. Yes, sir. Thank you, sir. (*Closes door*) Come on, Miss Kelly. The boss says he won't need us any more this evening.

MISS KELLY: I wonder how long he'll be working in there! Poor man, he must be awfully tired.

RED: Well, if he's tired, it isn't from seeing people. He's refused to see everybody who called this afternoon. Well, good night, Miss Kelly. See you tomorrow. (*He exits.*)

MISS KELLY: Good night, Red. I'll turn off the lights and lock the door. (*She turns off lights and exits. There is a glow of light from behind center door.*)

BILLY (*From behind filing cabinet; in stage whisper*): Pst! They've gone!

RUTH: Is the coast clear?

BILLY: Yes!

RUTH: I can't get out till you move this cabinet. I'm afraid I'll upset it.

BILLY: Take it easy. (*Footsteps from behind center door are heard.*) Sh! Hold everything. The General's coming out. (*The center door opens, and* GENERAL WASHINGTON *appears in the doorway. He wears a long military cloak over his uniform. He pauses, looking around the office in a tired and discouraged manner.*)

GENERAL: So this is what I mean to America! This is the way they remember the father of their country. (*Moves to desk and picks up letters*) Requests for radio appearances! Will I be on a quiz program? An offer of five thousand dollars to use my picture on a package of graham crackers! A park and swimming pool are to bear my name. (*Sinks down in desk chair*) Is it by things like these that the name of Washington is remembered in this noble country? (*The filing cabinet is suddenly pushed forward, and* BILLY *steps out. The* GENERAL *springs to his feet.*) Who's there?

BILLY: Only me, sir. Just a minute, I'll turn on the lights. (*Turns on lights*)

GENERAL: What are you doing here, lad? Explain your presence in my office and then leave immediately, please.

BILLY: I can explain everything, sir, but first, I must get my friend out from behind this other filing cabinet. (*Tugs at cabinet*) Come on out, Ruth.

RUTH (*Scrambling out of hiding place*): Oh, dear! I was scared to death that cabinet would topple over on me! (*Seeing the* GENERAL) Oh! For heaven's sake! Billy, look! He's wearing a George Washington costume!

GENERAL: And what did you expect I'd be wearing, young lady?

RUTH: But aren't you the General?

GENERAL: Of course. General Washington, at your service. (*Bows*)

BILLY: Jeepers! This is more than we bargained for. Come on, Ruth, let's get out of here.

GENERAL: Not so fast, young man. Not before you have made some explanations.

RUTH: But you *can't* be General Washington.

GENERAL: And why not?

RUTH (*Swallowing hard*): Because General Washington is dead. He died in . . . oh, dear . . . let me see . . . he died in . . . when was it, Billy? I never was any good at dates.

BILLY: Me neither . . . but it was a long, long time ago.

GENERAL: It was 1799, if the exact date is important to you.

RUTH: Then you're a ghost!

GENERAL: Call me that if you like. A ghost is a spirit . . . a spirit is a ghost . . . so why argue about what to call me?

BILLY: The spirit of Washington . . . remember, Ruth . . . the song we sing in school? "His spirit is here . . . His spirit is here . . ."

RUTH: Oh . . . now I understand . . . at least I think I do.

GENERAL: Sometimes I don't understand it myself. But when you have served your country as long as I have, you become a part of it. You just don't vanish forever because you happen to die. As for me . . . I've always wanted to return and see for myself how Americans use the freedom we won for them in 1776 . . . Now I know.

BILLY: And you're disappointed?

GENERAL: Yes . . . I am. I fancied that my name would always mean something to Americans. I thought they would remember the things I did, the ideals I stood for . . . but . . . well . . .

RUTH: But they do. Why, my goodness, General, your name is the best-remembered name of all our heroes.

GENERAL: Yes . . . but for what? I have become a series of bridges . . . schools . . . hospitals. . . . Whenever men don't know what to name a building or a street, or a hotel . . . they call it *Washington*. Even my wife's name and the name of Mount Vernon are not exempt from this commercial usage. How many Martha Washington Tea Rooms and Mount Vernon Real Estate Developments do you suppose there are in this country?

RUTH: But doesn't that prove that the people remember you, General?

GENERAL: No, child. It proves that they remember my name. But it doesn't prove they remember me, their commander, their chief, their first President.

BILLY: But we remember you, sir. The boys and girls in school remember you and the things you stood for.

GENERAL: I wonder if you do. Most children seem to think of me about once a year if my birthday falls on a school day. All they know about me is that old story about the cherry tree.

RUTH: Oh, no, sir. You're mistaken there. Why, right now, Billy and I have been studying what you had to say about military training. You see, Billy and I are on the debating team for our history class. That's really why we're here today, to get some material.

BILLY: The debate is: Resolved that the United States should adopt a system of compulsory military training. Ruth and I are defending the proposal, and we have to have our material ready by tomorrow. We thought if we came to see a real general and asked his opinion, it would help our side.

GENERAL: Do boys and girls take an interest in things like that today?

RUTH: Of course, they do. After all, we are the people who are most affected by compulsory military training.

GENERAL: That's right. And what do you propose to say in your debate?

BILLY: Well, sir, we've been basing our argument on a statement of yours.

GENERAL: A statement of mine?

BILLY: Yes, sir. You once said, "To be prepared for

war, is one of the most effectual ways of preserving peace."

GENERAL: So I did. So I did. Let me see . . . I think I said that in my first annual address to Congress in January, 1790. Dear me, that was a long time ago.

RUTH: And those words are still being quoted, General. So you see, you're not forgotten after all.

GENERAL: Perhaps you're right.

BILLY: Oh, yes, sir, you are remembered in more ways than you could possibly imagine. Our history teacher says you are influencing our country's foreign policy even today.

GENERAL: I am glad the people still remember.

RUTH: And that's not all they remember. You think all these people who name their products after you and your family are selfish and commercial. But it's a great compliment, General, if you just look at it in the right light.

BILLY: Sure. The name of Washington has always stood for truth and reliability and strength and greatness. That's why people are so anxious to name things after you because that name alone arouses the people's confidence and trust.

GENERAL: Well spoken, lad. You should be a statesman.

BILLY: Maybe I will. Our history teacher says that's what our country needs most . . . great statesmen like you and Mr. Franklin and Mr. Jefferson and the others who drew up such documents as the Declaration of Independence and the Constitution.

GENERAL: And do you think the people of today really appreciate and treasure those documents?

RUTH: Do we think they really appreciate and treasure those documents? Why, General Washington, those papers are the treasures of America. The Declaration of Independence, the Constitution and the Bill of Rights, every scrap of paper that has contributed to the freedom of this country is carefully preserved.

BILLY: Say, Ruth, I have an idea! On our next school vacation, let's take the General to the National Archives Building.

GENERAL: What is this National Archives Building?

RUTH: It's the place where America's most important documents are kept.

BILLY: The Constitution is there.

RUTH: And the Declaration of Independence, the Bill of Rights—some of the most precious papers in America.

GENERAL: And what are they selling there?

RUTH: Oh, dear! You can't forget about that selling idea, can you? Well, the Archives Building isn't selling anything.

BILLY: But it *is* selling the American people on the idea of remembering and cherishing their great American heritage. Why, each year, thousands and thousands of visitors come to see these documents, and they remember that, because of them, we can all enjoy the rights to life, liberty and the pursuit of happiness.

GENERAL: Wonderful! Wonderful! Then the people have not forgotten.

RUTH: No, indeed! When you see hundreds of people waiting patiently in line to see these great American papers, you know that they remember the men who wrote them and signed them.

GENERAL: I'd like to stand once more and look at that copy of the Constitution we argued over—so many years ago. (*Chuckles to himself*) I remember what good Ben Franklin said the day it was signed. He pointed to the picture of a half-disk of the sun that was painted on the back of my chair and said: "I have often and often in the course of the session and the vicissitudes of my hopes and fears as to its issue, looked at that behind the President without being able to tell whether it was rising or setting; but now at length I have the happiness to know that it is a rising, and not a setting sun." Well, he was right. It was a rising sun.

BILLY: And how!

RUTH: Well, General, will you come with us on our trip?

GENERAL: Of course! I don't want to miss such a fine opportunity, and I wouldn't have missed meeting you young people for anything. You have helped me understand this strange, new America a little better. I even believe I understand this thing you call advertising.

BILLY (*Taking candy bars from pocket*): In that case, General, have a candy bar.

GENERAL: No, thank you, I never eat candy.

RUTH: Oh, but you must try one. These are George Washington Bars.

GENERAL: In that case, my dear, I'll have one! If they're George Washington Bars, I have an idea they must be pretty good. (*Curtain*)

THE END

Production Notes

THE GENERAL RETURNS

Characters: 6 male; 4 female.

Playing Time: 30 minutes.

Costumes: Modern everyday dress for all except the General, who wears a long military cloak over a Revolutionary War uniform. On her second appearance, Miss Kelly wears a hat and coat and carries a handbag.

Properties: Letters, card file, envelopes, five-dollar bill, sheet of paper, calling card, bag of golf clubs, candy bars.

Setting: The General's outer office. There is a large desk at right, on which are several telephones, a typewriter, a card file, some letters, envelopes, and various papers. There is a door marked "Private" at center. Flanking this doorway are two large American flags in floor holders. There is a light switch on one wall; two filing cabinets stand against wall. Various chairs complete the furnishings. There is an exit at left.

Lighting: Lights go off briefly, during which time the stage is lighted by the light coming from center doorway.

Mother Beats the Band

Characters

MRS. SHERIDAN
MR. SHERIDAN
DEE
TUCKER } *their children*
SALLY
PINEAPPLE, *Sally's friend, a member of Junior Mechanics*
MRS. CALHOUN
MR. CALHOUN
CORNY CALHOUN
MRS. BRIGGS
MRS. PHIPPS
MRS. COHEN
MRS. GALLAGHER } *The Krazy Kitchen Kadettes*
MRS. GRIMM
MRS. RILEY

SETTING: *The Sheridan living room.*

AT RISE: DEE *is supervising her brother,* TUCKER, *in the moving of the living-room furniture. He staggers to center stage, almost bent double under an armchair, when she stops him.*

DEE: Hold it, Tuck! Hold it! I have a better idea.

TUCK (*Depositing armchair on floor with a thud, and draping himself over it*): Better make up your mind, Sis. Remember, you're paying for this by the piece, not by the hour.

DEE: If we move the table where the sofa is, and the sofa where the table is, we might be able to put the armchair over in the corner and bring down the little gate-leg table from the den.

TUCK: That will cost you thirty-seven cents extra plus twenty cents for the upstairs table, plus another twenty if I have to take it back. This operation is beginning to run into money.

DEE: You let me worry about that.

TUCK (*Picking up chair again*): O.K. You're the boss. But I'm just warning you so you won't start beefing when you get my bill.

DEE (*As* TUCK *starts to move chair*): Wait a minute! Wait a minute! We'll have to move Dad's smoking stand.

TUCK (*Depositing chair*): Where are we moving it?

DEE: It's really a moldy looking specimen. Let's put it in the attic.

TUCK: Oh, no! Nothing doing. You get yourself another moving van! I'm not being a party to moving Dad's smoking stand to the attic. I want to keep my happy home.

DEE: Don't be silly. I'll take all the responsibility.

TUCK: I've heard that one before!

DEE: Oh, all right! If you're going to be such a ninny, we'll leave it where it is. Now, come on!

TUCK: Come on *where?* This chair's heavy. Make up your mind.

DEE: Oh, dear! The upholstery is so faded. And look! That spot where you spilled the ink still shows.

TUCK: My heart is bleeding! Positively bleeding. Now where do you want it?

DEE (*Pointing*): Over in that corner. (*As he starts*) No! Better take it back where it was in the first place. Oh, dear! This room is positively impossible!

TUCK (*As he maneuvers chair into place and flops into it*): It never was impossible before. You always said you liked this room. After all, you helped pick the color scheme.

DEE: Yes, but that was ages ago. I don't see why we don't redecorate every year the way other people do. And you know, Tuck, we're the only family in the block without a picture window!

TUCK: So what? Do you want me to knock out the side of the house?

DEE: Don't be crude! Now go bring the footstool over here.

TUCK: Cost you a nickel.

DEE: It won't cost me a cent. That footstool goes with the chair.

TUCK: Not in *my* book! The bargain was that I get paid by the piece. That footstool counts as one piece. Five cents or it stays where it is.

DEE: But you can't have the chair in one corner and the footstool clear across the room.

TUCK: Five cents!

DEE: O.K. O.K. Five cents!

TUCK (*As he moves footstool*): And remember, you pay double if Mom says you have to put all this stuff back.

DEE: Honestly, Tuck, you are disgusting. I never saw anyone so crazy for the almighty dollar.

TUCK: Just thrifty, my girl! Just thrifty! It's the American system of free enterprise.

DEE: What's *free* about it, I'd like to know?

TUCK: What I'd like to know is what you're up to. You never took this much interest in housekeeping before.

DEE: Haven't you heard? We're having company.

TUCK: Who? When? Who's coming?

DEE: The Calhouns.

TUCK: The Cal—who's?

DEE: The Calhouns. Mr. and Mrs. Worthington Calhoun . . . and son!

TUCK: And son! You mean old Corny Calhoun from school?

DEE: Tucker Sheridan! Don't you dare call him *Corny*. There's nothing corny about him. He's the coolest, smoothest . . .

TUCK: But that's his name, stupid. Cornelius Calhoun. All the kids call him Corny.

DEE: Well, I don't.

TUCK: You mean you actually call him *Cornelius?*

DEE: Certainly. It's such a distinguished name, when you say it right . . . (*Giving every syllable full value*) Cor-ne-li-us! Cor-ne-li-us Calhoun! So aristocratic. Oh, Tuck, I'm so thrilled that he's bringing his parents over to-night, and I'm so anxious for everything to be just right.

TUCK: Everything's always all right when we have com-pany. Mom sees to that.

DEE: Oh, sure, but this is different.

TUCK: What do you mean, *different?*

DEE: The Calhouns are different. They're . . . well . . . they're very important people. They live in Windsor Heights. They have a yacht. Mr. Calhoun has his own plane . . . and . . . my goodness, Tuck, they even have a butler! Did you ever know anyone before who had a butler?

TUCK: Nope! But then I never knew anyone who had leprosy either!

DEE: Please be serious, Tuck. This visit is important to me. I want the Calhouns to like us.

TUCK: They'll like us all right. We're a likable family.

DEE (*Doubtfully*): Yes, I know. We're a likable family, but we certainly aren't stylish.

TUCK: Aw, who wants to be stylish?

DEE: I do . . . just this once. I want you to get out of those awful dungarees and force yourself into some decent clothes. I want Sally to comb her hair and put on her taffeta dress. I want Dad to keep his shoes on all evening and not smoke that terrible pipe . . . and I want Mother . . . (MRS. SHERIDAN *enters.*)

MRS. SHERIDAN: And what about Mother, pet? Merciful goodness! What's happened to the living room?

TUCK: Lightning just struck, Mom. We've been blitzed by the Calhouns!

DEE: Oh, Mother! You told me ages ago that I could invite Cornelius and his parents to call on us some evening. Well, they're coming tonight.

MRS. SHERIDAN: How nice, dear. But . . . really, is all this necessary?

DEE: Maybe not necessary, but you must admit it's a big improvement. Doesn't it look a hundred percent better?

MRS. SHERIDAN: Um-m-m . . . I'm not sure yet. And I don't know what your father will say about his armchair. However, if you think the Calhouns will like it, I guess it will be all right with the rest of us.

DEE: If only I had a little more time. I could take down

the drapes, and we could have washed the curtains, and —oh, my goodness, Tuck! We'll have to take every stick of furniture out of this room and turn the rug.

TUCK: You're not talking to me, gal.

MRS. SHERIDAN: What on earth has come over you, Dee?

DEE: But look, Mother! Just look! The moth hole shows with the sofa moved around this way. We'll have to turn the rug so the hole goes under the sofa.

MRS. SHERIDAN: Nonsense! That moth hole's no bigger than a pea. No one will notice it.

DEE: But, Mother! You don't understand. These are the Calhouns who are coming. They've probably never even seen a moth hole.

TUCK: Then it will do them good to see one. Even the Calhouns should know the facts of life.

DEE: This is no laughing matter, Tuck. We positively can't entertain the Calhouns in a living room where there's a moth hole.

MRS. SHERIDAN: Aren't you being a little intense about all this, dear?

DEE: Intense? Of course, I'm intense. Mother, you know how I've been raving about Cornelius Calhoun. All the girls are mad about him. And to think he's bringing his parents to call on *us!* It's . . . it's the most fantastic thing that's ever happened to me.

MRS. SHERIDAN: But, honey, is it worth getting so upset? You'll be so excited you won't be able to enjoy their visit.

DEE: I'll enjoy it all right, if I can just get this room to look respectable and if . . . well, if the family will just act a little more civilized than usual.

MRS. SHERIDAN: Civilized?

DEE: Oh, Mother, you know what I mean. You're all the dearest family in the world, but . . . well . . . you're just not . . . just not . . .

TUCK: Just not good enough for the Calhouns.

DEE: Tuck, I never said that.

TUCK: But that's what it adds up to, isn't it? Well . . . phooey on the Calhouns! I don't care how many moth holes we have in our rug. We're just as good as any Calhoun that ever drew breath.

DEE: Oh, dear, of course we are. I only meant . . .

MRS. SHERIDAN: What *did* you mean, dear?

DEE: Honestly, Mother, I don't know. I just want everything to be nice. I want the house to look nice. I want my family to look nice.

MRS. SHERIDAN (*Putting her arm around* DEE): I understand, dear. And don't worry. We'll do you proud. Tuck, you skip upstairs and take your bath. I'll catch Sally as soon as she comes in and get her washed and pressed.

DEE: And you'll wear your new dress, Mother? You look so sweet in that!

MRS. SHERIDAN: I'll wear anything you say, dear. Now, run along, Tuck.

TUCK: What about the moth hole?

MRS. SHERIDAN: Never mind about the moth hole. We can throw a scatter rug over it. Now get started, so Dad can have his shower when he gets home.

TUCK: Heads up! I'm on my way. (*He exits.*)

DEE (*Yelling*): And be sure to put out clean towels when you've finished.

TUCK (*Appearing in doorway*): I'll fold the dirty side in. That's just as good. (*He exits.*)

DEE: Honestly, Mother, how do you put up with that boy?

MRS. SHERIDAN: I don't *put up* with him, dear. I simply

couldn't get along without him. You must admit he has a refreshing personality.

DEE: Refreshing? Just plain *fresh* is my word for him. (SALLY, *who is 14, enters, wearing dirty coveralls and carrying a large oil can. A large, crumpled bandanna hangs from her hip pocket.*) Oh, my goodness! (DEE *points dramatically.*) Look what we have here!

SALLY: Hi, Mom! Where do you think I've been?

DEE: From the looks of you, I'd say you've been in a coal mine. (*With a screech as* SALLY *is about to flop into a chair*) Not there! Not there! Mother, don't let her sit in that chair. She'll stick fast!

SALLY: Well, listen to the dictator! Since when are you giving orders around here?

DEE: Now listen to me, Sally Sheridan!

MRS. SHERIDAN: Girls! Girls! Please, don't argue. You'd better not sit down any place, Sally, till you've changed your clothes. Where *have* you been, darling?

SALLY: Under Pineapple's car! Honestly, Mother, it was simply great, and I mean great! All those nuts and bolts and wires! You just can't imagine! And do you know where Pineapple's going to take me next Saturday?

MRS. SHERIDAN: Where, dear?

SALLY: Right down into the grease pit over at the garage. He and the rest of the gang are coming over tonight, and we're going to tear down that old engine Dad has in the cellar.

DEE: Not tonight, Sally! Mother, that awful Pineapple boy can't come over here tonight!

SALLY: And why not? What's the matter with Pineapple? He's teaching me to be a grease monkey.

DEE (*Hurling herself into a chair*): This is the payoff! Why should I be afflicted with a sister who wants to be a grease monkey? Mother, you simply have to do something about her!

MRS. SHERIDAN: Don't you think you're getting too upset over this, Dee?

SALLY: Over what? What's going on around here?

MRS. SHERIDAN: It's the Calhouns, Sally.

SALLY: What about them? Pineapple works for Mr. Calhoun, and he says Mr. Calhoun is a swell guy.

MRS. SHERIDAN: They're coming over here tonight.

SALLY (*Interrupting*): Great! Mr. Calhoun and Pineapple will have plenty to talk about.

DEE: Mother! Mother! Make her understand, please.

MRS. SHERIDAN: I'll try, dear. Listen, Sally, this visit is important to your sister. She wants everything to be especially nice, and she wants us to look and act our best.

SALLY: O.K. I'll cooperate. I'll change to my new jeans and put on that plaid shirt she gave me for Christmas.

DEE (*Moaning*): Jeans! A plaid shirt!

MRS. SHERIDAN (*To* SALLY): Jeans and a plaid shirt are out! I want you to wear your taffeta dress and heels.

SALLY: But Mother, I can't work in the cellar with the gang in my taffeta dress!

MRS. SHERIDAN: I really think you should call off the gang meeting for tonight, Sally.

SALLY: But, Mother, you said the Junior Mechanics could work in our cellar any time. You gave it to us as our headquarters.

MRS. SHERIDAN: I know I did, dear. But, please, call it off, just for tonight. This party should be strictly family.

SALLY: O.K. But can't I even have Pineapple? He's practically family.

DEE: That's just the trouble. We don't want people to think we've adopted him.

MRS. SHERIDAN: Dee, keep quiet. I'll handle this. Now you go upstairs, Sally, and call the gang. You can explain how things are. They'll understand.

SALLY: Well, I hope so. (*She exits.*)

DEE: Sometimes I can hardly believe Sally and I are even distantly related. She is so revolting!

MRS. SHERIDAN: Don't ever let me hear you use that word again in talking about your sister—even in fun!

DEE: I'm sorry, Mother, but I just don't understand Sally.

MRS. SHERIDAN: You mean you just don't appreciate her. She's a wonderful youngster, Dee, and that gang of hers are a fine bunch of teen-agers.

DEE: But do they have to *live* here?

MRS. SHERIDAN: They need a decent place for a hangout, Dee. As long as those Junior Mechanics want to work in our cellar—hammer and saw, take things apart, put them together again—your father and I are happy to have them.

DEE: But what about me? Don't I have some rights too?

MRS. SHERIDAN: Of course, you do, dear. And I want this to be a happy evening for you. Now come along. (*Phone rings and* DEE *grabs it.*)

DEE (*At phone*): Hello? (*Pause*) Yes, yes, she's here, Mrs. Briggs. (*Pause*) What? Oh, my goodness! Not tonight! (*With hand over phone*) Mother, it's Mrs. Briggs . . . Something about the Krazy Kitchen Kadette practice.

MRS. SHERIDAN: Oh, my! Let me talk to her. (*At phone*) Hello, Mrs. Briggs. (*Pause*) Yes, I know, but I must admit I had forgotten this was the night . . . (*Pause*) Why, certainly! (*Pause*) Yes, I know we need the practice.

DEE (*Making frantic motions*): Mother, not tonight! You can't have them tonight.

MRS. SHERIDAN (*At phone*): Well, I was wondering if we could practice a bit earlier this evening. (*Pause*) You can? When? (*Pause*) That will be fine. (*Pause*) Very well, Mrs. Briggs. I'll expect you. Thanks for calling. (*Hangs up*)

DEE: Mother! You can't. You simply can't have that awful band practice here tonight.

MRS. SHERIDAN: I couldn't get out of it, Dee. But they're coming early.

DEE (*Interrupting*): I don't care! I think it's terrible for you to have those horrible old women here when the Calhouns are coming!

MRS. SHERIDAN: Dee! What's come over you? Those "horrible old women," as you call them, are my Senior Citizens Club. This kitchen band is their greatest interest in life at the moment. I wouldn't think of disappointing them, not even for your Calhouns. After all, elderly people need to have fun, too.

DEE: Mother, you just don't understand!

MRS. SHERIDAN: You are the one who needs to understand, dear. The Calhouns are just people—very nice people—but just people. And my Kitchen Kadettes are just people, too. You can't make over the whole human race just because the Calhouns are coming.

DEE: But, Mother! Those Krazy Kitchen Kadettes are so awful! I'd be so ashamed if the Calhouns should run into them!

MRS. SHERIDAN: Then you'd have to be ashamed of me, too, Dee, because I'm their leader.

DEE: Mother, I didn't say I was ashamed of you . . . ever!

MRS. SHERIDAN: Well, it seems to me you're ashamed of your whole family in one way or another.

DEE: I'm not, Mother! Honestly, I am not! It's just that you do such weird things!

MRS. SHERIDAN: Like what, for example?

DEE: Well, like . . . Oh, Mother, why can't you play cards and go to receptions and luncheons and be on committees? Why do you have to organize such crazy things as those Kitchen Kadettes, and the Junior Mechanics, and the . . .

MRS. SHERIDAN: Those people need me, Dee. And I need them. I wish you could understand. (MR. SHERIDAN *enters carrying a very large carton which he drags into the middle of the floor.*)

MR. SHERIDAN: Hello, everybody! Where's Tuck?

MRS. SHERIDAN: What's that?

DEE: What's in the box, Dad?

MR. SHERIDAN: The peanuts! They came this afternoon. The Express Company called.

DEE: Peanuts? What peanuts?

MRS. SHERIDAN: Oh, I forgot to tell you, dear. They're for my Girl Scout Troop. We're selling them. This is Peanut Week, you know.

MR. SHERIDAN: Where's Tuck? I want him to help me put up the sign.

MRS. SHERIDAN: He's upstairs dressing.

DEE: What sign? What sign are you putting up, Dad?

MR. SHERIDAN: I left it out on the porch. It's the sign that came with the peanuts. Your mother wants it on the front gate.

DEE: A sign on our front gate? Oh, my heavens! What does it say?

MR. SHERIDAN (*Shouting*): Tuck! Tuck! Come on down. I need help.

TUCK (*Offstage*): O.K., Dad. Be there in a jiffy.

DEE: Mother, what does this sign say?

MRS. SHERIDAN: Nothing much, dear. It's just about the peanuts.

DEE: I insist on knowing what it says.

MR. SHERIDAN (*Chuckling*): It's kind of cute. It says, "Follow the Squirrels! Get Your Peanuts Here!"

DEE: And you mean to tell me you're putting that sign on our front gate?

MRS. SHERIDAN: Now, darling, don't be so upset.

DEE (*Screaming*): Upset! Who wouldn't be upset! What will the Calhouns think?

MR. SHERIDAN: What about the Calhouns?

MRS. SHERIDAN: Oh, nothing, dear. They're just dropping by this evening.

MR. SHERIDAN: Great! We ought to be able to sell them a bale of peanuts. Your Girl Scouts will be stopping here for their quotas tonight, Mother, so you and Dee had better separate them into packs.

DEE (*Sinking into chair*): Not tonight! Not tonight! (TUCK *enters.*)

TUCK: Hi, Pop. Where's this job you have for me?

MR. SHERIDAN: Out front, son. You and I are going to put up a sign. Come along. (*He exits.*)

TUCK: O.K. (*Starts to exit*) And don't worry about the towels, Sis. I put the clean side out! (*He exits.* MRS. SHERIDAN *stands for a minute watching* DEE, *who is sobbing bitterly.*)

MRS. SHERIDAN: Dee, child, listen to me. You're making a mountain out of a molehill. The sign will hardly show at all. After all, it isn't a neon sign. It's really just a small placard, quite neat and attractive.

DEE: I don't care what it is. The whole thing is disgusting. Now those horrible little Girl Scouts will be tramping in and out all evening.

MRS. SHERIDAN: Listen, dear. I'll get Tuck to take the peanuts down to the recreation room, and the girls can come to the back door.

DEE (*Wailing*): But that awful kitchen band!

MRS. SHERIDAN: We're having the rehearsal early, I told you. I'll have them in and out before the Calhouns make their appearance. I promise you.

DEE: There isn't time.

MRS. SHERIDAN: Yes, there is. Mrs. Briggs is rounding up the band and bringing them over before dinner. I'll cut the rehearsal short, we can have a bite to eat, and we'll all be sitting here as cool as cucumbers when the Calhouns call.

DEE: It will never work! Never! All those Girl Scouts and those peanuts!

MRS. SHERIDAN: Now don't worry. I'll take care of everything. Why don't you go upstairs and supervise Sally? Maybe she needs help with her hair, and you have such a way with it.

DEE (*Wearily*): Very well. But, Mother, I'm warning you . . . (*Doorbell rings.*) I'd better leave. I can't stand any more shocks. (*Starts to exit*)

MRS. SHERIDAN: Don't worry, dear. Everything will be under control. (DEE *exits; Kitchen Kadettes enter. Each one "plays" some sort of kitchen utensil in which is placed a kazoo or comb.* MRS. GALLAGHER *carries a dress box.*) Oh, good evening, girls. I'm so glad you came early.

MRS. BRIGGS: We just couldn't wait, Mrs. Sheridan. Could we, girls?

ALL: No, indeed!

MRS. PHIPPS: We have a surprise for you.

MRS. SHERIDAN: A surprise? For me?

MRS. COHEN: We do hope you'll like it. Go ahead, Mrs. Gallagher. You make the speech.

MRS. GALLAGHER (*Steps forward, holding dress box*): With pleasure, Mrs. Sheridan. You've been so good to us, and we've enjoyed ourselves so much that we want you to have this token of our proud esteem and fond appreciation. (*They all applaud as* MRS. GALLAGHER *hands dress box to* MRS. SHERIDAN.)

MRS. SHERIDAN: I can't imagine what in the world it could be.

ALL: Open it! Open it! (MRS. SHERIDAN *opens box which contains a bright-colored cape, a very tall drum major's hat and a baton.*)

MRS. SHERIDAN: This *is* a surprise. Why, I'm overcome.

MRS. COHEN: We want you to be the best-dressed leader in the district!

MRS. RILEY: Put it on. We want to see how it looks on you. (MRS. SHERIDAN *puts on cape and hat amid exclamations of pleasure from the Kitchen Kadettes.*)

MRS. SHERIDAN: I really don't know what to say, ladies. This is really wonderful.

MRS. BRIGGS: It's you who are wonderful, Mrs. Sheridan. I was just saying to the rest of the girls, I've never had such a good time in my whole life as I've had since you started the Kitchen Kadettes.

MRS. GRIMM: And I know that goes for all of us. (TUCK *and* MR. SHERIDAN *enter.*)

MR. SHERIDAN: Well, the sign's up.

TUCK: And it looks neat.

MR. SHERIDAN: Good evening, ladies.

TUCK: What's that you have on, Mom?

MRS. SHERIDAN: It's my new uniform, Tuck. The Kadettes gave it to me to wear at the district competition.

MR. SHERIDAN: You cut quite a figure in that, Nora.

TUCK: Say, that looks great, Mom! Come on, Dad. Let's get these peanuts organized.

MR. SHERIDAN: You ladies go right ahead with your rehearsal and don't mind us. We're going to separate these peanuts into packs and take them down to the recreation room.

MRS. SHERIDAN: Shall we line up and try our first number, girls? Where's Mrs. Edmonds?

MRS. GRIMM: She and Mrs. Hall couldn't come. They both have terrible colds.

MRS. SHERIDAN: Oh, dear! Now we won't have a pianist, and we're missing a funnel player.

MRS. GRIMM (*Placing instrument made out of a funnel on the table*): I brought Mrs. Hall's instrument along just in case she turned up at the last minute. (SALLY *and* DEE *enter.* SALLY *is wearing the taffeta dress.*)

MRS. SHERIDAN: How about you, Sally? Will you play for us? We're doing "I Get So Lonely" as our first number. (SALLY *goes to piano.*)

SALLY: Sure, Mom. I'll help you out.

DEE (*Looking with horror at her mother's uniform*): Mother, what on earth do you have on? Don't you realize it's almost six o'clock?

MRS. SHERIDAN: Sh! Not so loud. Go set the table, and we'll eat as soon as we've finished. (DEE *exits.*)

SALLY (*At piano*): Come on, let's go! (*Band plays any popular song of hillbilly variety.*)

MRS. SHERIDAN: That was fine, ladies. But let's try it again and take it a little faster. One . . . two . . . three . . . Go! (*As they play,* MR. CALHOUN, MRS. CALHOUN *and* CORNELIUS *enter, followed by* PINEAPPLE. *They stand in doorway and applaud at end of number.* DEE *enters on applause. As she sees the* CALHOUNS, *she gasps in surprise.*)

DEE: Cornelius! Mrs. Calhoun!

SALLY (*With crash on piano keys*): Pineapple! Where did you come from?

DEE: Cornelius! You said eight-thirty!

MRS. CALHOUN: You really must excuse us, barging in like this, Mrs. Sheridan. But I couldn't wait another minute!

MRS. SHERIDAN: This *is* a surprise, Mrs. Calhoun. I don't believe you folks have met all of my family. (*Gesturing*) This is Sally, Mr. Sheridan, and Tucker.

ALL (*Ad lib*): Hello. How are you? Nice to meet you. (*Etc.*)

MR. CALHOUN (*To* MRS. CALHOUN): Go ahead, Catherine, and tell the folks why we're here.

MRS. CALHOUN: We're here because we've just had the most wonderful news in the world. Mrs. Sheridan, you've really put our town on the map! And as president of our local Golden Rule Club I couldn't wait to come over and give you the news!

MRS. SHERIDAN: Oh, dear! What have I done now?

MRS. CALHOUN (*Laughing*): What have you done? Really, Mrs. Sheridan, you are the most modest woman in the world. (*She opens purse and produces a telegram which she reads with the aid of a lorgnette.*) Listen to this citation! "Mrs. Sheridan, because of your character and achievements as a wife and mother, because of the high moral character of your children, because of your courage, patience and devotion in the home, and because of your understanding and sense of social responsibility, you have been selected by the Mothers' Committee of the Golden Rule Foundation as the MOTHER OF THE YEAR!" (*There is a burst of applause and shouts of congratulations from the Kitchen Kadettes.*)

MRS. SHERIDAN (*In complete astonishment*): The *what?*

MRS. CALHOUN: The Mother of the Year! (*Coming forward and shaking hands*) I congratulate you, Mrs. Sheridan, and I am proud to know such a truly wonderful woman.

MRS. SHERIDAN: But I don't understand . . .

SALLY (*Throwing her arms around her mother*): Golly, Mom, I always knew you were the most wonderful mother in the whole U.S.A., but this proves it!

MR. CALHOUN (*Shaking hands with* MRS. SHERIDAN): Congratulations are in order, Mrs. Sheridan. It is a great honor, and I know you deserve it. All the community work you have done, the interest you have shown in young and old! It's truly remarkable. Pineapple just never stops talking about the Junior Mechanics and how you've given them a place to work and put up with their noise and confusion.

PINEAPPLE (*Moving forward to shake hands*): And I mean it, Mrs. Sheridan! Gosh, some of those fellows in Junior Mechanics never had any place for a workshop or never knew what fun they could have at home till they started coming here.

SALLY: Why, Pineapple! That was a wonderful speech.

PINEAPPLE: I'm glad to have the chance to make it, Sally. I might have missed the whole occasion if it hadn't been for the rattle in the rear end of Mr. Calhoun's car. I rode along over here to listen for it, and I found it. It'll only take half an hour to fix it once I get the car back to the garage.

CORNELIUS (*Shaking hands*): Congratulations, Mrs. Sheridan. Anyone who knows your three kids, knows you're a pretty swell mother.

MR. SHERIDAN: Well, Nora, I guess it's my turn to make a speech, but I think I'll have to make mine later. I'm sort of dumfounded myself.

TUCK: Me too, Mom. But I think it's swell.

DEE: Oh, Mother . . . I don't know what to say . . .

MRS. SHERIDAN: And neither do I, Dee. My goodness! I haven't been this flustered since the day I got married. Let me find chairs for everybody.

MR. CALHOUN: No, indeed, Mrs. Sheridan. We can't stay. Catherine was so excited when she got the telegram, she insisted on coming right over. And this evening, we want you and your whole family to be our dinner guests. I know we were coming over here later, but in view of such a tremendous occasion, I suggest we do the entertaining. How about it?

MRS. SHERIDAN: Thank you. We'd be delighted.

CORNELIUS: I have some new records I want you to hear after dinner, Dee. Sally and Tuck will like them, too.

MRS. CALHOUN: If Pineapple can tear himself away from those Junior Mechanics for one evening, maybe he'd like to join us.

PINEAPPLE: Thanks, Mrs. Calhoun. That would be swell. But I'll have to fix that rear-end rattle first.

MR. CALHOUN: Then we'd better take the car down to the garage right now. Goodbye, Mrs. Sheridan. We'll expect you about seven. And before I leave I want to tell you how happy we are that Corny is a welcome visitor in your home.

MRS. SHERIDAN: Thank you, Mr. Calhoun. He's a fine boy. We all enjoy him.

MR. CALHOUN (*To* MRS. CALHOUN, *who has picked up funnel instrument and is fingering it wistfully*): Coming, Catherine?

MRS. CALHOUN: Would you mind waiting for me in the car a few minutes, dear? I used to play one of these things in college, and I'd just love to have a go at it, if Mrs. Sheridan wouldn't mind.

MRS. SHERIDAN: We'd love it, Mrs. Calhoun. We just happen to be short a funnel player at the moment.

MRS. CALHOUN: I might be a bit rusty, but I used to blow a mean funnel in my time.

MR. SHERIDAN: Tuck and I will see you out to your car, Mr. Calhoun. I'd like you to take a look at the sign we just put on the gate. Coming with us, Dee?

DEE: Not right now, Dad. I'm going to help Mother get these peanut packs ready for her Girl Scouts. If Mom is the Mother of the Year, it's high time I started acting like her daughter. I want her to be as proud of me as I am of her . . . and believe me, she's something to live up to. (TUCK, MR. SHERIDAN, MR. CALHOUN, CORNY *and* PINEAPPLE *exit.* DEE *starts to unpack the peanut carton.*)

MRS. SHERIDAN (*To Kitchen Kadettes*): Well, ladies, what shall it be?

MRS. GALLAGHER: Let's make it, "For She's a Jolly Good Fellow." Come on, gals, let 'er rip! (*As Kitchen Kadettes play song,* DEE *goes to stand beside her mother.* MRS. SHERIDAN *gives her a hug with her free arm as she directs the band. Curtain.*)

THE END

Production Notes

Mother Beats the Band

Characters: 5 male; 10 female; female extras to be additional Krazy Kitchen Kadettes, if desired.

Playing Time: 25 minutes.

Costumes: Modern everyday dress. Tuck wears blue jeans at the beginning of the play. He later appears in a suit. Dee wears an attractive party dress. Sally wears a pair of dirty coveralls for her first entrance. She later appears in a dressy taffeta dress. The Krazy Kitchen Kadettes wear bright-colored capes over their dresses. They all have on matching band hats. Mrs. Calhoun has a lorgnette and carries a purse, in which is a telegram.

Properties: Large oil can, bandanna, very large carton, kitchen instruments containing kazoos or combs for the Krazy Kitchen Kadettes, dress box containing bright-colored cape and drum major's hat and baton for Mrs. Sheridan, funnel instrument, telegram.

Setting: The Sheridan living room. There is a piano at left and a large sofa upstage center. There is an entrance from outside upstage right, and there is a door at left, leading to the rest of the house. There are several armchairs placed about the stage, one of which Tuck is carrying as the curtains open. One of the armchairs has a matching footstool. A smoking stand, telephone, radio, tables, lamps, bookcases, etc., complete the furnishings of the room.

Lighting: No special effects.

Dial M for Mother

Characters

Topper Marlow
Skipper Marlow
Lucy Marlow
Peggy Marlow
Jason Jones
Bongo Johnson, *Topper's friend*
Policeman
Maggie, *the housekeeper*

Time: *A morning in May, shortly before Mother's Day.*
Setting: *The Marlow living-dining room.*
At Rise: Topper *enters right, goes directly to table, pours a glass of orange juice, unfolds paper and scans first page. Carrying orange juice and paper, he crosses to living room area, sits on sofa, and examines paper more closely. After turning several pages, he utters an exclamation, sets orange juice on coffee table and reads intently. Then, rising swiftly, he searches in a desk drawer, pulling out a sheaf of papers which he piles on top of desk, until he finds a pair of scissors. He carefully cuts out an article from the center of one of the inside*

pages of the newspaper, and tucks the clipping in his wallet. Next, he refolds the paper, and returns it to its original place on the breakfast table. He crosses to telephone on stand and dials.

TOPPER: Hello, is this Mr. Johnson? (*Pause*) May I please speak to Bongo? (*Pause; he glances furtively over his shoulder from time to time.*) Hello, Bongo? Topper here. Have you seen the morning paper? (*Pause*) It's there all right! (*Pause*) You bet I'm lucky Mom went to her college reunion. (*Pause*) Dad? Oh, he won't be home till tonight. (*Pause*) No, no, of course not! And I've taken good care they *won't* see it! I have it right here in my wallet. (*Pause*) Listen, Bongo, what time does that bus leave? (*Pause*) O.K. (*Pause*) Sure, I can make it. Meet you at the bus station in ten minutes. And, Bongo, remember—mum's the word! (*As he hangs up phone,* MAGGIE *enters.*)

MAGGIE: Land sakes, it's *you!* How do you want your eggs? Soft-boiled or sunny-side?

TOPPER: No eggs for me this morning, thank you, Maggie.

MAGGIE: What's the matter? You sick or something?

TOPPER: Nothing's the matter, Maggie. I'm just in a rush.

MAGGIE: Well, you can't rush out to mow lawns in your best suit. Now go upstairs and change, and I'll fix your eggs.

TOPPER: I'm not mowing lawns this morning, Maggie. I—I have some business to attend to.

MAGGIE: Business or no business, you're not leaving this house on an empty stomach. What would your mother say? You start on your cereal, and I'll hustle those eggs. Sunny-side will be quickest. (*She exits*)

TOPPER (*Calling after her*): Don't bother, Maggie. I'm

not hungry. I couldn't eat a bite. (*Carries orange juice glass back to table and sticks a pastry into his mouth*) Not a bite! (*Takes a second roll and pops a third one into his pocket*) I'll be seeing you. (*Starts to run off left, turns, runs back, snatches newspaper from table, and sticks it under sofa cushion. He exits, and* MAGGIE *re-enters.*)

MAGGIE (*Hands on hips*): Now, look here, Topper Marlow, I don't want any arguments. Everybody in this house eats a decent breakfast! (*Looks around and calls*) Topper, Topper, you come back here. (*To herself*) Honestly, that boy! What's wrong with him this morning? (LUCY *enters right.*)

LUCY: Morning, Maggie. Where's Topper?

MAGGIE: Who knows! Rushed off without his breakfast! And in his best suit, too! He wouldn't do that if his mother were home.

LUCY (*Pouring orange juice*): Don't let it bother you, Maggie. He won't starve! Not from the looks of these buns! (*Sits at table*) And at least he won't be underfoot while we're getting ready for the party.

MAGGIE: Heavenly days! The party! I plumb forgot! Well, that settles it! I'll just call my sister and tell her I can't come—operation or no operation!

LUCY: What on earth are you talking about? What's the matter? Who had an operation?

MAGGIE (*Sitting down, taking off her apron and twisting it*): Oh, Lucy, I'm that upset! It's my brother-in-law. My sister called early this morning. Ed has appendicitis. They rushed him to the hospital, and she wants me to come over and stay with the children. But I'll ring her up right now and tell her to try to get Mrs. Murphy.

LUCY: You'll do nothing of the sort. Those children need you, and we can manage.

MAGGIE: I don't see how! Not with the party and everything. You've never baked a cake in your life.

LUCY: Then it's time I learned. Or better yet, I'll just skip the cake and have strawberries and ice cream.

MAGGIE: That might be a good idea. I have three boxes of berries in the refrigerator, and you can pick up three more when you do the marketing.

LUCY: Good. Do you have the market list?

MAGGIE (*Rising, leaving apron on chair*): I'll get it. It's all made out. Your mother said you should watch the paper for weekend specials on lamb chops.

LUCY: I'll look. (*Reaches for paper*) Where is the paper? Hasn't it come yet?

MAGGIE: It's right there on the table.

LUCY: No, it isn't.

MAGGIE: But I put it there myself, when I brought it in.

LUCY: Well, the paper's not here now.

MAGGIE: Maybe Topper took it with him. Honestly, that boy! He sure has a bee in his bonnet this morning. (*She exits as* PEGGY *enters, wearing high heels and carrying a pocketbook. A pretty sweater is draped over her shoulders.*)

PEGGY (*Breezily*): Hi, pet. What's for breakfast? (*Going to table*) Um-m! Danish! And with nuts! (*Helping herself*) These are delish! Just the kind I love!

LUCY: And where do you think you're going, Mademoiselle Marlow?

PEGGY: Downtown to pick up my dress at Murray's.

LUCY: Not in my good sweater!

PEGGY: Oh, Lucy, be a doll, and let me wear it, pu-leeze!

LUCY: I will not be a doll, and I will not let you wear it!

So just march right upstairs and take it off, pu-leeze!

PEGGY: O.K., soon as I finish the Danish.

LUCY: You'll get it all smeared up with icing.

PEGGY: No, I won't! Oops! (*Brushing herself off*) Oh, well, just a few crumbs.

LUCY: Please, Peggy, don't be difficult! Maggie has to stay with her sister's children today. Her brother-in-law is having an emergency operation. She didn't want to go because of the party. But I said we could manage.

PEGGY: Sure, we can. I'll make the sandwich filling as soon as I come back from Murray's.

LUCY: I thought you could do the breakfast dishes first. Murray's doesn't open till eleven.

PEGGY: They open at nine on Saturdays.

LUCY: Eleven.

PEGGY: Nine! Look, I'll show you their ad in the paper.

LUCY: *You* look! We can't even find the paper. It's disappeared.

PEGGY: By the time Mom gets home, we won't be able to find anything in this house.

LUCY: Nonsense! I think we're doing fine! I just hope this nice weather holds for her reunion.

PEGGY: Poor Mom! I'll bet she has butterflies about her big speech!

LUCY: She'd have bigger butterflies if she knew Maggie was leaving.

PEGGY: I wonder if we should call her.

LUCY: And ruin her day? I should say not!

PEGGY: That's right. It's quite an honor for Mom to be speaker of the day—the star performer after twenty-five years!

LUCY: They're lucky to get Mom. She's a real orator when she gets started.

PEGGY: They should have a piece about her in the paper. . . . Mrs. Andrew Marlow—Guest Speaker at College Reunion.

LUCY: Maybe there is an article, if we could just find that paper.

PEGGY: It must be around someplace.

LUCY: I guess Topper took it with him. Try to remember to pick up another copy when you're downtown, Peggy. (MAGGIE *enters carrying market list.*)

MAGGIE: Here's the list, Lucy. And don't let them fool you with those strawberries. Sometimes they put all the big ones on top.

PEGGY: I'm sorry about your brother-in-law, Maggie. I hope he'll be all right.

MAGGIE: Thanks, Peggy. I sure do hate to leave you like this. I know your mother was depending on me to hold the fort here.

PEGGY: Don't worry about us.

MAGGIE: If you need me, you can always call. I'm going to run upstairs and pack a bag. There's a bus in half an hour.

LUCY: I'll drop you off at the bus station on my way to market.

PEGGY: You might as well take this sweater upstairs, Maggie. Hard-Hearted Hannah won't let me wear it. (*Hands sweater to* MAGGIE)

LUCY: And tell Skipper to get a move on, will you, please, Maggie? We'll give him the dish-washing detail.

MAGGIE: I'll rout that young man out in a hurry. (*She exits.*)

PEGGY: I can't wait to wear my new dress, Lucy. It's positively dreamy!

LUCY: Poor Jason! He'll be absolutely dazzled!

PEGGY: Jason! Pooh! I'm sick and tired of Jason! It's high time I started dating somebody more exciting.

LUCY: And just whom do you consider more exciting than Jason Jones?

PEGGY: I'm not telling! But wait till you see him! He's . . . well . . . he's sort of a surprise!

LUCY: Now, look here, Peggy Marlow, don't you try any tricks while Mother's away. You know how she feels about Max Callahan.

PEGGY: Who said anything about Max Callahan? Besides, Mom always lets us choose our own friends.

LUCY: But not that dreadful Max Callahan. You know she doesn't approve of him.

PEGGY: It's not fair to judge a boy by his haircut. Maybe if she'd get to know Maxie, she'd like him.

LUCY: But she can't get to know him when she's not home. And it's not fair to take advantage of her being away. You know she wouldn't stand for it if she were here.

PEGGY: But she's not here, and you're not going to pick my date for the party, Lucy Marlow, so there!

LUCY: Peggy, please, listen to me.

PEGGY: Sorry! I'm in a hurry! (*She exits.*)

LUCY: Oh, dear! I wonder if I should call Mother after all. (*Crosses to phone table and searches through papers*) She left a number here someplace. (*As* LUCY *looks through numbers on phone pad,* SKIPPER *enters. He goes to table, picks up a Danish, holds it in his teeth, then juggles box of cereal, milk bottle, and cereal bowl. He crosses to sofa, makes a safe landing on the coffee table, and stretches out on sofa.*)

SKIPPER: Looking for something, sis?

LUCY: I'm looking for the phone number Mother left in case of an emergency.

SKIPPER: Are we having an emergency? (*In squirming about to get comfortable, he kicks sofa cushion out of the way, and reveals newspaper, which he proceeds to read as he munches the pastry.*)

LUCY: Not yet, but we're headed for one, if that Max Callahan shows up for the party tonight.

SKIPPER: Max Callahan! That jerk! Who invited him?

LUCY: Your sister Peggy thinks he's exciting.

SKIPPER: So do the police.

LUCY: The police!

SKIPPER: Sure. He's always bad news. It says right here in the paper he's lost his driver's license again.

LUCY: The paper? (*Turns and sees he has paper*) Where did you get that paper? We couldn't find it after Topper left.

SKIPPER: It was right here under the cushion. (*Turns page to place where clipping was cut out*) And some joker has been operating on it with the scissors.

LUCY: Let me see that. (*Looks at paper*) Well, that's funny. What do you suppose Topper cut out of this? (MAGGIE *enters, wearing a coat and hat and carrying a suitcase.*)

MAGGIE: Skipper Marlow, what are you doing on that sofa? You'll have crumbs all over everything.

SKIPPER: I'm making a time and motion study. You have no idea how much time and motion you save when you eat lying down.

MAGGIE: I'm only interested in the time and motion required to clean up after you. Now, scat!

SKIPPER (*Reluctantly moving food to table*): Women! They never appreciate scientific data!

LUCY: If you're ready, Maggie, we'd better get started. Skipper can do the dishes.

SKIPPER: Thanks for volunteering.

MAGGIE: I'd feel better about leaving if we called your mother. I put her phone number in the desk for safekeeping.

LUCY: So that's why I couldn't find it.

SKIPPER: You told me you were only going to your sister's, Maggie. You sound as if you were taking off for Timbuktu!

MAGGIE: I just hate the idea of leaving you alone like this.

SKIPPER: Dad will be home tonight, and in the meantime, I'll try to protect my two delicate sisters!

MAGGIE: You! You have enough trouble looking after yourself. (*Peering at him more closely*) Let me look at you, Skipper. Do you feel all right?

SKIPPER: I felt fine till I got the message about these dishes.

MAGGIE (*Feeling his forehead*): Your face looks a mite flushed. You're not coming down with something, are you?

SKIPPER (*Shaking off her hand*): Of course not! It's just dish-washing-itis! We'll be O.K., Maggie, honest.

LUCY: Now stop fussing, Maggie. You don't want to miss that bus. (MAGGIE *and* LUCY *exit.*)

SKIPPER (*Putting on* MAGGIE'*s apron*): When K.P. is inevitable, why not enjoy it? (*Stacks dishes in a fantastic pile*) This should be good for a whole paragraph in my time and motion study. (*He exits. A crash is heard.* SKIPPER *re-enters shouting.*) Hey, Maggie, where's the dustpan? (*Shrugs*) Oh, well, my study will show whether it's quicker to sweep up or wash up. (*He exits. Doorbell rings several times, and* JASON *enters with letter.*)

JASON: Hey, where is everybody? (SKIPPER *enters with box of strawberries.*)

SKIPPER: Hi, Jason. I was just topping off my breakfast with some strawberries. Have some?

JASON: Sure, thanks. (*Boys sit on sofa, eating berries*) Hey, Skip, are you feeling O.K.?

SKIPPER (*Eating another berry*): Sure, I feel great. Why?

JASON: You look funny. Kind of splotchy!

SKIPPER: That's my new sun tan. Have another berry. There are plenty more in the refrigerator.

JASON: Oh, I almost forgot. The mailman left this as I came in.

SKIPPER (*Taking letter from* JASON): It's from Dad. (*As he opens letter, check falls out.*) Well, what do you know?

JASON: Anything wrong?

SKIPPER: He's all tied up and can't get home till Monday, so he sent a check for Mom's Mother's Day present. (*He puts letter on sofa.*)

JASON (*Picking up newspaper*): Hey, did you see the good news about the measles epidemic? If it gets worse, they're going to close the schools.

SKIPPER: No kidding! I didn't see that! Where is it?

JASON: Right here on the same page with the story on the teen-age vandalism.

SKIPPER: What teen-age vandalism? I didn't see that either.

JASON: No wonder . . . look! Somebody cut it out of your paper. It was right here! (*Points to hole in paper*) See, there's the bit about the epidemic.

SKIPPER: But why should the story about vandalism be cut out of our paper?

JASON: The police are investigating two teen-agers.

SKIPPER: I don't get it. I just don't get it. Nobody saw the paper after Topper left this morning.

JASON: Do you think Topper cut it out?

SKIPPER: But why? And why would he have put the paper under the sofa cushion?

JASON: You mean he actually *hid* the paper?

SKIPPER: I didn't say he *hid* it. I just said nobody could find it.

JASON: Golly . . . you don't suppose . . .

SKIPPER (*Rising*): I don't suppose anything! And don't you start supposing either. Topper would never be mixed up with anything like this vandalism.

JASON: But where is he?

SKIPPER: How should I know? (PEGGY *enters from front door, carrying suit box and newspaper.*)

PEGGY: Hi, Skip. (*Seeing* JASON) Oh, I didn't know you had company! (*Crossing to right exit*)

SKIPPER: Wait a sec, Peggy. Do you know where Topper is?

PEGGY: Topper? How should I know? He left early.

JASON (*Pointing to* PEGGY'*s newspaper*): Is that the morning paper?

PEGGY: Yes. I bought one downtown. We couldn't find ours this morning.

SKIPPER: I found it. Someone hid our paper under the sofa cushions.

PEGGY: Who did that?

SKIPPER: I think maybe Topper did.

PEGGY: Why? What's all the mystery?

SKIPPER: Let me see your paper. (*Takes paper and opens it*) Now, Jason, where's that story? (*He turns the pages, and* JASON *looks over his shoulder.*)

JASON (*Pointing*): See . . . there it is. Right in the middle of the page. POLICE SUSPECT TEEN-AGERS OF VANDALISM

—CONSIDERABLE DAMAGE DONE TO PUBLIC BUILDINGS.

SKIPPER: Gee, I wish Mom were home.

PEGGY: What *is* all this? What's the matter? (LUCY *enters with grocery bags.*)

LUCY: Wow, these are heavy. Take them to the kitchen for me, will you please, boys? (*Boys exit with bags. To* PEGGY) Well, I see you got your dress.

PEGGY: Oh, wait till you see it, Lucy. It's a dream . . . a positive dream.

LUCY: I *did* see it, remember?

PEGGY (*Opening box*): You didn't see *this* one. When I got down there, Murray's was having a sale, so I got *this* one for the same price. Look! (*Holds up sophisticated black sheath evening dress*)

LUCY: Oh, for heaven's sake, Peggy. You can't wear that. Why, it's for somebody twice your age.

PEGGY: It is *not!* The clerk thought it was just right, and so do I.

LUCY: Well, it isn't! You march that right back and buy the one you and Mom picked out.

PEGGY: I will not. I'm buying this with my own money . . . my birthday money, and Mom said I could spend it on anything I want.

LUCY: Well, she never thought you'd want anything like that. Now be sensible and take it back.

PEGGY: I won't take it back. Ever since Mom's been gone, you've been pulling this big sister act, telling me what I can and can't do.

LUCY: Peggy, be reasonable. I'm not trying to boss you, honest, I'm not. But you know Mother wouldn't let you keep that dress.

PEGGY: She would so, and I'm going to call her up and ask

her. I'm going to call her this very minute. (*Going to desk*) Her number's here someplace.

LUCY: If you call Mom, I'm going to talk to her, too. (*Both girls search desk for number, knocking papers off on floor.*)

PEGGY: Now see what you've done. (*Scrambling for papers*)

LUCY: Here's the number— Salisbury, M-900. I'll put the call in.

PEGGY: Don't you dare. It was my idea to call Mom. (JASON *and* SKIPPER *enter.*)

SKIPPER: Who's calling Mom and why?

LUCY *and* PEGGY: I am.

SKIPPER: Well, let me do it. I have something important to tell her.

LUCY: What? What do you have that's so important? (*Suddenly looking at him in horror.*) Skipper! (SKIPPER*'s make-up has been touched up so that he has a heavy, red rash*) What's wrong with you? What's wrong with your face?

SKIPPER: My face? There's nothing wrong with my face.

PEGGY: But there is! You should see yourself! You have spots all over!

JASON: Holy mackerel! You've got measles!

SKIPPER: Don't be silly!

JASON: It's not silly, Skip! Believe me . . . I've had them!

LUCY: Skipper, you get right to bed. I'll make you some hot tea.

SKIPPER: But I'm not sick. I feel fine.

PEGGY: Ye gods! The party! We can't have it if Skip has measles.

LUCY: I'll call Dr. Wertz right away.

SKIPPER: Lucy, put down that phone. I tell you I do not

have measles, and I am not going to bed, Dr. Wertz or no Dr. Wertz.

LUCY (*Dialing*): Now look, Skip, measles can be serious. After the doctor comes, I'm going to call Mother. (*Door-bell rings*)

PEGGY: I'll get it. (*She exits left.*)

SKIPPER (*Making a lunge for the phone*): Put down that phone, I tell you. I'm not sick. *I do not have measles!*

LUCY (*Putting down phone*): Stop yelling, Skip. I'm only getting a busy signal. Try not to get excited. You'll just get more spots. (PEGGY *enters with* POLICEMAN.)

PEGGY: I'm sorry, Officer, but Topper isn't here just now.

POLICEMAN: That's too bad. I wanted to talk to him.

SKIPPER: I'm sure he'll be back soon, Officer.

POLICEMAN: Perhaps I could talk to Mrs. Marlow.

LUCY: She isn't here, either. Mother is away for the week-end.

POLICEMAN: Then perhaps your father could help me.

SKIPPER: He won't be home until Monday, sir.

JASON: Maybe Bongo Johnson would know where Topper is, Officer. They're always together.

POLICEMAN: Yes, I know. We want both of them, so I might as well stop at the Johnsons'. (*At door*) When Topper comes in, ask him to come down to Headquarters, will you please?

LUCY: Certainly, Officer.

POLICEMAN: I see you've been reading the paper, so you know the whole story. Quite a pair, aren't they?

SKIPPER (*Laughing grimly*): Yeah! Yeah! You took the words out of my mouth, quite a pair!

POLICEMAN: Say, young fellow, you'd better see a doctor! Looks to me as if you have a fine case of measles!

LUCY: I was just dialing Dr. Wertz when you came in.

POLICEMAN: I hope you reach him. The doctors are running themselves ragged with this epidemic. All three of my kids are down with measles.

LUCY: That's too bad.

POLICEMAN: You won't forget to tell your brother we want to see him?

LUCY: No, sir. I'll be sure to give him your message.

PEGGY: I'll show you to the door, Officer. (PEGGY *and* POLICEMAN *exit.*)

LUCY: Well, what do you suppose *that* was all about?

SKIPPER (*Picking up paper*): It was about this! The article that Topper cut out of the paper this morning.

LUCY: What did he cut out?

JASON (*Pointing*): It was this . . . this article about the teen-agers who are suspected of vandalism.

LUCY: But Topper didn't have anything to do with that!

JASON: You heard what the policeman said!

LUCY: But it's impossible!

JASON: Then why did he cut the story out of the paper?

SKIPPER: And why did he hide the rest of the paper under the sofa cushion? (PEGGY *re-enters.*)

PEGGY: We have to find Topper right away and warn him that the police are looking for him.

JASON: How can we warn him when we don't know where he is?

LUCY (*Suddenly sitting on sofa*): Oh, my goodness!

ALL: What's the matter?

LUCY: When I took Maggie to the bus station, Mr. Grimm at the ticket window said something about Topper and Bongo almost missing the bus this morning.

JASON: Don't tell me he's skipped town!

SKIPPER: That doesn't sound like Topper.

PEGGY: Or Bongo, either! Oh, Lucy, I'm scared. Maybe we'd better call Mom.

LUCY: If only we could talk it over with Dad.

SKIPPER (*Picking up letter from sofa*): He sent us a letter today. He's tied up until Monday.

LUCY: I hate to do this, but if this isn't an emergency, I don't know what is. (*At phone*) Long Distance, please. I want to place a person-to-person call to Mrs. Andrew Marlow, Salisbury, Long Island. The number is M-900. (*Pause*) That's right. M—as in Mother. M-900. (*To others*) They're ringing her now.

SKIPPER: Don't you dare tell her I have measles.

LUCY (*Into phone*): Hello? (*Pause*) No one answers. (*Pause*) Yes, thank you. I wish you would. Our number is Center-6000. (*Hangs up*) Mom must be out. The operator will try again in fifteen minutes. I'll try Dr. Wertz again. Peggy, try to straighten up a bit before the doctor comes. (*Dials, as* PEGGY *picks up papers from floor*)

SKIPPER (*Making a dash for the phone*): Lucy, stop it! I tell you I will not have you calling the doctor.

LUCY: Be reasonable. We're in enough trouble now without your making things worse. (*Pause*) Oh, dear! The line is still busy! (*Hangs up*)

PEGGY (*Looking at papers she has picked up*): Well, what do you know about this!

ALL: What?

LUCY: What's the matter now? Don't tell me anything else can happen.

PEGGY: These papers! They're the notes for Mom's speech . . . the speech she's supposed to make this afternoon.

LUCY: Put them in the desk.

SKIPPER: Maybe she can use the same speech next year.

PEGGY (*Reading notes*): Oh, Lucy, this is terrible. Simply terrible! And it's all about us!

LUCY: I don't believe Mom wrote anything terrible about us.

PEGGY: Oh, she didn't. What she wrote is wonderful. But it's so terrible that she'll never get to say it. Listen to this: (*Reading*) "Twenty-five years ago, when I was graduated from this college, I was voted the girl most likely to succeed. Well, I never made headlines, and I never made a fortune. But I do feel that I have succeeded beyond all expectations in that I became the mother of four wonderful children."

SKIPPER: Is that what she says . . . four *wonderful* children?

PEGGY: Yes, and there's lots more. Listen: "Oh, they're not the most talented or the most brilliant children in the world, and they have their share of faults. Skipper, the youngest, is at the stage where he no longer eats to live. He lives to eat!" (*All laugh.*)

JASON: That's a good one!

PEGGY (*Reading*): "Peggy, my younger daughter, is working overtime proving that she's grown up."

JASON: That's even better!

PEGGY (*Reading*): "Lucy, the next in line, will be a real executive when she learns how to control her bossiness."

LUCY: I am *not* bossy!

PEGGY (*Reading*): "And Topper—Topper is my first-born, the strong, silent man of action! He acts first and tells us about it later."

SKIPPER: That's Topper all right.

PEGGY (*Reading*): "But in spite of these faults, my children have one quality which makes me feel I am a successful mother. Each one, in his own way, is self-reliant. Through the years, I have tried to teach them to face their problems squarely, and work out their own solutions. If I have not given my children anything else, I have given them this gift of independent thinking, the ability to stand on their own two feet, and make their own decisions based on their own integrity. This is important to me, as it should be to every mother, because it is what America needs most in her young people of today."

SKIPPER: Golly! How could we ever let Mom down?

PEGGY: And to think I was going to run to Mother because of that silly old dress. I'll take it back right away. I knew all along it was too old for me.

LUCY: I'm sorry I was so bossy about Max Callahan, Peggy.

PEGGY: I never said I invited Max, Lucy. That was your idea. If you hadn't made me so angry, I would have told you I invited Bongo Johnson.

SKIPPER: For Pete's sake! What makes you think Bongo Johnson's any more exciting than Jason here?

PEGGY: Well, if you must know, I only invited Bongo because Katy Keller told me Jason was asking her.

JASON: Why that little schemer! I invited her only because she told me you wanted to invite Bongo!

SKIPPER: Of all the dopes!

LUCY: I guess we're all dopes, Skipper! We don't deserve a mother like Mom.

JASON: After all she said about self-reliance, I guess you can handle a case of measles.

PEGGY: And we can easily cancel the party.

SKIPPER: But what about Topper?

PEGGY: We have to help him!

LUCY: According to Mother, Topper is perfectly capable of helping himself, if we just give him the chance.

JASON: How can you give him the chance when he's run away?

SKIPPER: Will you stop saying things like that, Jason? How do we know he's run away? All we know for sure is that he cut an article out of the paper. (*Holds up paper in time for* TOPPER *to see it, as he enters with* BONGO.)

TOPPER: Well, I see the news is out! You've read the paper.

ALL: Topper!

LUCY: Topper, how could you!

SKIPPER: How could you think you'd get away with it by cutting out the clipping?

TOPPER: I didn't want anyone to know!

LUCY: But we were bound to find out!

PEGGY: Oh, Topper, the police have been here. They want you down at Headquarters.

BONGO: Yes, they've been to my house, too.

JASON: So you decided to come home and face the music?

TOPPER: What music?

SKIPPER: We never would have known if Jason hadn't seen the article.

PEGGY: And I bought another copy of the paper downtown.

BONGO: Well, what do you think of your headline brother and his pal? I guess this town will sit up and take notice! Two hometown boys making the big time!

JASON: You've made the big time all right.

SKIPPER: What will Mom and Dad say?

TOPPER: They don't know it yet.

LUCY: I've already called Mother.

TOPPER: You what!

LUCY: I thought she ought to know.

TOPPER: Lucy, this was none of your business. It's my place to tell Mom.

LUCY: Well, you can have that pleasure when she calls back. The operator is still trying to get her.

TOPPER: I never saw such a bunch of busybodies! A guy can't keep a secret in this house for five minutes.

BONGO: Oh, what's the difference? The whole town knows by this time that we made it.

JASON: That's a funny way to put it.

SKIPPER: Yes, what do you mean that you *made it?* Made what?

TOPPER: Well, you certainly ought to know. You read the article. (*Seizing paper and reading*) "TWO LOCAL BOYS CHOSEN FOR INTERNATIONAL SWIMMING MEET."

ALL (*Scrambling to read paper; ad lib*): Where is that? What are you reading? Let me see!

BONGO: What have you been yapping about all this time? (*Looking over* TOPPER*'s shoulder and reading*) "Charles Marlow, better known to the sports world as Topper, and Marvin (Bongo) Johnson have been chosen to represent their state in the international swimming meet scheduled for Geneva, Switzerland, in August. The local competition is sponsored by the Police Athletic Club. Marlow and Johnson are well known in state and district competition and both are honor students in the local high school."

LUCY: Oh, Topper! Topper! This is absolutely wonderful!

PEGGY: And to think we thought . . .

SKIPPER: Jason Jones, I have a good notion to punch you right in the nose.

JASON: Well, gee whiz! How was I to know what was printed on the other side of the page?

TOPPER: What's the matter with all of you? What are you jabbering about?

LUCY: Topper, we owe you an apology. We thought . . . or that is, Jason thought . . .

JASON: Now everybody's blaming the whole thing on me. Look, let me have the paper. I'll show you what happened. (*Takes paper from* TOPPER) On one side of the page, we have an article about Marlow and Johnson, swimming champions and honor students. (*Turns page over and points*) And on the other side of the same page —an article on teen-age vandalism. We thought you had cut out the report on vandalism.

TOPPER: You mean you thought I was mixed up in that?

LUCY: We didn't really, Topper. But then we found out you had left town.

BONGO: We just hopped on a bus to Milford. There's a guy we know over there who does passport pictures.

PEGGY: And then the police came.

TOPPER: But of course they came. Mom and Dad have to give their permission and sign a million forms.

LUCY: Oh, Topper, we're so ashamed. Please forgive us.

PEGGY: What are we going to tell Mom if she calls back?

TOPPER: Don't you dare tell her anything. This is *my* big news, and I want to save it as a Mother's Day surprise.

JASON: You can always tell her about the measles.

SKIPPER: You shut up.

TOPPER: Measles? Who has measles?

LUCY: Skipper. Look at him!

TOPPER: Measles? You're crazy! That's nothing but a

strawberry rash. He's been making a pig of himself again. How many boxes did you eat?

SKIPPER (*Pointing to box on coffee table*): I was just finishing the third box! Golly, I forgot they always give me a rash.

PEGGY: Oh, boy, now we can have our party after all!

LUCY: Topper and Bongo can be the guests of honor. (*Phone rings.*)

SKIPPER: I'll bet that's Mom.

LUCY (*At phone as others cluster about*): Hello (*Pause*) Yes, this is Center-6000. (*To others*) It's Mom all right. (*Into phone*) Hello, Mother? (*Pause*) No . . . no . . . nothing's wrong. We're all fine, just fine. But we're worried about you. We found the notes for your speech —how are you going to talk without them? (*Sighing with relief; to others, with hand over phone*) She says those notes were just to get something on paper, and that she remembers the words by heart.

PEGGY (*Taking phone*): It's a wonderful speech, Mom. And we're so proud that you're giving it. (*Pause*) Yes, yes, Skipper's here. Skip, Mom wants to talk to you.

SKIPPER (*Taking phone*): Hi, Mom. (*Pause*) Nothing but a small strawberry rash. (*Pause*) Sure, sure, I'll be careful. I won't eat another strawberry this whole weekend! And, Mom, that was some speech you wrote. I know you'll be a wow!

TOPPER: Let me talk to her. (*Taking phone*) Hello, Mom. (*Pause*) Sure, everything's under control. Have a good time and don't worry about a thing. And, say, Mom, I have a little surprise for you when you get home. (*Pause*) Nothing doing. I'm saving it till I see you. (*Pause*) Nope, you'd never guess in a million years. (*As others crowd around phone*) Wait a minute . . . they all want to say something. (*Pause*) Jason and Bongo are here, too. Just a minute. I'll hold up the phone so you can hear everybody. (*Holds up phone*) Let 'er go, gang.

ALL: Happy Mother's Day! (*Curtain*)

THE END

Production Notes

DIAL M FOR MOTHER

Characters: 5 male; 3 female.

Playing Time: 30 minutes.

Costumes: Modern everyday dress. When Peggy first enters, she wears a pretty sweater draped over her shoulders. She wears high heels and carries a pocketbook. Maggie wears an apron and housedress when she first appears; later she wears a coat and hat and carries a suitcase. Topper wears a suit, and the Policeman wears a uniform. While Skipper is offstage, taking the grocery bags into the kitchen, his make-up should be touched up so that he has a heavy red rash on his face.

Properties: Two newspapers (one for Peggy), plate of Danish pastries, box of cereal, bottle of milk, pitcher of orange juice, plates, glasses, spoons, scissors, papers, wallet for Topper, market list and suitcase for Maggie, letter containing check for Jason, suit box containing black sheath evening dress, grocery bags, box of strawberries.

Setting: The Marlow living-dining room. The table in the dining area, at right, is set for four and holds a plate of Danish pastries, a box of cereal, a bottle of milk, a pitcher of orange juice, and a neatly folded newspaper. Other furnishings include chairs; a desk with a drawer in which are a sheaf of papers and a pair of scissors; a telephone stand, holding a telephone and a phone pad; a sofa with cushions; a coffee table. An exit at right leads to kitchen and rest of house; left exit leads to front door.

Lighting: No special effects.

Part-Time Hero

Characters

BILL STEVENS, *a war veteran*
PATSY STEVENS, *his sister*
MRS. STEVENS, *their mother*
CAPTAIN JOHN FERRIS
ELLEN JACKSON
ELLEN BRADY

SCENE 1

TIME: *The night before Memorial Day, 1947.*
SETTING: *The Stevens living room.*
AT RISE: BILL STEVENS *is sprawled on the living-room couch;* PATSY, *his little sister, is perched beside him, holding a book.*

PATSY: Aw, come on, Bill. Just see if I know the first stanza, will you? They're going to broadcast our Memorial Day Program. Just think, I'll be on the air.
BILL: So what?
PATSY: I have to be letter perfect.
BILL: You will be. All of us Stevenses have good memories.

PATSY: But, Bill, I'm scared I'll forget it.

BILL: You won't forget it. Why, I can still say the *Gettysburg Address* without missing a word. "Fourscore and seven years ago our fathers brought forth on this continent a new nation, conceived in liberty, and dedicated to the proposition that all men are created equal. Now we are engaged in a great civil war, testing whether that nation, or any nation so conceived and so dedicated, can long endure." Now, what do you think of that? And I haven't looked at it in years.

PATSY: It's wonderful, Bill, but it isn't helping me a bit.

BILL: O.K.! O.K. Peace at any price. Give me the book. (PATSY *hands him the book.*) And mind you, no mistakes.

PATSY: Oh, thanks. I'd rather die than forget. I get butterflies in my stomach just to think of it. I'm so scared.

BILL: Stop squawking about being scared. Let's have the speech. What is it? Some silly old poem?

PATSY: Yes. I mean no. It's a poem, but it isn't silly. It's beautiful and terribly sad. Miss Doyle says I put a lot of expression into it.

BILL: I can imagine. But let's have it, expression and all.

PATSY: All right. It's on page 28. (*Assuming a stiff unnatural pose for reciting*)

"Cover them over with beautiful flowers,
Deck them with garlands, these heroes of ours.
Lying so silent by night and by day,
Sleeping the years of their manhood away.
Give them the meed they have won in the past;
Give them the honors their future forecast;
Give them the chaplets they won in the strife;
Give them the laurels they lost with their life.

(*Refrain*)

Cover them over, yes, cover them over,
Parent and husband, brother and lover,
Crown in your hearts these dead heroes of ours.
Cover them over with beautiful flowers." *

BILL (*Slamming down the book*): Stop! Stop! That's enough. Stop!

PATSY: But that's just the beginning. There are three more verses.

BILL: I don't want to hear them. I've heard all I can stand of that truck!

PATSY: But it's not truck! It's poetry.

BILL: Well, it's more truck than poetry, I can tell you that. Heroes! What does a hero care about being covered over with flowers—beautiful or otherwise—what good does that do him? A hero wants something while he's living, not after he's dead.

PATSY (*Almost in tears*): But, Bill, it's for Memorial Day in memory of Civil War heroes.

BILL: Civil War heroes! Don't make me laugh! People have forgotten the heroes of our own century and you talk about remembering Civil War heroes!

PATSY: Oh, Bill! You're awful! Why do you always talk like that?

BILL: And why not? It's only the dead heroes who are remembered. The living ones come home and have no jobs, no homes, no . . . no . . .

PATSY (*Angrily*): Go ahead. Why not say it? "No girls!" That's what you mean, isn't it? Just because you broke off with Ellen Jackson . . .

BILL: Shut up!

PATSY: I won't shut up, and you can't make me!

BILL: I'll show you what I can do. (*Starts after her*)

* Decoration Day Hymn (Anonymous)

PATSY (*Screaming*): Mother! Mother! Make Bill stop! Mother! Bill's chasing me! Make him stop! (MRS. STEVENS *enters.*)

MRS. STEVENS: Children! Children! Stop it. Stop it! Patsy! Bill! You should be ashamed of yourselves carrying on like this.

PATSY (*Running to her mother and half crying*): He made fun of my Memorial Day poem.

BILL: I said it was a lot of truck, and I repeat it! "Cover them over with beautiful flowers!" Bah!

MRS. STEVENS: Oh, Bill . . .

BILL: And there's one thing I want understood around here. That child is to keep her mouth shut on the subject of Ellen Jackson.

MRS. STEVENS: Oh, Patsy, you didn't . . .

BILL: Yes, she did.

MRS. STEVENS: Patsy, I'm surprised at you, teasing Bill like this.

PATSY: I wasn't teasing him. (BILL *begins to put on hat and coat.*)

MRS. STEVENS: Bill, dear, where are you going?

BILL: Out! Out to find a couple of heroes so I can cover them over with beautiful flowers! (*Exits*)

MRS. STEVENS (*Sitting down on couch*): Oh, Patsy, don't you know better than to upset Bill like this?

PATSY: I only asked him to hear my Memorial Day poem.

MRS. STEVENS: But you know any mention of war upsets him.

PATSY: But this is only the Civil War!

MRS. STEVENS: Only the Civil War! What kind of talk is that? War is war. Any war is bad enough. And why did you have to mention Ellen Jackson?

PATSY: Well, if you ask me, I think we make entirely too much fuss over Bill. We carry him around on a silver platter all the time, just so he won't get upset.

MRS. STEVENS: Well, nobody asked you, and in any case, I'm not going to have him disturbed. He's been through enough.

PATSY (*Half remorsefully*): Yes, I know. Say, Mother, it does seem a shame about Bill and Ellen, doesn't it?

MRS. STEVENS: Yes, Ellen is such a sweet girl. And smart, too. She writes for the *Morning Herald*.

PATSY: Know something? I think Ellen still likes Bill.

MRS. STEVENS: I'm sure she does.

PATSY: Well, then, if he still likes her, why don't they do something about it?

MRS. STEVENS: They'll have to do something about it themselves. But first of all, Bill will have to straighten himself out.

PATSY: Why doesn't he get a job or go back to school?

MRS. STEVENS: He can't seem to make up his mind as to what he wants to do. He refuses to go back to school. One minute he talks about going to New York for a job, and the next minute he's decided to go to California. (*Sighs*) Oh, well, I guess he'll work things out sooner or later. And in the meantime, young lady, why don't you go on with your poem and forget about Bill?

PATSY: Oh, Mom! Will you hear me say it?

MRS. STEVENS: Of course.

PATSY (*Handing her the book*): I'll start with the refrain. That's the saddest.

"Cover them over, yes, cover them over,
Parent and husband, brother and lover.
Crown in your hearts these dead heroes of ours.
Cover them over with beautiful flowers."

MRS. STEVENS (*Who has not been paying attention*): That was fine, dear.

PATSY: But, Mother, you weren't even listening. You're thinking about Bill.

MRS. STEVENS: I'm afraid you're right, Patsy. He's the only hero that I can think of at this minute. I wonder where that boy went.

CURTAIN

* * * *

SCENE 2

SETTING: *A section of the public park.*

AT RISE: CAPTAIN JOHN FERRIS *enters, wearing an overcoat, the collar of which is turned up. He walks with a cane. He goes over to the bench and sits down.* BILL *enters, pauses by the bench, walks up and down a few times and then stands beside it, as if waiting for someone.*

FERRIS (*Clearing his throat*): Good evening. Waiting for someone?

BILL: Er—no, not exactly.

FERRIS: Is this some sort of public park?

BILL: Oh, yes. This is Union Square, one of the historic spots in our little burg. Are you a stranger in town?

FERRIS: In a way. (*Pauses*) Looks as if they're getting ready for some sort of celebration. I see they're building a platform over there under the trees.

BILL: Yes. That's the speakers' stand for tomorrow where the old windbags will deliver their Memorial Day speeches.

FERRIS: Oh, really?

BILL (*Sitting down*): Yes. It sure gives me a laugh. They make speeches to honor the dead heroes while they kick the live ones around.

FERRIS: Are you a hero?

BILL: What? Well, no . . . no . . . of course not. I'm just a returned vet. (*Taking a closer look at* FERRIS) You look as if you've been in the wars. Have you?

FERRIS: That's right.

BILL: Then you know how it is. All the flag waving and cheering till you come home, and then what do they hand you?

FERRIS: There is a difference.

BILL: And how! The colleges are so crowded you can't get in edgewise.

FERRIS: I gave up my education.

BILL: I'm in the same boat. What are you aiming to do?

FERRIS: I guess I'm just a drifter.

BILL: Got any folks?

FERRIS: Not any more. My parents are both dead.

BILL: Too bad. Say, you haven't had many breaks, have you? Wounded too, I see.

FERRIS: Yes, my leg was shot up a bit.

BILL: I guess I was luckier than most. I never got a scratch. (FERRIS *coughs.*) You shouldn't be sitting out here in this dampness. That's a bad cold you have, chum.

FERRIS: Oh, it's nothing. Just a little hacking cough I picked up. A prisoner of war doesn't lead too healthy a life.

BILL: Prison! Say, they really gave you the works. What was it like?

FERRIS: That is something that is better forgotten.

BILL: So is the whole messy business. But how can we forget when we have to fight another war here on the home front to get our rights?

FERRIS: I see what you mean.

BILL: You remind me of someone I've met before. Your face is familiar. Are you sure we don't know each other? My name is Bill Stevens.

FERRIS: Glad to know you, Stevens. My name is Ferris. John Ferris.

BILL: Ferris. Ferris. Gee, the name sounds familiar too, but I can't place you. Are you stopping at a hotel or visiting here?

FERRIS: I guess you'd say I was just visiting. Tell me, Bill, do you know a girl named Ellen Brady?

BILL: Ellen Brady? Are you sure you don't mean Ellen Jackson?

FERRIS: No, this girl's name is Brady.

BILL: Sorry. I don't know her.

FERRIS: I'm sorry, too. I'd like to find her.

BILL: Well, gee whiz! I know most everybody in town. But I never heard of Ellen Brady. What does she look like?

FERRIS: She's beautiful. Sort of tall and slim. Has red-gold hair and a smile that you remember always.

BILL: Say, fella, the more you talk, the more that girl sounds like Ellen Jackson.

FERRIS: I guess I should know her name. (*Takes ring from pocket*) Here's a ring I gave her before the war.

BILL: Gosh! Were you engaged?

FERRIS: That's what I thought. But you see, there was someone else. Someone who stayed right here in town. I guess she saw a lot of him. Anyhow, I was jealous, we quarreled, and . . . well . . . here's the ring.

BILL: By jiminy, you and I must be kindred spirits for

sure. So your girl threw you over for a guy who stayed home and took things easy.

FERRIS: That's what I thought, but I know now that I was wrong. If only I hadn't lost my temper and made a fool of myself. (ELLEN BRADY *enters, wearing long hooded coat.*) But look! Here she comes.

BILL: Why, that's Ellen!

FERRIS: Yes, Ellen Brady. As lovely as the first time I saw her.

BILL: Ellen Brady, nothing! That's Ellen Jackson. I guess I should know. She's my girl. Er . . . uh . . . I mean she *was* my girl.

FERRIS: Sh! I must speak to her. (*Stepping forward*) Ellen!

ELLEN: John!

FERRIS: Oh, Ellen, I've come back. I realize now I was wrong. We should never have quarreled. I was unreasonable and suspicious. I didn't use my head. I'm sorry.

ELLEN: I'm sorry too, John.

FERRIS: Then you'll forgive me?

ELLEN: It's too late, John. You see, my name is Mrs. Jackson.

FERRIS: Ellen! (*Steps back*)

ELLEN: I'm sorry, John. Things could have been different. (*She exits.* FERRIS *sinks down on bench and hides his face in his hands.*)

BILL: Say, what is this? What goes on here? Who is she? And who are you?

FERRIS: Just a returned veteran like yourself, a hero who won victory on the battlefield and lost everything he loved at home.

BILL: I don't get it. Are you a real hero?

FERRIS: If you call it being a hero to stand off an entire

regiment with a handful of men, blow up a bridge and capture a strategic town from under the enemy's nose, then I'm a hero.

BILL: Gosh! I must have seen your picture in the news. What outfit were you in?

FERRIS: I was with the Army of the Potomac under General McClellan.

BILL: The Army of the Potomac! General McClellan! Why, that's the wrong war! I thought you said you were a returned vet.

FERRIS: So I am, but I returned in 1865.

BILL: Then you must be . . . Holy smokes! What are you? A ghost?

FERRIS: Call me what you will. You say my face looks familiar. You're right. You've seen it many times.

BILL: But where?

FERRIS: On the statue, over there in the park. Didn't you ever stop to read the name?

BILL: Then you must be Captain Ferris, the town hero.

FERRIS: At your service, sir. Yes, I'm the town hero, the great fighter who lost everything I've fought for.

BILL: Why? How?

FERRIS: Because I didn't know how to live like a hero.

BILL: What do you mean?

FERRIS: First of all, I refused to continue my education, quarreled with my folks about that, and finally left home to go out West and get rich quick. You see, I thought all the good jobs had been snapped up by the stay-at-homes.

BILL: You mean the men who didn't have to serve—who couldn't pass the Army physical.

FERRIS: In my day, a man could buy himself a substitute for a hundred dollars, and plenty took advantage of that loophole. Then my next mistake was to quarrel with Ellen, like a jealous fool.

BILL: I guess you had combat nerves or something, and it took you a while to get adjusted.

FERRIS: We didn't know about things like that in 1865. But people are people, and war is war, and those are the mistakes I made. You see, I thought everybody was down on me. I guess that's why I turned out to be such a failure.

BILL: But you weren't a failure. You were a hero.

FERRIS: A battle hero, yes . . . but a peacetime hero, no.

BILL: But tomorrow, the whole town will turn out to pay tribute to you. They'll put a wreath on your statue. The Mayor will speak. The bands will play. Why, at this minute my little sister is learning a poem to recite, in memory of you and all the other heroes.

FERRIS: That is nice of them, and it is good to be remembered as a hero. But if I had my life to live over again . . . oh, well . . . we all make mistakes, don't we, Bill?

BILL: I'll say we do . . . and gosh . . . talking with you has sort of reminded me of a few of my own. Maybe I can straighten some of them out, before it's too late.

FERRIS: I'm sure you can. And by the way, if you'd ever like to talk to me again, you know where to find me. I'm always on duty in the park, except on nights like this, when I get restless and walk around a bit. Goodbye, Bill.

BILL: Goodbye, John, er . . . I mean, Captain.

FERRIS: Just call me John. I'm "Captain" only when I'm over there on my bronze pedestal. (*Exits*)

BILL: Gee! I feel funny. I don't know if I've been asleep or not. And yet I could hardly go to sleep sitting here on this iron bench. (ELLEN JACKSON *enters.*) For Pete's sake! Here comes Ellen. (BILL *stands up as she approaches.*) Pardon me, young lady, could you spare a few kinds words for a hometown boy?

ELLEN: Why, Bill! (*Laughs uneasily*) How come you're standing out here in the park?

BILL: Maybe I was sort of hoping I'd see you. We used to meet here lots of times—remember? You'd go to the library to study, and I'd hang around and bring you home.

ELLEN: Yes, I remember. I was at the library tonight.

BILL: Doing some more studying?

ELLEN: Not exactly. But I was looking up some material for a human interest story on Captain Ferris. The paper always runs a special Memorial Day article.

BILL: And did you find anything very startling?

ELLEN: Well, yes, I did. I found mention of some correspondence with a girl in this town. And guess what her name was?

BILL: Was it Ellen Brady?

ELLEN: Why, Bill! How could you know a thing like that? You never stick your nose inside a history book.

BILL: Yes, but sometimes you learn a lot of things outside of books.

ELLEN: Well, smarty, did you know my great-grandmother's maiden name was Ellen Brady?

BILL: Not till this minute. But I could have guessed as much.

ELLEN: Why? How?

BILL: Because she had red-gold hair, and a smile that you would remember always.

ELLEN: Why, Bill! That's right. And you've never even seen a picture of her, have you?

BILL: That's right, and yet I have seen her just as plainly as I see you now.

ELLEN: You sound awfully crazy tonight! But nice! Don't you think it was romantic that the great Captain Ferris wrote letters to my great-grandmother? I wonder what they wrote about.

BILL: Someday, if you're very, very good, I'll tell you. But right now, I want to issue an invitation.

ELLEN: What is it?

BILL: If I promise to stop acting like a jealous, ill-tempered fool, if I stop squawking about being kicked around, and go back to college in the fall—in other words, if I begin to act like a civilized civilian, will you . . .

ELLEN: Will I what?

BILL: Will you go to the Memorial Day Exercises with me tomorrow and help lay a wreath in front of Captain Ferris's statue?

ELLEN: Why, Bill, that's the craziest invitation I ever had.

BILL: I know it sounds crazy, but I'm serious. Will you do it?

ELLEN: You know I will . . . if you'll let me add a few flowers of my own for Great-grandmother Ellen Brady.

BILL: By all means. (*Taking her arm*) And now let's go to my house. There's something I have to do.

ELLEN: What?

BILL: I have to help my kid sister study her poem for the exercises tomorrow. I want her to be letter-perfect.

ELLEN: But Patsy always does very well.

BILL: "Very well" isn't good enough. She must be super because tomorrow your Great-grandmother Brady and Captain Ferris will be listening. (*Curtain falls as* BILL *and* ELLEN *exit.*)

THE END

Production Notes

Part-Time Hero

Characters: 2 male; 4 female.

Playing Time: 30 minutes.

Costumes: Bill wears khakis. Captain Ferris wears an overcoat and carries a cane. He has a ring in his pocket. Ellen Brady wears a long hooded cloak. Ellen Jackson, Patsy, and Mrs. Stevens wear everyday modern dresses.

Properties: Book, ring.

Setting: Scene 1: The Stevens living room. At rise, Bill's hat and coat are on the sofa. Scene 2: A section of the public park. A park bench and a street light complete the setting.

Lighting: During Scene 2, the stage is dimly lit.

Gathering Sticks

Characters

BARRY WARREN, *a high school senior*
PEGGY WARREN, *his sister*
ZIP WARREN, *his younger brother*
MR. WARREN } *their parents*
MRS. WARREN }
ELOISE CARTWELL, *Barry's girl friend*
BEETLE BAGLEY
BECKY FOSTER, *Zip's girl friend*
JUDGE COOPER

TIME: *Graduation day.*
SETTING: *The Warren living room.*
AT RISE: PEGGY WARREN *is taking a snapshot of her brother,* BARRY, *and* ELOISE CARTWELL *in their caps and gowns.* MRS. WARREN *is superintending the photography.*

PEGGY (*Looking through camera*): Move in a little closer to Barry, Eloise. That's good.
ELOISE: Is my cap on straight?
MRS. WARREN: It's just fine, dear, and ever so becoming.

PEGGY: Try to relax, Barry. You look so stiff.

BARRY: I feel stiff. Whoever thought up this monkey suit should have his head examined.

MRS. WARREN: Wait a minute, Peggy. His mortarboard is slipping.

BARRY: Tell me what it is, and I'll glue it fast.

PEGGY: It's your hat, silly.

BARRY: You could have fooled me.

ELOISE: Here, let me fix it. You're supposed to wear it perfectly square, not at an angle. (*Adjusts mortarboard*) There. How's that?

MRS. WARREN: That's fine, dear. Now give us a nice big smile, both of you! After all, commencement is a happy time.

BARRY: I don't feel happy.

PEGGY (*Brightly*): Watch the birdie! (*Clicks camera*) There! (*Winds film*) That should be a good one.

ELOISE: Now, let's take one of Barry by himself. (*Steps aside*)

BARRY: Well, hurry up. My face is freezing in this stupid grin.

ELOISE: Say "cheese" and stop looking as if you smell something.

BARRY: Maybe I do . . . Limburger!

PEGGY: Hold your head a little higher . . . more to the right. Now, a little to the left. No, that's too far. Now pull in your chin. Good! (*Snaps*) I've got it.

BARRY: And I've had it.

MRS. WARREN: Now let's try one sitting down. Maybe he'll look more natural.

BARRY: Nothing doing! Enough is enough, even for you, Mom. Besides, I have a date.

PEGGY: Don't be in such a rush. Eloise will wait.

ELOISE: Oh, the date's not with me, Peggy. Perish the thought. It's with the one and only Beetle Bagley!

BARRY (*Apologetically*): We have a little work to do on the car this afternoon.

PEGGY: Oh, no, not again!

MRS. WARREN: Barry Warren, I simply will not have you messing about in that garage this afternoon. I don't want Judge Cooper to meet you under a layer of grease.

BARRY: What's a little grease between friends? Anyhow, I'm sure Old Coop's met plenty of mechanics in his day.

MRS. WARREN: But you're not a mechanic. You're the president of the Senior Class, and I want you to look and act the part, at least while the Judge is here.

BARRY: For Pete's sake, Mom, what's the matter with you? You'd think Old Coop was the King of Siam instead of the high school commencement speaker.

PEGGY: Well, he just happens to be one of the most important men in the whole state, Barry Warren.

ELOISE: My father says he'll probably be our next governor.

PEGGY: That's right, so you'd better stop calling him Old Coop.

BARRY: That's what Dad calls him all the time. "Good Old Coop!" "Old Cooper-Dooper!" That's all I've heard for the past month.

MRS. WARREN: That's all right for your father. They grew up together, but you should show him more respect.

BARRY: Wait till he gets here, Mom. I'll show him plenty of respect.

ELOISE: I should think you'd be thrilled to have such an important man staying at your house. I'm dying to meet him.

BARRY: Women! Always impressed with big names! Look at Mom, all shook up over entertaining a judge.

MRS. WARREN: I'm not "all shook up," as you call it, Barry. I just want everything to go well.

PEGGY: And by that, brother mine, she means she wants you to steer clear of all arguments with Dad.

BARRY: I'll try, Mom, but if Dad starts giving me the business about the old school tie, I'm liable to sound off. And, furthermore, if he's called in Judge Cooper as a one-man M-Squad to strong-arm me into the legal profession, it's no dice.

MRS. WARREN: But, Barry, you know your father was ready to enroll you at Crescent University the day you were born.

PEGGY: And Dad's been trying to make a lawyer out of you since you had your first haircut.

BARRY: If somebody in this family has to become a lawyer, let Zip do it. He always knows how to win an argument.

MRS. WARREN: Oh, good heavens! I forgot all about Zip. I wonder where he is.

BARRY: Call Becky Foster. He's over at her house most of the time.

PEGGY: Not today. He's out mowing lawns. Zip has developed a terrific interest in making money lately.

BARRY: See what I mean? Zip's the go-getter in the family. Why doesn't Dad try out his legal psychology on him?

PEGGY: I'll admit Dad's a better psychologist in the courtroom than he is at home.

MRS. WARREN: And you're just as bad, Barry. This constant harping on what you call your right to choose for yourself only antagonizes him.

BARRY: But I do have the right to choose for myself, Mom.

ELOISE: Then why don't you hurry up and choose? One minute you're going to write the great American novel, the next minute you're going to be a second Henry Ford, and the next minute you're up in the clouds with the spacemen.

BARRY: I'm trying to keep an open mind, Eloise. But I still think every fellow has a right to lead his own life.

MRS. WARREN: Your father thinks you're too young to know what you really want.

BARRY: I know. He's always telling me I'm not dry behind the ears. After all, if a man of eighteen doesn't know what he wants to do, who does? And if I don't want to go to Crescent and take up law, that's *my* business (BEETLE BAGLEY *enters, wearing coveralls.*)

BEETLE: Hi, there! Good afternoon, Mrs. Warren. Hello, Peggy. Hi, Eloise. (*Steps back in amazement*) Well, if it isn't the Sweet Boy Graduate himself, all done up in his black *muumuu!* I take it you're being preserved for the family archives.

BARRY: How about joining me in the rogues' gallery, pal? Be my guest. (*Throws cap and gown to* BEETLE, *who promptly tosses them back.*)

BEETLE: No thanks, chum. I'm not the academic type—not even in a snapshot.

MRS. WARREN (*Taking cap and gown*): Barry Warren, give me that gown! Just look at it! Nothing but a mass of wrinkles. Now I'll have to press it.

ELOISE (*Taking cap and gown*): Don't bother, Mrs. Warren. I have to press mine so I might as well do both.

PEGGY: That's sweet of you, Eloise. You can do them right here, if you like. The ironing board is all set up in the kitchen. Mother and I will really have to step on it if we want to finish our errands before Dad gets back from the station with Judge Cooper. Come along, I'll show you where the iron is. (ELOISE *and* PEGGY *exit.*)

MRS. WARREN: Now remember, Barry, I want you to be

presentable, and if Zip shows up, shove him under the shower and try to get him into a white shirt and tie.

BARRY: O.K., Mom. I'll get him washed, dead or alive. Now take it easy, will you?

MRS. WARREN: I'll try, dear. (*With a sigh*) Maybe I do worry too much, but your Dad and I are so terribly proud of you, and we do want you to have the very best.

BARRY: I know, Mom.

PEGGY (*Calling from offstage*): Hurry up, Mother. We'll miss the bus.

BARRY: So long, Mom.

BEETLE: 'Bye, Mrs. Warren.

MRS. WARREN: Goodbye, boys. (*Exits*)

BARRY (*Shaking his head*): Mothers! There's nothing like 'em!

BEETLE: You can say that again. (*Briskly*) Well, have you told your folks?

BARRY: Well . . . er . . . not exactly.

BEETLE: What do you mean, "not exactly"?

BARRY: Well, I've told Zip, but somehow the words just stick in my throat when it comes to telling Mother and Dad.

BEETLE: Not chickening out, are you?

BARRY: Nothing of the sort. I've already written to Crescent cancelling my registration and turning down the scholarship.

BEETLE: Good! We'll have to act fast, boy. It's later than we think.

BARRY: What do you mean?

BEETLE: I mean that Mr. Jake Callahan is coming here this afternoon to close the deal. He's arriving on the two o'clock plane.

BARRY: Jake Callahan! Are you off your rocker? Why is he coming here of all places?

BEETLE: Where else? The car's in your garage, isn't it?

BARRY: Sure, but for Pete's sake, Beetle, Judge Cooper will be here.

BEETLE: So what? We'll get the papers signed before your Dad gets home with the Judge.

BARRY: Do you really think he'll sign us on?

BEETLE: But natch. When old Callahan sees the job we've done on that Stutz Bearcat, we'll be in business.

BARRY: Gee, I hope so.

BEETLE: Barry and Beetle, the Boy Mechanics of the Callahan Stock Car Circuit! We've got it made, sonny!

BARRY: It's our big chance, Beetle. Come along upstairs while I change, and let's map out our strategy. (*As they start to exit,* ELOISE *enters with both graduation gowns on hangers.*)

ELOISE: I've just given this a lick and a promise, Barry, but I think it will do if you can manage to take it upstairs without rumpling it again.

BARRY (*Taking his gown*): Thanks, Eloise. I'd ask you to stick around and watch us work on the car, but . . .

ELOISE: No thanks. I've seen enough of that car. Besides, I must go home and make myself beautiful for tonight.

BARRY: You suit me just as you are, but you girls are never satisfied.

ELOISE: Flatterer! You know you have eyes for nothing else but that decrepit automobile. But I grin and bear it.

BEETLE: Now that's what I call a sensible woman.

BARRY: So long, Eloise. I'll see you tonight. And I promise you that I won't even mention the word "car" at the party after graduation. Come along, Beetle. (BEETLE *and* BARRY *exit.*)

ELOISE: I don't see how Mrs. Warren stands it! (*As she opens door to leave, she collides with* JUDGE COOPER, *who was about to enter. His coat is slung over his shoulder; his shirt is open at the neck and a handkerchief is bound around his forehead. With one hand he is fanning himself with his hat and in the other he carries a brief case.*) Oh, I'm terribly sorry.

JUDGE: That's quite all right. I'm Judge Cooper, and you must be Peggy Warren.

ELOISE: No, I'm Eloise Cartwell, otherwise known as "the girl next door." Mrs. Warren and Peggy have gone out for a little while. Mr. Warren was expecting to meet you at the station.

JUDGE: At the last minute I decided to come by plane. It's a long hot ride out here from the airport. Feels good in here, nice and cool.

ELOISE: I was just leaving, but please make yourself at home, sir. I'll tell Barry you're here. (*Calling*) Barry, your guest has arrived! (*To* JUDGE) I hope to see you later, Judge Cooper. Our class really feels honored to have you as our speaker. (*She goes to door.*)

JUDGE: Thank you. I hope they still feel that way after my speech. (ELOISE *exits.* JUDGE *mops his face and looks around.*) Well, well, old Mac has done all right for himself. It will be fun to meet his boy. (BEETLE *enters excitedly.*)

BEETLE: Well, well, well. It's good to see you, sir. We're sure glad you could make it.

JUDGE: The trip from the airport took longer than I expected. Did you get my wire?

BEETLE: We sure did, sir, and it was like money from home. Barry will be down in a minute.

JUDGE: Barry? But I thought you were Barry.

BEETLE (*Laughing*): Oh, no, sir. I'm Beetle. Beetle Bagley. Barry's my partner, and this is his house. We wanted you to come here to save time. The car is in his garage.

JUDGE: The car?

BEETLE: Yes, the Bearcat. We have our workshop out there, so you can really see the whole works. (*Calling*) Hey, Barry, better bring down an extra pair of coveralls.

JUDGE: Coveralls?

BEETLE: Sure, we don't want you spoiling your good clothes out there in that dump . . . well, it's not exactly a dump, and we do try to keep it cleaned up, but you know how things are in a garage. ,

JUDGE: Yes, yes, I know . . . (BARRY *dashes in wearing coveralls and carrying an extra pair.*)

BEETLE: Aha, here he is, my partner, Barry Warren. Barry and Beetle, the *B and B Mechanics,* we call ourselves. The B and B also stand for Brain and Brawn, and you'll agree we need both in this business, sir. Barry's the brain, and I'm the brawn.

JUDGE: Indeed!

BARRY (*Shaking hands with* JUDGE): Glad to meet you, sir. It's really quite an honor to have you come here in person. I know how busy you must be.

JUDGE: Yes, yes, quite so.

BARRY (*Hustling* JUDGE *into coveralls*): And now, I guess you'd better climb into these, sir. I know you'll want to look the Bearcat over from stem to stern, and we don't want to take a chance with that good suit of yours.

BEETLE: You'll excuse us for rushing you, sir, but—er—

well, Barry's folks are expecting company, and we'd like to get our business out of the way before they arrive.

JUDGE: I see . . . at least I *think* I see!

BARRY: It does sound a bit confusing, sir, but tonight is our high school commencement, and the speaker is an old friend of my dad's, so he's staying here.

JUDGE: Are both of you young men in the graduating class?

BEETLE: Hard to believe, isn't it? Oh, it's not hard to believe that Barry's getting a diploma. He's a real brain. But me . . . well, I'm strictly a carburetor man myself.

JUDGE: But what about college?

BEETLE (*Shocked*): College?

JUDGE: Or some form of higher education?

BARRY: Don't let that bother you, sir. As a matter of fact, I was enrolled at Crescent University, but I've decided against it.

JUDGE: And your parents, how do they feel about this decision?

BARRY: They'll understand why I couldn't pass up an opportunity like this, sir.

JUDGE: Isn't your father a professional man?

BEETLE: Heck, yes. Barry's old man is a lawyer, one of the best, too.

BARRY: But I want to hoe my own row, sir . . . make a career of my own. Naturally, Dad would like to see me follow in his footsteps, but, well, I just can't see it.

BEETLE: Wait till you see this boy operate, sir. He's really a genius when it comes to motors.

BARRY: Stop being my press agent, Beetle, and speak for yourself. It's really Beetle who has most of the know-how. Gosh, sometimes I think he knows what an engine's going to do before it does it. (*Doorbell rings.*)

BEETLE: How about taking a look at the Bearcat right

now, sir? That will give you some idea of what we can do. We've built her up from scratch, and boy, oh boy, is she a dream! (BEETLE *practically drags* JUDGE *offstage, talking vehemently as* BARRY *heads for the door.*)

BARRY (*As doorbell rings again*): Holy smokes, I'm coming! Can't you wait a minute? Why does everything have to happen at once around here? (*Before he can open door,* BECKY FOSTER *enters.*)

BECKY (*In great excitement*): Oh, Barry, I'm so glad you're home. You've got to do something right away. There's no time to lose.

BARRY: For heaven's sake, Becky, what's the crisis? What are you talking about?

BECKY: It's Zip! Oh, Barry, the most awful thing has happened.

BARRY: What's happened to Zip? Has he been in an accident? Is he hurt? Where is he?

BECKY: No, no, he's not hurt. Oh, dear, I know he'll kill me for coming here, but you've just got to stop him.

BARRY: Stop him from what? Becky, stop sputtering and start making sense.

BECKY: Your crazy brother is leaving school. He's taking a full-time job at the Miracle Mart.

BARRY: He's done what?

BECKY: That idiot manager down there has convinced him he's the boy wonder of the paint department.

BARRY: But he can't do that! He's just a kid!

BECKY: Try telling him he's a kid and see where you get! (ZIP *enters from front door.*)

ZIP: Well, it's the "kid" himself, blabbermouth, so you can deliver the message in person!

BARRY: For Pete's sake, Zip, what's the matter with you? You can't quit school now.

ZIP: Who says I can't? I'm sixteen years old, and I have a job, a good job, too. Fifty bucks a week to start, with the promise of a regular salesman's territory at the end of the first year—that's if I don't go back to school in the fall—and they'll give me a car, too.

BARRY: So that's it, a car? Good night! Here you are, ready for your senior year, with every chance at a first-rate scholarship, and all you can think of is a car!

ZIP: You're a fine one to talk! Who's throwing away a college education so he can be a mechanic on the Stock Car Circuit?

BARRY: That's different. In the first place, I'm older, and I want to see something of the world before I settle down to something really serious.

ZIP: And how much of the world do you think you'll see flat on your back under an automobile with oil dripping all over your face?

BARRY: I can see you're in no mood to listen to reason.

BECKY: I told you. He's crazy . . . just plain crazy.

ZIP: You keep out of this. You had no business coming over here in the first place, spilling the beans.

BARRY: May I ask when you are planning to tell Mom and Dad about this mighty decision?

ZIP: About the same time you figured on breaking your own bad news.

BARRY: Now look, Zip, you're a smart kid. Start acting your age, and think this thing over. Right now, fifty bucks a week looks like big money to you.

ZIP: I'll say it does, and I'm going to grab it while I have the chance.

BARRY: But that's just the point. By quitting school now, you're throwing away all of your chances to make something out of your life.

ZIP: And whose life is it, big brother? I've heard you tell Dad a thousand times that every guy has a right to lead his own life and make his own choices without any strings.

BARRY: But you're only sixteen. You're not even dry behind the ears.

ZIP: Now you're talking just like Dad.

BARRY: But he's right, Zip . . . at least about this. How do you know what you're going to want in five or ten years? And by that time, it will be too late.

ZIP: I never thought I'd live to see the day you'd be dishing out those arguments, Barry. You've sure climbed over to the other side of the fence.

BARRY: Maybe I have. But I just can't stand by and see you make such a fool of yourself. After all, if you don't care anything about yourself, what about Mom and Dad? How do you think they're going to feel about this?

ZIP: Pretty much the same way they're going to feel about your cutting loose from college. But you said yourself, they'll adjust to the idea in time.

BARRY: Well here's somebody who's not going to adjust to the idea—now or later. You're going to march right down there to that Miracle Mart and tell that wise guy he can get himself another boy.

ZIP: Is that so? And who's going to make me?

BARRY (*Grabbing hold of him*): If necessary, I am. (*The boys start to fight as* MR. WARREN *enters.*)

MR. WARREN: Hey, you two, what's going on here?

ZIP: Let go of me! Look out, you're tearing my shirt.

BARRY: I'll tear more than your shirt if you don't get some sense into that head of yours.

BECKY: Oh, Mr. Warren, isn't this awful? Make them stop.

MR. WARREN (*Separating them*): Here, here, cut this out! Behave yourselves, both of you.

ZIP: You keep out of this, Becky Foster.

MR. WARREN: Barry—stop! What's wrong with you two? Why, you haven't acted like this since you were in grade school. Barry, I'm ashamed of you.

BARRY: I'm sorry, Dad.

MR. WARREN: Zip, you sit down over there and cool off. Then maybe somebody can give me an explanation of this.

ZIP: Barry can do all the explaining. Ask him.

MR. WARREN: It's a good thing Judge Cooper isn't with me. I wouldn't have wanted him to walk in on a scene like this.

BARRY: Judge Cooper? What became of him? I thought you were meeting his train.

MR. WARREN: Can't imagine what happened to him. He never showed up. (BEETLE *enters with* JUDGE COOPER. *Both are well smudged with grease.*)

BEETLE: Hey, Barry, what's the delay?

MR. WARREN (*Rushing forward to greet the* JUDGE): Well, well—if it isn't old Coop! Where in the world have you been, old boy?

JUDGE: Didn't you get my wire that I was flying in?

MR. WARREN: I wouldn't have been cooling my heels down at the station if I had heard from you. But what are you doing in that outfit? You look as if you've been in a grease pit.

JUDGE: That's exactly where I have been, Mac. Boy, oh boy, it's good to see you. You haven't changed a bit.

BARRY: Judge Cooper!

BEETLE: Oh, my achin' back! It's the Judge!

BARRY: But I thought . . . Jiminy! We thought you were Jake Callahan.

MR. WARREN: Jake Callahan? Who's he?

BEETLE: Owner of the Callahan Stock Car Circuit, Mr. Warren. We thought—or rather—I thought . . . Well, gee whiz, sir, why didn't you tell us you were Judge Cooper?

JUDGE: I never had the chance, son. You were so sure I was Jake Callahan, you had me out in that garage before I could say Jack Robinson. Now before we have any more cases of mistaken identity, I'd like to find out who the rest of you are. Is this your daughter Peggy?

MR. WARREN: Oh, no, this is Becky Foster. Becky, this is Judge Cooper.

BECKY: How do you do, sir.

MR. WARREN: Becky is Zip's girl friend, Coop.

ZIP: Not any more, she isn't!

MR. WARREN: Why, Zip! What a thing to say. I'm almost ashamed to introduce you as my youngest son.

JUDGE (*Shaking hands with* ZIP): Glad to meet you, Zip. I can almost tell by looking at you, you're going to be the lawyer in the family. A chip off the old block, I'd say.

ZIP: Oh, no, not me, sir. Barry's the legal light of the family.

JUDGE: But I thought Barry . . .

BARRY: We seem to be having a rough afternoon, sir. Maybe it's a good thing you are a judge and used to handling disputes.

BECKY: I . . . I think I'd better go.

ZIP: Oh, no, you don't. You started this, young lady. (*Pointing to a chair*) Now, you can just sit down and see it through.

Mr. Warren: What's the matter with everybody? Has somebody hidden a charge of dynamite around here? You all look ready to explode.

Zip: Go ahead, Barry. I dare you to touch off the fuse!

Barry: Dad, I hate to upset you like this with Judge Cooper here and everything, but . . .

Judge: Don't mind me, son. Fire away.

Barry: Well, the fact is—I know this is going to hit you pretty hard, but . . .

Zip: Go ahead, tell him—tell him the whole blooming business!

Barry: Well, sir, the fact is that I guess I've made a pretty silly mistake.

Zip: Now you call it a mistake.

Barry: Yes, I do call it a mistake and it was you who made me see just what a terrible mistake it was. Gee, Dad, I'd give a lot to undo what I've done, but . . .

Mr. Warren: For heaven's sake, boy, get to the point. What is this mistake? What have you done?

Barry: Well, I know how much you've counted on seeing me through law school, and when I was a kid I was pretty much sold on the idea myself. But lately, well, maybe I was tired of hearing you pound away at the idea. Somehow or other I began thinking that four years of college and three years of law school were just too long to wait to begin to lead my own life. So Beetle and I have cooked up a deal with the Callahan Stock Car Circuit.

Beetle: They're always on the lookout for good mechanics, and Barry's one of the best.

Barry: So I decided to cancel my registration at Crescent and go on the road for a year or two.

Mr. Warren: But your scholarship!

BARRY: There are plenty of other guys who can use that scholarship, Pop.

MR. WARREN: But this is incredible! You can't do a thing like this.

BARRY: But it's done, Dad. I've already written to Crescent and cancelled the whole thing.

MR. WARREN (*Dropping into a chair*): I don't see how you could do such a thing, Barry. You know what plans your mother and I have had for you.

JUDGE (*Putting his hand on* MR. WARREN*'s shoulder*): We can't lead their lives for them, Mac. They have to go it alone.

MR. WARREN: But he's a bright boy, Coop, a talented boy. Madge and I wanted him to have the very best.

BARRY: I know, Dad. I've always known how you and Mom felt, but I never really understood until this afternoon. Not till I saw someone I care about doing the same darned thing.

MR. WARREN: What do you mean?

ZIP: He means me, Dad. You see, well, I got a job this afternoon, too.

BECKY: He's going to quit school, Mr. Warren, and sell paint for the Miracle Mart.

MR. WARREN: Is that so? Well, I can tell you right now, young lady, he's going to do no such thing. As long as I am boss of this household, no son of mine is going to quit school before he gets his diploma. I'll see to that.

JUDGE: Easy, Mac, easy!

BARRY: I know we've let you down, Dad, but don't be too hard on Zip. Actually, the whole thing is my fault.

ZIP: How do you figure that?

BARRY: You might never have cooked up this harebrained scheme, Zip, if I hadn't kept harping on leading my own life, making my own choices, jumping the gun on everything and everybody. When you stood there quoting me chapter and verse, spouting all that big talk about a life of your own, I suddenly realized how I must look to Mom and Dad. I can tell you it made me pretty sick.

ZIP: You don't have to take the blame, Barry. I guess I just got carried away with the idea of making my own money, having my own car, doing the things I'd like to do right now instead of waiting. I knew I'd have to buck Mom and Dad, but I never had any idea you'd take it this way.

BARRY: Well, now you know. I've thrown away my own chance, but I can't stand by and let you do the same thing. (PEGGY *and* MRS. WARREN *enter, carrying packages.*)

MRS. WARREN: Oh, dear, I'm sorry we're late, but the bus service in this town is simply dreadful.

PEGGY: We were standing in the square forever. Sorry, Dad.

MR. WARREN: It's all right, Peggy. So far, you've missed nothing but trouble.

MRS. WARREN: Trouble? I do hope nothing happened to Judge Cooper.

JUDGE (*Stepping forward*): Nothing that a little soap and water won't cure, Mrs. Warren. It's a pleasure to meet you. And this young lady, I presume, is your daughter. (*Shakes hands*)

MRS. WARREN *and* PEGGY: Judge Cooper!

MRS. WARREN: Barry Warren, you've had the Judge out in that filthy garage!

BEETLE: It's my fault, Mrs. Warren. I—er—made a mistake.

MR. WARREN: This seems to be our day for mistakes, Madge. And our two worst mistakes, so far, seem to be our sons.

MRS. WARREN: I don't understand. Has something happened?

MR. WARREN: Everything has happened. Barry has chucked his scholarship at Crescent; Zip is talking about quitting school. . . . I—I just don't know how to explain it to you.

MRS. WARREN: Are you serious, Mac?

MR. WARREN: I was never more serious in my life. It seems you and I have really made a mess of things as parents.

BARRY: Don't say that, Dad.

ZIP: Nobody could ask for better parents than you and Mom.

MR. WARREN: Then what's the answer? You tell me.

JUDGE: Maybe it's time for me to speak my little piece, Mac. Remember I came here to deliver the commencement address, and this seems the right time for rehearsal.

MR. WARREN: Don't make jokes, Coop. I'm not in a laughing mood.

JUDGE: Neither am I, old friend. If you recall, I accepted this invitation for purely personal reasons. I wanted to visit you and meet your family.

MR. WARREN: Well, you've met them, and I hope you're impressed.

JUDGE: As a matter of fact, I am. You have a charming wife, a lovely daughter and two fine sons.

ZIP: I don't think we look very fine to him right now, Judge.

JUDGE: No, I suppose not. But then you don't look very

much different to him than he appeared to his father thirty-four years ago.

BARRY: What do you mean?

JUDGE: Sit down, everybody, and let me talk for a few minutes. (*All sit.*) I've made a lot of commencement speeches in my time, and I'm fed up with them. It's usually hot, the auditorium is overcrowded and the graduates couldn't care less about what the speaker has to say. So two years ago I started sending my regrets. But when your invitation came, I reconsidered.

MR. WARREN: That was good of you, Coop.

JUDGE: Naturally, because of you, Mac, I wanted to do an especially good job. But for the life of me I couldn't think of anything that hadn't been said before or that these young people would want to hear. Then I had an idea.

MR. WARREN: Knowing you, I'll bet it was a good one.

JUDGE: It occurred to me that the people who care most about commencement are the parents. So I decided to address the parents instead of the graduating class. After all, it's a commencement for them, too, the beginning of their career as parents of young adults; and that's quite different from being the parents of children—even of adolescents. I'm calling my address "Gathering Sticks."

MRS. WARREN: "Gathering Sticks." That's a strange title.

JUDGE: It's not original. I borrowed it from a young poet I once knew, and I also borrowed his verse as the keynote of my speech. Listen. Here is youth addressing the adult world:

> "You ask me what I am doing, man?
> Why am I so busy
> Rushing here and there?

I'm going to set the world on fire!
I'm going to shape the sun again.
So, please, don't bother me now.
I'm gathering sticks!"

MR. WARREN: Gathering sticks! I can't say I understand exactly what it means. . .

JUDGE: You should understand, Mac. You wrote it.

MR. WARREN: I *what?* What are you talking about, Coop?

JUDGE (*Taking book from briefcase*): It's right here, Mac, here in our old *Tatler*—our class poem. See— (*Shows book to* MR. WARREN) Class Poem, "Gathering Sticks," by MacKenzie Warren.

MR. WARREN: Well, I'll be darned!

BARRY: Did you really write that, Dad?

ZIP: I never knew you were a poet, Pop!

PEGGY: Neither did I.

BECKY: And can't you even remember that you wrote it?

MRS. WARREN: Why, I think that's wonderful, dear, just wonderful.

BEETLE: Just what does it mean, Mr. Warren?

MR. WARREN (*Clearing his throat*): Well—er—I guess it means . . .

JUDGE: It means that you were just like Barry and Zip back in those days. It means you wanted to set the world on fire, but you weren't sure how to go about it. And you certainly couldn't wait for any advice from an old fuddy-duddy like your father. So you went rushing around collecting the first sticks you could find to make a mighty blaze. Trouble is—you picked up some pretty green wood! All it did was burn your fingers and make an awful smudge! If you remember, that was the year you left home to join the Clark Brothers Traveling Circus and Carnival Circuit.

PEGGY: Oh, no! Not Dad! I can't believe it!

MRS. WARREN: MacKenzie Warren! I never knew you were with a circus!

BARRY: A circus! Dad, what got into you?

ZIP: Now I've heard everything!

BEETLE: What were you, sir, a lion tamer?

MR. WARREN: No, of course not! I—I was in the business end.

JUDGE: Come off it, Mac. You were on the business end of a shovel most of the time. Oh, they did let you sell tickets and help with the bookkeeping, but they never did offer you the partnership they promised you when you signed up.

PEGGY: Heavens, Dad, you must have been a real sucker!

JUDGE: No worse than I was, Peggy. That same year I took a flyer in the used car business.

BARRY *and* BEETLE: Used cars!

JUDGE: Only I used up all my money on the deal. Before the year was out, both of us had to call for help. Fortunately we had parents who could and would answer the call.

BARRY: I get the point, Judge. You picked up the wrong sticks. They just wouldn't burn!

JUDGE: But we had a chance to find the right sticks, Barry, thanks to our parents. And that's the whole point of my commencement address. I want to advise mothers and fathers to sit tight and keep their faith in their young people during this difficult period of gathering sticks.

BARRY: I hope they get the message, Judge, and I hope the kids get it, too, before it's too late.

ZIP: You don't have to worry about me, Dad. I'll tell the man down at the Miracle Mart to offer his green wood to some other guy. (*To* BECKY) Come along, Nosey Foster. You might as well be in on the kill.

BECKY: Oh, gee, Zip, then you're not really mad?

ZIP: That remains to be seen. Come along. See you later, Judge. (ZIP *and* BECKY *exit. Knocking is heard from offstage.*)

PEGGY: That must be someone at the back door. I'll go see who it is. (*Exits.*)

BARRY: Gosh, Dad, if there were only something I could do!

MR. WARREN: I don't know what it would be, son, but most of us get another chance. If and when yours comes along, I'll try to be as good a father as my dad was.

MRS. WARREN: I just can't imagine you in a circus, Mac.

MR. WARREN (*With a chuckle*): Well, Madge, I guess I've changed a mite in thirty-odd years! (PEGGY *enters with two telegrams*)

PEGGY: Telegram for you, Dad. (*Hands it to him*) And one for B. Bagley. (*Hands it to* BEETLE) Even Western Union seems to know this is your second home, Beetle.

MRS. WARREN: Anything important, dear?

MR. WARREN: Not any more. It's from a fellow I know who changed his plans from train to plane.

BEETLE: Well, here goes our bundle of sticks, pal. Listen to this. (*Reading*) "Sorry—deal is off. Hired two mechanics today. No more openings. Signed J. Callahan."

BARRY: Of all the rotten luck!

JUDGE (*Trying to take off his coveralls*): If I can just take off this rig, I may have something that will interest you, Beetle. When I mentioned that used car business, I didn't tell you I still hold a share in it. I have the card here somewhere. (*Steps out of coveralls*) Here . . . here it is. Capitol Used Car Lot. It's right around the corner from my office. If you go out there on Monday and ask for Nick Burney, he might have something for you. Tell him I sent you.

BEETLE: Gee, Judge, thanks a lot.

JUDGE: And if you take my advice, you'll arrange for some training on the side. A good automotive engineer is always in demand.

BEETLE: Automotive engineer? Wow! But you've forgotten something, sir. It's Barry who's the brains of the outfit. I'm just the brawn.

JUDGE: I've seen enough to know better than that, Beetle. That Stutz Bearcat will get you a letter of recommendation from me anytime.

BEETLE: I—I just don't know what to say, sir.

JUDGE: Then don't say anything. I'm sort of a carburetor man myself in my spare time, and I think we speak the same language.

MRS. WARREN: I'm sure you'll want to take your things upstairs, Judge Cooper, and clean up. I never thought you'd have such a greasy reception. Peggy, take this filthy garment out to the garage. (*As* PEGGY *picks up coveralls, a letter drops from the pocket.*)

PEGGY: Just a minute; there's a letter here. (*Picking it up*) Its addressed to Dr. E. P. Curtis, Registrar, Crescent University.

BARRY (*Grabbing letter*): I don't believe it! I just don't believe it.

MR. WARREN: What is all this?

BARRY: Look! Look, Dad, it's my second chance! It's my letter! My letter to Crescent! I could have sworn I mailed it, and all the time it was right here in these coveralls.

MRS. WARREN: Why, it's like a miracle, a real miracle.

BARRY: I don't deserve a second chance, Dad, but I'm sure going to make the most of this one for you and Mom.

PEGGY: Maybe you'll have a law partner after all, Dad.

MR. WARREN: Now, now, Peggy, let's not be gathering any more sticks for Barry. With four years at Crescent, he'll have plenty of time to gather his own. There will be no more speeches about the legal profession from me. From now on, Barry is his own man, and he can make his own choices and start his own bonfires. Come along, Coop, I could do with some cleaning up myself. (MR. WARREN *and the* JUDGE *exit.*)

PEGGY: Well, Mom, how about our heading for the kitchen?

MRS. WARREN: Good idea. With a house full of men to feed, we'd better be starting a fire of our own under the roast beef. (PEGGY *and* MRS. WARREN *exit.*)

BARRY (*As he picks up the "Tatler"*): Do you really think we can do it, Beetle?

BEETLE: Do what, chum?

BARRY: Do you really think we'll ever set the world on fire?

BEETLE: I'm not sure, Barry, but the two of us wooden heads can sure give it a good hard try! (*Curtain*)

THE END

Production Notes

GATHERING STICKS

Characters: 5 male; 4 female.

Playing Time: 30 minutes.

Costumes: Modern everyday dress for Mr. and Mrs. Warren, Peggy, Zip, Eloise, and Becky. Barry and Eloise wear caps and gowns at opening. Later Barry changes to coveralls. Beetle wears coveralls. Judge enters with coat over his shoulder, shirt open, and a handkerchief around his forehead. Later he wears coveralls over his clothes. Coveralls should be greasy when Judge Cooper and boys return from garage.

Properties: Camera, hangers for commencement gowns, hat, brief case containing class yearbook, packages, telegrams, card, letter.

Setting: The Warren living room. An exit at right leads to the rest of the house. The front door is at center stage.

Lighting: No special effects.